The Probability Handbook

The Probability Handbook

Mary McShane-Vaughn

ASQ Quality Press
Milwaukee, Wisconsin

American Society for Quality, Quality Press, Milwaukee 53203
© 2016 by ASQ
All rights reserved.
Printed in the United States of America
21 20 19 18 17 16   5 4 3 2 1

Library of Congress Cataloging-in-Publication Data
Names: McShane-Vaughn, Mary, 1963– | American Society for Quality.
Title: The probability handbook / Mary McShane-Vaughn.
Description: Milwaukee, Wisconsin : ASQ Quality Press, 2015. | "American
   Society for Quality." | Includes bibliographical references and index.
Identifiers: LCCN 2015045483 | ISBN 9780873899222 (hardcover : alk. paper)
Subjects: LCSH: Probabilities—Popular works.
Classification: LCC QA273.15 .M44 2015 | DDC 519.2—dc23
LC record available at http://lccn.loc.gov/2015045483

Acquisitions Editor: Matt Meinholz
Managing Editor: Paul Daniel O'Mara
Production Administrator: Randall Benson

ASQ Mission: The American Society for Quality advances individual, organizational, and community excellence worldwide through learning, quality improvement, and knowledge exchange.

Attention Bookstores, Wholesalers, Schools, and Corporations: ASQ Quality Press books, video, audio, and software are available at quantity discounts with bulk purchases for business, educational, or instructional use. For information, please contact ASQ Quality Press at 800-248-1946, or write to ASQ Quality Press, P.O. Box 3005, Milwaukee, WI 53201–3005.

To place orders or to request a free copy of the ASQ Quality Press Publications Catalog, visit our website at http://www.asq.org/quality-press.

  Printed on acid-free paper

Quality Press
600 N. Plankinton Ave.
Milwaukee, WI 53203-2914
E-mail: authors@asq.org
The Global Voice of Quality®

For my husband, Jim, who walked into graduate orientation at Georgia Tech at exactly the same time that I did. What are the chances?

Table of Contents

List of Figures and Tables

List of Formulas

Preface

As a graduate student, I worked in the statistics tutoring lab in the Industrial and Systems Engineering (ISyE) Department at Georgia Tech. The ISyE program at Georgia Tech is ranked number one in the country,[1] so it comes as no surprise that the undergraduate students were exceptionally bright and certainly very adept in math. Still, we got a lot of business in the tutoring lab. The funny thing is that students hardly ever came in to the lab for help with their statistics classes. Instead, most of the tutoring requests were for the probability course, a prerequisite for the statistics sequence.

In the intervening 20 years I've worked as a quality engineer, statistician, university professor, and Six Sigma training developer, and I've witnessed a similar phenomenon: even those fairly well versed in statistical analysis balk at the prospect of tackling probability. Granted, probability is tough. Many of the concepts seem counterintuitive at first, and the successful student must in effect train herself to think in a totally new way. It takes a lot of time, and mastery of probability only comes from solving many, many problems.

How, then, can probability be taught effectively? When I think back to my days spent in the tutoring lab, one barrier to student success stands out. The undergraduate probability textbook at Tech was a slim and elegantly written volume, but it made little sense to the students. As tutors, we reinterpreted the tidy mathematical exposition of the text into everyday words and solved example problem after example problem. Eventually, the engineering students caught on and were successful, in spite of their textbook.

Accordingly, the aim of this text and its companion, *The Probability Workbook*, is to present the subject of probability as a tutor would. Probability concepts are explained in everyday language and worked examples are presented in abundance. In addition to paper-and-pencil solutions, solution strategies using Microsoft Excel functions are given. All mathematical symbols are explained, and the mathematical rigor is kept on an algebra level; calculus is avoided.

This book is written for quality practitioners who are currently performing statistical and probability analyses in their workplaces, and for those seeking to learn probability concepts for the American Society for Quality (ASQ) Certified Quality Engineer, Reliability Engineer, Six Sigma Green Belt, Black Belt, or Master Black Belt exam.

---

[1] See https://www.isye.gatech.edu/news/2015-us-news-world-report-isye-undergraduate-program-maintains-no-1-ranking.

Chapter 1 traces the origins of probability as an academic subject and high-lights the pervasiveness of statistics and probability in today's popular culture. Chapter 2 introduces the reader to counting techniques to determine how many ways particular outcomes can occur. Counting possible outcomes is a fundamental piece of probability calculations. In Chapter 3, we begin the hard and rewarding work of learning probability concepts and rules, including the concepts of mutual exclusivity, sampling with and without replacement, odds, conditional probabil-ity, and Bayes' theorem. Seven detailed examples are included at the end of the chapter to help solidify your understanding. After studying the first three chap-ters and completing the practice problems included in the companion workbook, readers will be prepared to answer any number of probability questions, from picking socks out of a drawer, to selecting lottery numbers, to choosing colleagues for committees, to deciding whether a manufacturing lot should be shipped to the customer.

Chapter 4 introduces commonly used "named" discrete probability distribu-tions: the discrete uniform, binomial, hypergeometric, geometric, negative bino-mial (also known as the Pascal), and Poisson. The formulas, parameters, and uses for each distribution are introduced, and worked examples are shown for each dis-tribution type. Useful approximations among the distributions are also presented, and a summary of the distributions is tabulated at the end of the chapter.

Chapter 5 covers continuous probability distributions, among them the well-known normal (also known as the Gaussian), standard normal, Student's t, F, chi-square, and Weibull distributions. Lesser known but useful and interesting distributions are also included in this chapter: the uniform, triangular, gamma, Erlang, exponential, Rayleigh, lognormal, beta, and Cauchy. In addition, key theo-rems such as the law of large numbers and Chebyshev's inequality are presented and explained. At the end of the chapter, a summary of the distributions appears for quick reference. After studying the material in Chapters 4 and 5 and complet-ing the practice problems in the companion workbook, the reader will be able to select the appropriate distribution for a wide range of scenarios, state the formulas for the mean and variance for various distributions, and correctly evaluate prob-ability statements.

The appendices contain the distribution road map, a graphic of all the probabil-ity distributions presented in the text and how they are related. Probability tables for the binomial and Poisson distributions as well as cumulative probability tables for the binomial, Poisson, standard normal, Student's t, chi-square, and F distribu-tions are also provided.

As extensive as the list of rules, theorems, and distributions covered in the text happens to be, this book is by no means comprehensive! The distributions pre-sented in the text were carefully chosen for their applicability to the types of prob-lems that arise in the quality field. Univariate distributions not covered include the Laplace and extreme value distributions, as well as the Pearson series of distribu-tions. There also exists a multitude of multivariate distributions in which arrays of random variables are modeled. These distributions include the Dirichlet, mul-tivariate normal, Hotelling's T^2, and the Wishart and require a working knowl-edge of matrix algebra. To learn more about these distributions, you can consult a thicker and more densely written text!

Even though my outline was carefully crafted, I did experience scope creep in the writing process. Just as soon as I would finish one section, I would invariably have an idea in the shower of yet another formula, relationship, example, or interesting fact to add. Finishing the book was becoming a Sisyphean task. In order to send a completed manuscript to the publisher, I had to either stop showering or decide that, as it stood, the book more than covered what was necessary. To my family's great relief, I chose the latter option.

It is my hope that as you read this book you underline new terms, highlight formulas, write in its margins, and refer to it often. It would be gratifying to see dog-eared copies of *The Probability Handbook* on office shelves or opened up during certification exams.

Feel free to contact me with comments or questions about the book or to learn more about courses based on the book. Visit http://www.6sigma.university.

Acknowledgments

I'd like to thank the staff at ASQ's Quality Press for their patience and support during the writing process and in the production stages. I'd also like to thank the copyeditor at Kinetic Publishing Services, LLC, for making the paragraphs read so smoothly.

In addition, I am extremely grateful to the reviewers for their careful reading and excellent suggestions, all done on a tight deadline. Dr. Sandy Furterer, Dr. Abbe Herzig, and Dr. Bindu Viswanathan, I am proud to count you among my colleagues and my friends. Your work has made this text an infinitely better and more readable book.

1

Introduction

The lottery has been characterized as a tax on the mathematically naive. Consider a player who uses a "system" to carefully curate his picks based on his anniversary date, his child's age, and the current phase of the moon. Unfortunately, all the superstition in the world can't overcome the tyranny of random chance: a player choosing the numbers 1 2 3 4 5 has the same probability of winning as our player using his "system." As the popular financial advisors on television tell us, in the long run it would be better to invest the dollar than to spend it on a lottery ticket. But what would be the fun in that?

The lure of easy money is nothing new. For centuries, gamblers have tried to outsmart other players, as well as fate, in the hopes of scoring the big win. Not surprisingly, the study of probability traces its origins to games of chance. Unlike the lottery, which is based on pure luck, many games involve decision making and strategy that can be crafted by using probability concepts. Girolamo Cardano (1501–1576), by turns quite a successful professional gambler, mathematician, and physician, wrote the first treatise on winning betting strategies for cards and dice using the concepts of probability. The work was published posthumously almost a century later in 1663.[1] At about this same time, the mathematicians Blaise Pascal and Pierre de Fermat were conducting a lengthy correspondence concerning the solution to the "Problem of Points," in which the stakes in an unfinished game of chance involving coin flips must be fairly divided between two players.[2]

Probability has since evolved beyond rolls of the dice and flips of a coin to influence almost every aspect of our lives. Medical researchers, meteorologists, and even online dating sites use probability to estimate disease risk, create weather forecasts, and match clients, respectively.

Probability and statistics have even migrated into our popular culture. Suddenly, the field of probability and statistics is cool. Take, for example, the popularity of Nate Silver's FiveThirtyEight blog, in which he correctly predicted the outcome of the 2012 presidential election for all 50 states.[3] In their book *Freakonomics*, Steven Levitt and Stephen Dubner apply probability principles to draw novel comparisons between, say, schoolteachers and sumo wrestlers, or to postulate on the reasons why drug dealers still live with their mothers. The book

---

[1] For more information on Cardano, refer to http://www.britannica.com/biography/Girolamo-Cardano.

[2] For more on the "Problem of Points," see http://mathforum.org/isaac/problems/prob1.html.

[3] http://fivethirtyeight.blogs.nytimes.com/2012/11/08/election-night-replay/.

Outliers by Malcolm Gladwell examines how hidden advantages and culture affect an individual's success. Along the way, he uncovers and explains unexpected relationships, such as the fact that most professional hockey players were born in the month of January. Michael Lewis gives a gripping account of how probability and statistics were successfully used to recruit undervalued baseball players for the Oakland A's in his book-turned-movie *Moneyball* (starring Brad Pitt, no less!). *USA Today*[4] reports that demand for data analysts is outstripping supply. Now seems like the perfect time to dive in and learn the theorems and apply the techniques.

---

[4] http://www.usatoday.com/story/money/business/2012/10/01/hot-tech-jobs-demand/1593105/.

2

Learning to Count

There are many counting systems in existence. For example, the indigenous Walpiri tribe in Australia has only three words in its language for numbers, which translate to *one, two,* and *many*.[1] Using this system to calculate probabilities would greatly simplify things since the results would take the form of *not likely, more likely,* or *very likely*. Probability lecture over in 15 minutes, tops. However, we give up precision for ease with this approach. For example, it would be impossible to know if we've achieved the Six Sigma ("Many" Sigma?) standard of 3.4 defects per million opportunities using such a lumpy measurement scale.

On the other end of the spectrum, the ancient Sumerians counted using a base-60 number system, meaning that they used 60 unique symbols and names for the numbers 0–59. It probably would have taken children until seventh grade to memorize their phone numbers, if, of course, there had been phones in ancient Sumeria. Our base-10 counting system seems like a welcome relief to these alternate methods, especially since we can conveniently cheat using our fingers.

Still, counting, even in base 10, is not necessarily straightforward. There are entire graduate classes on counting processes, and those so inclined can earn their PhD in a field called combinatorics, which is essentially the study of fancy counting.[2] Consider, for example, some classic counting questions:

- How many ways can four friends be arranged in a line at a movie theater?

- How many unique license plates can be made using three letters and three numbers?

- How many different committees of 6 people can be selected from a group of 30 people?

- How many possible combinations are there for a state lottery?

- How many unique product combinations can be created?

- How many times do I need to ask my children to clean their rooms before they look up from their iPhones? (OK, maybe this one isn't a classic question, but I'd still like to know the answer. The Walpirians would wisely answer "Many.")

---

[1] See *The Story of 1*, a 2005 BBC documentary narrated by Terry Jones and directed by Nick Murphy.

[2] See http://grad-schools.usnews.rankingsandreviews.com/best-graduate-schools/top-science-schools/discrete-mathematics-rankings.

In this chapter, several counting techniques will be presented, starting with enumeration, factorials, combinations, and permutations, along with Microsoft Excel functions to calculate counts.

2.1 ENUMERATION

To figure out how many ways something-or-other can happen, we can simply write down all the possible ways the particular event can occur and then count them up. This "brute force" technique is known as *enumeration,* or a listing of all possible events. For example, if we wanted to find the number of ways four friends can be arranged in a line at a movie theater, we would list all the possible orderings of the people and then count the number of orderings.

Let the four people be named Arnoldo, Beth, Cameron, and Daniel. We can line them up for the movie as shown in Table 2.1.

Counting the number of unique orderings in Table 2.1, we see that four friends can be lined up in 24 different ways.

Solving small problems via enumeration is not too difficult; however, as the number of outcomes grows larger, enumeration becomes quite time-consuming and fraught with errors of omission. For example, if another friend, Eve, were to join our group of four, there would be 120 unique orderings for the movie line.[3] Add Fred, and now we have 720 different ways the six friends could arrange themselves! A computer program could handle the enumeration quite easily, but writing out all the possibilities by hand would be prohibitively tedious.

Still, enumeration can come in handy when we are learning probability concepts. Classic examples include the outcomes of tossing a fair coin a certain number of times or throwing a pair of dice. Having a table of the possible outcomes allows us to see probability concepts in more concrete terms. For example, the possible outcomes of tossing a coin three times are enumerated in Table 2.2, and the 36 possible outcomes of tossing two dice are shown in Table 2.3. We will revisit this technique in Chapter 3.

Table 2.1 Four friends arranged in a movie theater line.

A B C D	B A C D	C B A D	D B C A
A B D C	B A D C	C B D A	D B A C
A D B C	B D A C	C D A B	D A B C
A D C B	B D C A	C D B A	D A C B
A C B D	B C A D	C A B D	D C B A
A C D B	B C D A	C A D B	D C A B

---

[3] The calculation of this figure is explained in Section 2.2, "Factorials."

Table 2.2 Enumeration of possible outcomes when tossing a fair coin three times.

First flip	Second flip	Third flip
H	H	H
H	H	T
H	T	H
H	T	T
T	H	H
T	H	T
T	T	H
T	T	T

Table 2.3 Enumeration of possible outcomes when throwing two dice.

1 1	1 2	1 3	1 4	1 5	1 6
2 1	2 2	2 3	2 4	2 5	2 6
3 1	3 2	3 3	3 4	3 5	3 6
4 1	4 2	4 3	4 4	4 5	4 6
5 1	5 2	5 3	5 4	5 5	5 6
6 1	6 2	6 3	6 4	6 5	6 6

2.2 FACTORIALS

A more convenient way to determine the number of possible orderings of items is to use a *factorial*. A factorial of a positive integer (meaning 1, 2, 3, etc.) is the product of all the positive integers from 1 up to that number. For example, the factorial of 3 is equal to $1 \times 2 \times 3 = 6$. The factorial of 4 is $1 \times 2 \times 3 \times 4 = 24$. The mathematical operator for the factorial is kind of unusual, and surprisingly pleasant: an exclamation point (!). The factorial of 4 is denoted as 4! and is read as "4 factorial."

Factorials can help us figure out how many ways items can be arranged. Recall our friends, still waiting in line for their movie. If there are four friends, they can stand in 4! different orders. Why is this so? Imagine the first position in line. Among Arnoldo, Beth, Cameron, and Daniel, how many people do we have to choose from to put in the front of the line?

As shown in Figure 2.1, there are four choices for the first spot in the line. Once we have chosen someone to stand in front, we then have three friends to choose from for the second spot, then two for the third spot, and then the remaining friend will stand at the back of the line. Hence we have $4 \times 3 \times 2 \times 1 = 4!$ ways to arrange

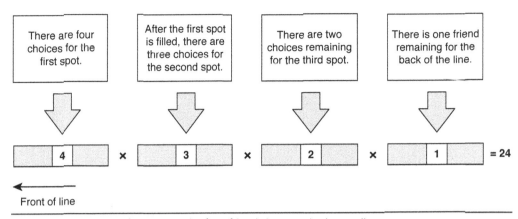

Front of line

Figure 2.1   Number of ways to order four friends in a movie theater line.

Arnoldo, Beth, Cameron, and Daniel.[4] If Eve comes along, we now have 5! = 5 × 4 × 3 × 2 × 1 = 120 arrangements. If Fred tags along with Eve, we have 6! = 720 unique orderings.

Note here that 4! can be written as 4 × 3!, 5! as 5 × 4!, 6! as 6 × 5!, and 7! as 7 × 6!. Noting this pattern, we can say in general that n items can be arranged in $n \times (n-1)!$ ways, as shown in Formula 2.1.

Formula 2.1   Factorial

$$n! = n \times (n-1)!$$

We can also denote the factorial formula using a multiplication operator, the capital letter pi, $\prod$, as in Formula 2.2.

Formula 2.2   Factorial, alternate version

$$\prod_{i=1}^{n} i = n!$$

Let's break down the meaning of Formula 2.2. The multiplication operator, denoted by the Greek capital letter pi ($\prod$), tells us to multiply the integers starting with 1 and increasing one step at a time until we get to n. It is read as "the product of i, as i goes from 1 to n." For $n = 3$, we can find 3! by using the formula:

$$\prod_{i=1}^{3} i = 1 \times 2 \times 3 = 3!$$

This is an elegant way to succinctly represent the factorial formula.

---

[4] Note that 4 × 3 × 2 × 1 = 1 × 2 × 3 × 4, due to the commutative property of multiplication.

Now, what would happen if no one came to the movie? For example, what if the theater offered a 6 a.m. showing of the 1987 film *Ishtar*?[5] How many ways can zero people stand in a line? Is it zero? Or is it one? In fact, there is exactly one way for zero things to be arranged in order. *Therefore, as a special case, zero factorial, or 0!, by definition, equals one.* This fact will become quite useful in the upcoming sections when we discuss permutations and combinations.

In our previous factorial examples, each member of our set of friends could be distinguished from the others. However, if we want to order n items, in which some items are identical to the others, we will need a slightly different strategy.

Say we are arranging five cubes in a row. Three of these cubes are red and are identical to each other, and the remaining two cubes are green and are also indistinguishable from each other. How many ways can these five cubes be arranged? If all 5 cubes were different colors, we would have 5! = 120 ways to line them up. But in the current case, we can only tell red and green cubes apart. We are right to suspect that the red/green orderings will be less than 5!. The number of unique orderings in this situation is

$$\frac{5!}{3!\,2!} = 10$$

In general, if we have n items with r_1 identical items in one group, r_2 identical items in another group, and so on for a total of g groups, the items must be ordered as shown in Formula 2.3.

Formula 2.3   Orderings for groups of identical items

$$\frac{n!}{r_1!\,r_2!\ldots r_g!}$$

Note that the sum of the r's in Formula 2.3 must equal n.

A more mathematically tidy way to display the equation would be to use the pi multiplication operator, as shown in Formula 2.4. Note, too, that we more formally state that the sum of the r_i must equal n using summation notation.

Formula 2.4   Orderings for groups of identical items, concise version

$$\frac{n!}{\prod\limits_{i=1}^{g} r_i!} \quad \text{and} \quad \sum\limits_{i=1}^{g} r_i = n$$

---

[5] For those of you too young to remember this box-office disaster, *Ishtar* starred two of the leading stars of the day, Warren Beatty and Dustin Hoffman. The movie cost $51 million to make but grossed only a little over $14 million in the United States. See http://www.imdb.com/title/tt0093278/.

2.3 PERMUTATIONS

Our four friends are now running in a 5K, and we'd like to know how many different ways they could place first, second, and third. We again could solve this by using enumeration, or by using a diagram as shown in Figure 2.2.

Let's try another problem to see if we can pick up a pattern. Now say that five friends, Arnoldo, Beth, Cameron, Daniel, and Eve, are running in the 5K. The number of possible outcomes is shown in Figure 2.3.

We notice in each of these cases that the number of ways the friends can come in first, second, and third is equal to or less than the number of ways they can line up at a movie theater. In the movie line example, each person had a specific spot to fill. Here, in the race example, we are only concerned with filling three spots. In general, the number of ways *n* items can be arranged in *r* places, *in which order matters*, can be written using the *permutation formula* shown in Formula 2.5.

Formula 2.5   Permutation formula

$$_nP_r = \frac{n!}{(n-r)!}, r \le n$$

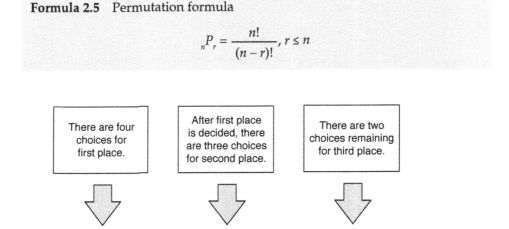

Figure 2.2   Number of ways for four friends to place in a race.

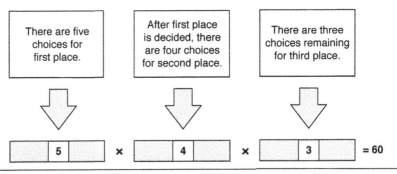

Figure 2.3   Number of ways for five friends to place in a race.

We read this formula as "n permute r equals n factorial divided by the quantity n minus r factorial." Note that the number of positions we have, r, must be less than or equal to the number of items we have, n.

For n equal to 5 and r equal to 3, we have:

$$_5P_3 = \frac{5!}{(5-3)!} = \frac{5!}{2!} = \frac{5 \times 4 \times 3 \times 2 \times 1}{2 \times 1} = 5 \times 4 \times 3 = 60$$

When n and r themselves are equal, the permutation formula simplifies to n factorial. For example, if $n = 5$ and $r = 5$, we get

$$_5P_5 = \frac{5!}{(5-5)!} = \frac{5!}{0!} = \frac{5 \times 4 \times 3 \times 2 \times 1}{1} = 5!$$

Recall that 0! equals 1 by definition.

2.4 COMBINATIONS

Many times when we choose r items from a total of n items, we aren't concerned with the order of the selections. For example, say that our five friends Arnoldo, Beth, Cameron, Daniel, and Eve are throwing a party and need to choose three people from among themselves to be on the planning committee. How many ways could they choose these three people? The possible configurations of the committee are enumerated in Table 2.4.

In contrast to running a race, note here that the committee membership denoted by ABC in Table 2.4 would be exactly the same if we chose ABC, ACB, BAC, BCA, CAB, or CBA. Clearly, order of selection does not matter. Instead of permutations, in our committee case we are calculating *combinations*. Because there are fewer configurations when order does not matter, *for given values of* n *and* r, *the number of combinations will always be smaller than or equal to the number of permutations*.

In general, the number of ways r items can be chosen from a total of n items, *in which order does not matter*, can be written using the *combination formula* in Formula 2.6.

Formula 2.6 Combination formula

$$_nC_r = \frac{n!}{r!\,(n-r)!}, r \leq n$$

Table 2.4 Number of ways for five friends to be chosen for a committee of three.

A B C	A B D	A B E	A C D	A C E
A D E	B C D	B C E	B D E	C D E

We read the term $_nC_r$ as "*n* choose *r*." In many texts, the combination term is presented as $\binom{n}{r}$, as shown in Formula 2.7. I often refer to this representation as "the cool way" to write the combination formula.

Formula 2.7   Combination formula, alternate notation

$$\binom{n}{r} = \frac{n!}{r!\,(n-r)!}, r \le n$$

Let's solve our committee problem using the formula. We have $n = 5$ and $r = 3$.

$$_5C_3 = \binom{5}{3} = \frac{5!}{3!\,(5-3)!} = \frac{5!}{3!\,(2)!} = \frac{5 \times 4 \times 3 \times 2 \times 1}{3 \times 2 \times 1 \times (2 \times 1)} = \frac{5 \times 4}{2 \times 1} = 10$$

There are 10 unique committees of three that can be chosen among our five friends.

If we compare the permutation calculation in Formula 2.6 and the combination calculation in Formula 2.7, we find that the combination has an extra term in the denominator, $r!$. *For a given* n *and* r, *the number of permutations will always be greater than the number of combinations by a factor of* $r!$. Note that if *r* equals zero or one, the number of combinations will equal the number of permutations. Contrasting the formulas for our example, we see

$$_5P_3 = \frac{5!}{(5-3)!} = \frac{5!}{2!} = \frac{5 \times 4 \times 3 \times 2 \times 1}{2 \times 1} = 5 \times 4 \times 3 = 60$$

$$_5C_3 = \binom{5}{3} = \frac{5!}{3!\,(5-3)!} = \frac{5!}{3!\,2!} = \frac{5 \times 4 \times 3 \times 2 \times 1}{3 \times 2 \times 1 \times (2 \times 1)} = \frac{5 \times 4}{2 \times 1} = 10$$

The number of permutations (60) is greater than the number of combinations (10) by a factor of $3! = 6$ because of the expression $3!$ in the denominator of the combination formula.

For a given number of items *n*, there is mirror symmetry in the number of combinations as we increase *r* from 0 to *n*. Table 2.5 shows us this phenomenon for the case of $n = 5$.

Table 2.5   Mirror symmetry for combinations, $n = 5$.

$\binom{5}{0} = \dfrac{5!}{0!\,(5-0)!} = 1$	$\binom{5}{5} = \dfrac{5!}{5!\,(5-5)!} = 1$
$\binom{5}{1} = \dfrac{5!}{1!\,(5-1)!} = 5$	$\binom{5}{4} = \dfrac{5!}{4!\,(5-4)!} = 5$
$\binom{5}{2} = \dfrac{5!}{2!\,(5-2)!} = 10$	$\binom{5}{3} = \dfrac{5!}{3!\,(5-3)!} = 10$

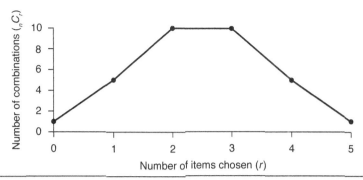

Figure 2.4 Combinations for $n = 5$.

Note that for both $r = 0$ and $r = 5$, the denominators equal 5, resulting in the same number of combinations. Similarly, $r = 1$ and $r = 4$ result in 5 combinations, and $r = 2$ and $r = 3$ result in 10 combinations. Figure 2.4 shows calculated combinations in graphical form.

In practical terms, we can think about choosing a committee of, say, three from five friends by either choosing three people outright or choosing the two that will not be on the committee. Both approaches yield the same result.

Finally, our friends decide to go out for pizza after their movie. The pizza parlor offers a choice of 3 kinds of crusts: deep dish, thin, or traditional. Each crust can be made from either white or wheat flour. The parlor is running a special on pies. Customers can add one type of meat (pepperoni, sausage, or ham) for the same price as a plain cheese pizza. Our friends decide to order the special. How many possible combinations of pizza can be created using these options?

The possible combinations can be enumerated by drawing a tree diagram as shown in Figure 2.5. By inspecting Figure 2.5, we can see that there are 18 possible pizza configurations. The number of unique pizzas can also be calculated outright as follows:

$$3 \text{ crusts} \times 2 \text{ flours} \times 3 \text{ meats} = 18 \text{ pizza configurations}$$

In general, we multiply the number of choices for each option to determine the total number of possible configurations. More formally, we can say we have a number of options from $i = 1$ to g, and each option i has a number of choices defined as n_i. Then the total number of configurations is calculated as shown in Formula 2.8.

Formula 2.8 Total number of configurations

$$n_1 \times n_2 \times \ldots \times n_g = \prod_{i=1}^{g} n_i$$

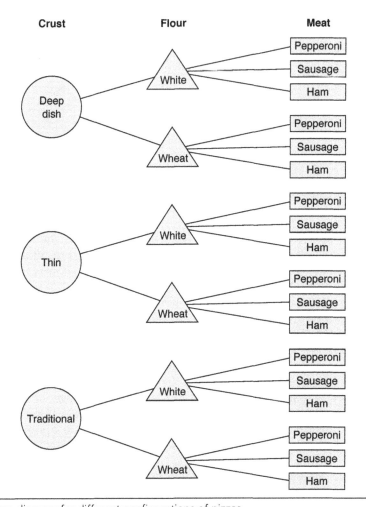

Figure 2.5   Tree diagram for different configurations of pizzas.

2.5 MICROSOFT EXCEL FUNCTIONS FOR COUNTING

The factorial, permutation, and combination formulas presented in this chapter can be evaluated using Microsoft Excel functions. The factorial function, shown in Figure 2.6, is *=fact()* and takes a number as its only argument. For example, to calculate 5!, we would enter *=fact(5)*.

A permutation can be calculated using the *=permut()* function shown in Figure 2.7. The function takes two arguments: number and number chosen. For example, $_5P_2$ would be entered as *=permut(5,2)*.

A combination can be calculated using the *=combin()* function shown in Figure 2.8. The function takes two arguments: number and number chosen. For example, $_5C_2$ would be entered as *=combin(5,2)*.

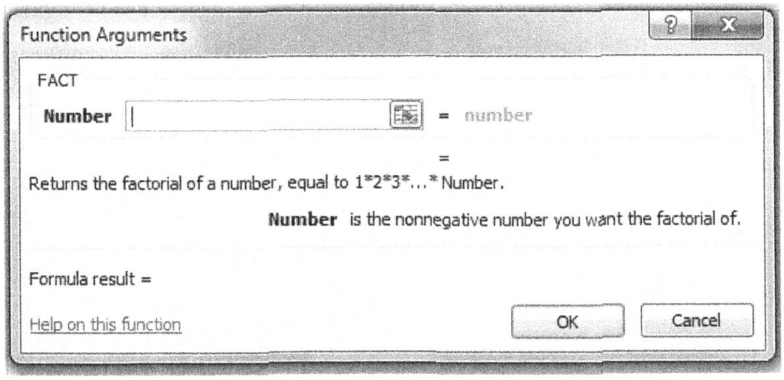

Figure 2.6 Microsoft Excel function =*fact()*.

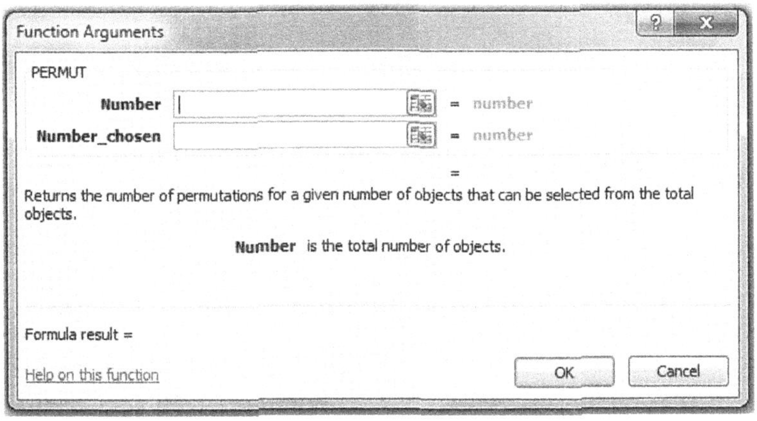

Figure 2.7 Microsoft Excel function =*permut()*.

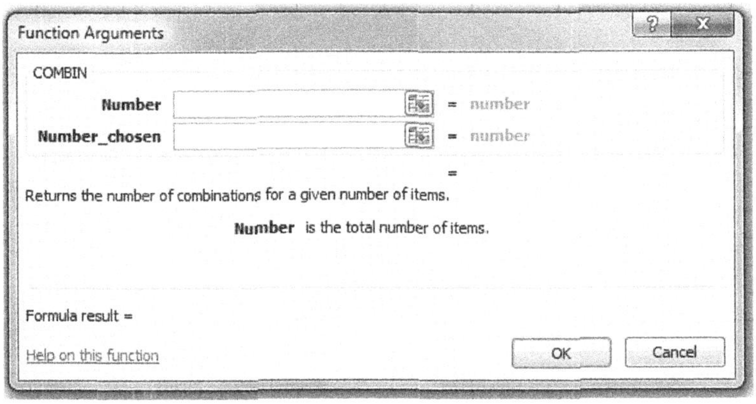

Figure 2.8 Microsoft Excel function =*combin()*.

3

Rules of the Game

If you have ever attempted to follow a cricket match on television, you might have wondered what exactly it was the players were doing, what with their wickets and pitches and bowlers. A ball and bat are involved, but it certainly is not baseball: cricket crowds cheer for seemingly incomprehensible reasons. Even the vocabulary of the game is at once familiar and strange. Why is it that bowlers are sometimes referred to as rabbits, or even ferrets? What exactly is a maiden over, and should we clap or groan when this happens? Most important, how is the score kept?[1]

It is easy to concede that the purpose of the game of cricket, let alone its specific rules, cannot be gleaned from casual observation. The same is true for probability. If we want to be able to formulate and solve probability problems, we will need to learn the basic terminology and rules of the game. Otherwise, probability becomes just another inscrutable cricket match. (It will hearten you to know that in the end, probability is a lot easier to understand than cricket.)

In this chapter, types of data and data collection, or sampling, methods are introduced. The terms, concepts, and rules that allow us to solve many types of probability problems are defined in detail. Finally, seven probability problems are presented that make use of the terms and rules in various, illuminating ways.

3.1 TYPES OF DATA

There are two main types of data: qualitative and quantitative. Qualitative data are generally verbal, such as the information we collect through voice of the customer (VOC), in which we ask our customers for feedback on ways we can improve our service. In quality, this kind of data is typically collated and summarized. On the other hand, quantitative data are used in a vast array of quality applications, such as counting defective products, measuring the dimensions of finished goods, and timing the production cycle. We will focus on quantitative data in our study of probability.

Quantitative data can be further divided into two types: discrete and continuous. Discrete data deal mainly with counts, especially in quality applications. Examples include counts of defectives (such as the number of lightbulbs that fail a go/no go test) and counts of defects (such as tallying up the surface defects found

---

[1] For a gentle introduction to the terms used in cricket and the rules of the game, visit https://www.cs.purdue.edu/homes/hosking/cricket/explanation.htm.

on a refrigerator door panel). Chapter 4 is devoted to probability distributions for this type of count data.

The second classification of quantitative data is continuous data. We collect these data whenever we use an instrument to make a measurement. Examples include measuring the length of a steel beam in inches, the tensile strength of a weld in pounds per square inch, and the changeover time of a production line in minutes. Chapter 5 covers probability distributions used for this type of data, including the normal, or Gaussian, distribution.

3.2 SAMPLING

As quality professionals, we pride ourselves on making decisions based on data, whether the data are qualitative or quantitative, continuous or discrete. When we collect subsets, or samples, from a population, the goal is to have a sample that is representative of the population as a whole. This way, we can make predictions and inferences about the population of interest. As always, good predictions require good data. How, then, can we collect samples that yield reliable information about the population? There are several methods that we can use, including random sampling, stratified sampling, systematic sampling, cluster sampling, and convenience sampling. All of these (except for convenience sampling) can be effective in collecting a sample that is indicative of the population.

The first step in designing a sampling plan is to define the population and list or describe all the members of the population in a *sampling frame*. The population of interest could be all the families in your neighborhood, or just the ones in the cul-de-sac, or all the widgets a department produces on second shift. The goal is to collect a representative sample that can be analyzed to make inferences about the population.

In a *random sampling* scheme, each unit in the population has an equal probability of being chosen for the sample. In *simple random sampling*, each sample of size n has the same probability of being selected as every other sample of the same size. We can use simple random sampling to choose three families in the neighborhood to answer a few survey questions, or to select 25 widgets from second shift for inspection. For the first scenario, we can put all the family names in a bag and then randomly select three. For the second, we can assign an identification number to each widget manufactured, and then choose 25 identification numbers at random to make up the inspection sample.

We can also select members of the population using a *stratified sampling* scheme. Here, each member of the population is first placed into one of several predefined strata. Then, a simple random sample is performed on each stratum. The size of each sample can be constant, or it can be proportional to the size of the population in each stratum. For example, we can define our population as all of the company's customers in the United States, and then we can stratify customers by state. We can either sample n customers per state or randomly select n_i customers per state, where sample size is based on that state's total customers. Using a stratified sample ensures that each state is represented in the sample. By making sample size proportional to stratum population, states with the most customers will have the most representation.

In a *systematic sample*, items in the population are ordered in some way and every kth item is chosen. This sampling scheme can be used to sample every twentieth widget as it moves down the line in an assembly plant, or to select shoppers for a survey as they move past a storefront in the mall, for example.

In a *cluster sampling* scheme, the population is divided into groups called clusters. Clusters are randomly chosen, and then each unit in the selected cluster is included in the sample. For example, say a company wants to determine whether a new training program will improve quality. Using a cluster sampling scheme, the company randomly chooses n departments and trains all the workers in those departments.

Finally, there is *convenience sampling*, which is always the last resort. Convenience samples are chosen solely for their ease of collection and are notoriously unrepresentative of the population. For example, an inspector could select 10 units from the closest machine in a department, or a pollster could simply ask all of her friends who they are voting for in the next election. In each case, the data collector would draw conclusions at his or her own peril.

In probability, we also have the notion of sampling *with* and *without replacement*. For example, say we have a standard deck of 52 cards and want to choose two cards, one after the other. If we sample with replacement, we return our chosen card back to the deck before we pick again. If we sample without replacement, we choose one card, keep it, and then choose a second card from the 51 remaining cards in the deck. The possible outcomes of the second draw change depending on whether there is replacement.

3.3 GRAPHICAL DISPLAYS OF DATA

When presented with a data set, an analyst's first impulse should be to graph it. By graphing we learn about the central tendency, dispersion, and shape of the data distribution and are able to identify any outliers. There are several options for graphing data sets, including the dot plot, histogram, stem and leaf plot, box and whisker plot, and probability plot. Probability plots are introduced in Section 5.5.4.

A dot plot displays a dot on the number line for each point in a data set. It is used for relatively small data sets, say $n \leq 50$. An example is shown in Figure 3.1. This dot plot shows that the data have two peaks occurring at 14 and 25. There is also a data point with value equal to 1, which seems to be an outlier. The analyst would need to investigate whether this outlier was a true reading or whether there was a data entry or measurement error.

The histogram is similar to a dot plot and is more appropriate for graphing larger data sets. The data are broken into nonoverlapping categories, and the frequency of data points in each category is represented by a vertical bar. The histogram gives the analyst a sense of the shape of the distribution of the data set. The histogram displayed in Figure 3.2 shows that the data distribution is fairly symmetric. The most frequently occurring category is the one centered on the value of 24.

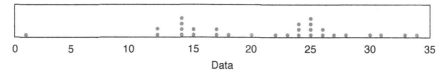

Figure 3.1   Example dot plot.

Note that we cannot determine the most frequently occurring value in the data set (also called the mode) from the histogram. We can only determine the most frequently occurring category.

For sample data sets of 50 points or fewer, we can also create a stem and leaf plot. The graph uses the actual data values to create a frequency plot. In contrast to a dot plot or histogram, the original data can be reconstructed from a stem and leaf plot. An example is shown in Figure 3.3 using the same data as the histogram in Figure 3.2.

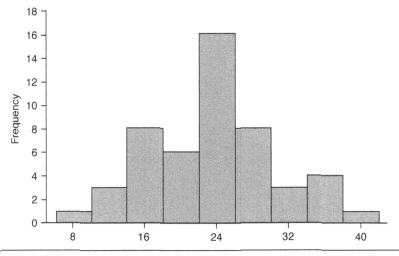

Figure 3.2   Example histogram.

```
Stem-and-leaf of data_1   N = 50
Leaf Unit = 1.0

 1     0    9
 1     1
 4     1    222
 8     1    4445
12     1    6777
14     1    89
18     2    0001
23     2    22333
(11)   2    44444445555
16     2    66666677
 8     2
 8     3    0
 7     3    33
 5     3    455
 2     3    6
 1     3
 1     4    0
```

Figure 3.3   Example stem and leaf plot.

The stem and leaf plot in Figure 3.3 consists of three main sections. The center column contains the stem and, here, represents the tens place of the data. Immediately to the right of the stem column is the leaf column, which represents the ones place of the data. For example, in the third row, which is shaded, the stem is 1 and there are three leaves with value equal to 2. This means that there were three values of 12 in the data set. The first column is the cumulative frequency of the data. The frequencies are totaled from both the top and the bottom of the stem and leaf plot, until they meet the row that contains the center point of the data, or the median. The frequency of the median row is shown in parentheses. Here, the median row contains the values 24 and 25, and there are 11 values in that row. Note that if we turn the stem and leaf plot 90° counterclockwise, we will see the same shape as shown in the histogram, but with the added advantage of seeing the values of the original data.

Finally, we have the box and whisker plot. My students would often ask if this plot was named after the famous twentieth-century statistician George E. P. Box. The answer is no. Sometimes a box is just a box.

The box and whisker plot graphically displays a five-point summary of a data set. The minimum and maximum, as well as the first, second, and third quartiles, are displayed. The first quartile, Q1, represents the point that has 25% of the data less than it. Q1 is also referred to as the 25th percentile. Q2 is the 50th percentile mark, or the median of the data, and Q3 is the 75th percentile of the data. The difference between Q3 and Q1 is known as the interquartile range (IQR). By definition, half of the data are contained within the IQR. The three quartile values are used to create the "box" of the chart. The minimum and maximum values are then plotted and connected to the box with lines that form the "whiskers." Sometimes, a sixth bit of information, the mean, is included in the plot as well.

Figure 3.4 shows a box and whisker plot for the same data as are shown in the dot plot in Figure 3.1. The median of the data is around 24, and 50% of

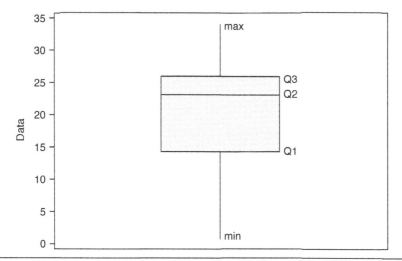

Figure 3.4   Example box and whisker plot.

the data fall between 14 and 26, based on Q1 and Q3. Because the median does not fall in the center of the box, we know that the data distribution is skewed. There is more of a spread of data below the median than above the median since there is more area in the lower part of the box. In addition, we see that the minimum is quite far away from both the median and the Q1 line, indicating a possible outlier.

3.4 EVENTS, TRIALS, AND OUTCOMES

The basic building blocks of probability are events, trials, and outcomes. Each unique possible occurrence for a particular scenario is known as a *simple event*. These simple events have an equal probability of occurring and are collected into a *sample space* Ω (omega). The sample space contains all the possible simple events that can occur for a particular experiment or procedure. For example, if we toss a single die, the sample space for this procedure is composed of six simple events: {1, 2, 3, 4, 5, 6}. If we toss a coin two times, the sample space would contain the simple events {HH, HT, TH, TT}. A *compound event* can be any combination of simple events that are of interest. For example, we could define a compound event A as rolling a number less than 3. Or, for our coin toss, we could define a compound event R as having at least one head in two tosses. We see that event R is mapped to the simple events {HH, HT, and TH}.

By actually throwing the die, or tossing the coin two times, we are performing a *trial* of the experiment or procedure. The result of the trial is the *outcome*. Any outcome can be mapped to a simple event in the sample space. In summary, simple events are possible occurrences, and outcomes are actual occurrences, or results, of a trial. Compound events are a collection of two or more simple events.

3.5 CLASSICAL VERSUS EMPIRICAL PROBABILITY

There is a *classical definition of probability* that is predicated on the fact that the probability of each simple event in the sample space is known and equal. This will be true for cases such as die or coin tosses, or selecting cards from a standard poker deck. The classical definition of the probability of an event A, then, is shown in Formula 3.1.

Formula 3.1   Classical definition of probability

$$P(A) = \frac{\text{number of ways A can occur}}{\text{number of total simple events}} = \frac{s}{N}$$

Note that $P(A)$ is read as the probability that A occurs, or simply the probability of A. By definition, probabilities are between 0 and 1. A probability of zero means that the outcome is impossible, and a probability of 1 means that the outcome is certain.[2]

For situations in which the probabilities of the simple events are not known, we can perform an experiment with several trials, count the number of favorable outcomes, and divide by the number of trials. This is referred to as *empirical probability* or *relative frequency*. We can calculate the relative probability of event A using Formula 3.2.

Formula 3.2 Empirical, or relative frequency, definition of probability

$$P(A) \approx \frac{\text{number of times A occurred}}{\text{total number of trials}} = \frac{a}{n}$$

Note that the empirical probability is an estimate of the true $P(A)$. As the number of trials increases, this estimate will get closer and closer to the true probability of event A.[3] Unless we are counting cards in Vegas (something I do not recommend or condone![4]), the empirical probability formula is more practical for most real-world situations in which all simple events or probabilities are not necessarily known a priori.

3.6 UNIONS AND INTERSECTIONS

We can calculate the probability of two or more events occurring by using the ideas of *union* and *intersection*. The union of two events A and B contains the total number of unique simple events that make up each event. For example, for a single die toss, let event A be defined as rolling either a 1 or a 3, and event B as rolling either a 1 or a 5. The union of these two events is {1, 3, 5}. We can write this by using the symbol for a union, $\cup$:

$$A \cup B = \{1, 3\} \cup \{1, 5\} = \{1, 3, 5\}.$$

Note that $A \cup B$ is equivalent to $B \cup A$. We can think of the union set as the numbers that will satisfy A OR B.

An intersection between two events A and B contains the simple events they have in common. The intersection of events A and B, then, is {1}. We can use the symbol for intersection, $\cap$:

$$A \cap B = \{1, 3\} \cap \{1, 5\} = \{1\}.$$

---

[2] This statement is true for discrete event probability, which is presented in this chapter and in Chapter 4. For the continuous probabilities introduced in Chapter 5, this statement does not hold for certain cases.

[3] See Section 5.2.1, "The Law of Large Numbers."

[4] To further convince you that this is a bad idea, you can read *Bringing Down the House: The Inside Story of Six MIT Students Who Took Vegas for Millions* by Ben Mezrich or watch the 2008 film *21*, inspired by the book.

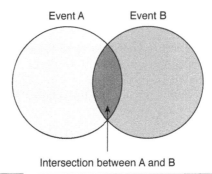

Intersection between A and B

Figure 3.5   Venn diagram with intersection.

Note that A ∩ B is equivalent to B ∩ A. The intersection is the set of simple events that satisfy A AND B.

The intersection of events A and B can be represented in a Venn diagram, as shown in Figure 3.5.

3.7 COMPLEMENT RULE

The *complement* of an event A includes all the simple events in which A *does not* occur. The notation for the complement of A is $\overline{A}$, read as "not A." The probability of $\overline{A}$ is equal to $1 - P(A)$. Conversely, $P(A)$ can be found by $1 - P(\overline{A})$. The complement rule comes in handy when we need to find the probability of event A but the calculation is laborious. We can instead find the probability of $\overline{A}$ and subtract the result from 1.

For example, if we wanted to find the probability of rolling a die and getting a number greater than or equal to 2, we would need to solve:

$$P(X \geq 2) = P(X = 2) + P(X = 3) + P(X = 4) + P(X = 5) + P(X = 6)$$

Using the complement, we instead can calculate the simpler expression to arrive at the same answer:

$$P(X \geq 2) = 1 - P(X = 1)$$

3.8 INDEPENDENCE

Two events A and B are said to be *independent* if the occurrence of one event does not influence the occurrence of the other. For example, let event A be the outcome of a single toss of a coin, and event B the outcome of a second coin toss. Events A and B are independent because the outcome of the first toss does not influence the outcome of the second. Regardless of what transpires on the first toss, the simple events for B are still {H, T}, each with probability 0.50.

We can also think of independence in terms of the transfer of information from trial to trial. If events A and B are independent, knowing if event A has occurred does not give us any additional information on the possible outcomes of B.

If events A and B are independent, then the following statements concerning intersections are true:

$$P(A \cap B) = P(A)P(B)$$

$$P(A \cap \overline{B}) = P(A)P(\overline{B})$$

$$P(\overline{A} \cap B) = P(\overline{A})P(B)$$

$$P(\overline{A} \cap \overline{B}) = P(\overline{A})P(\overline{B})$$

To show that two events A and B are independent, the following condition must be met:

A and B are independent iff $P(A \cap B) = P(A \text{ and } B) = P(A)P(B)$

where "iff" means "if and only if."

For example, a company determines that 25% of its customers are located in-state, 68% of customers are members of the reward program, and 17% of customers are both in-state and reward members. We can prove that event A = in-state location and event B = reward member are independent by showing $P(A \cap B) = P(A)P(B)$:

$$P(\text{In-state and Reward member}) = 0.17$$

$$P(\text{In-state})P(\text{Reward member}) = (0.25)(0.68) = 0.17$$

In this example, independence of the events implies that customer location does not influence whether a customer joins the reward program, and vice versa. Knowing that a customer is in-state does not give us any information about whether the customer is a reward member.

However, if events A and B are not independent, then knowing the status of event A gives us information about the sample space for event B. In fact, for cases in which A and B are not independent, the sample space of B cannot be fully determined until the status of event A is known.

Let's imagine that we have 10 socks in a drawer: 6 are white and 4 are black. This is the classic "socks in a drawer" problem encountered in all college introductory statistics courses. If we select two socks from the drawer, one after the other, what is the chance that we will get two matching socks? Of course, the answer would be 100% if we just turn on the light and look in the drawer for the socks. However, in the twisted scenario described in the statistics textbooks, it is dark, we are late, and we are willing to take our chances.

Let event A be defined as the color of the sock on the first trial, and event B be the color of the sock chosen on the second trial. When we first open the drawer, we have a probability of 6/10 of choosing a white sock and 4/10 of selecting a black sock.

What is the probability of choosing a particular color of sock on the second trial? It depends. If we choose a white sock on the first trial, then the drawer is left with five white socks and four black socks. Choosing a black sock first would leave six white socks and three black socks. Since the sample space for event B depends on the outcome of event A, we say that events A and B are not independent.

We can sketch the possible outcomes using a tree diagram shown in Figure 3.6.

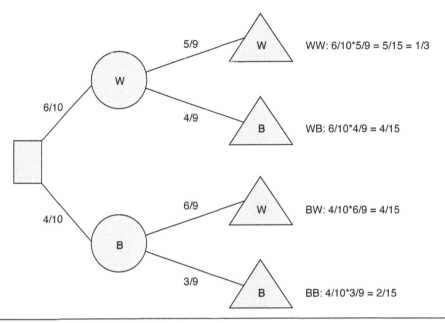

Figure 3.6 Tree diagram for socks in a drawer.

The probability of choosing a white sock on the first draw and a white sock on the second is 6/10*5/9 = 1/3. For a black match, we have 4/10*3/9 = 2/15. The probability of an unmatched pair is 8/15.

3.9 MUTUALLY EXCLUSIVE EVENTS

Two events A and B are said to be mutually exclusive if they cannot occur at the same time. For example, if we toss a coin one time, we cannot simultaneously flip a head (H) and a tail (T). As soon as the coin lands on heads, we know with surety that the coin has not landed on tails. In quality inspection, when we check the dimensions of a part with a go/no go gage, the part will either pass or fail, not both.

In terms of information transfer, mutually exclusive events are *completely dependent* since knowing that one event has occurred gives us perfect knowledge about the outcome of the second event.

A Venn diagram of two mutually exclusive events shows no overlap between the event circles, as shown in Figure 3.7.

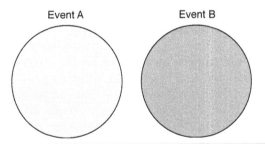

Figure 3.7 Venn diagram of mutually exclusive events.

3.10 CALCULATING ODDS

In addition to calculating the probability of an event, we can also calculate the *odds in favor of* or *odds against* an event occurring. The odds in favor of event A are calculated as the number of ways event A can occur (success) versus the number of ways event A cannot occur (failure). The result is expressed as a ratio separated by a colon, as shown in Formula 3.3. For example, when we flip a coin, we can calculate the odds in favor of getting heads as follows. There is one way to get heads, and one way to get tails, so the odds in favor of heads are written 1:1. Since the number of ways to succeed is equal to the number of ways to fail, we can use a statistical oxymoron and state that the odds are even.

Formula 3.3 Odds in favor of event A

$$\text{Odds in favor of A} = \text{number of ways A can occur:number of ways A cannot occur} = P(A):P(\overline{A})$$

To determine the odds against event A, we use Formula 3.4. Here we take the number of ways event A will not occur and compare it with the number of ways event A can occur.

Formula 3.4 Odds against event A

$$\text{Odds against A} = \text{number of ways A cannot occur:number of ways A can occur} = P(\overline{A}):P(A)$$

Formulas 3.3 and 3.4 show that odds can also be calculated using the success and failure probabilities of an event. For example, the probability of the coin landing on heads is equal to $1/2$, as is the probability of getting tails. The odds in favor of heads are equal to $1/2:1/2$, which is equivalent to 1:1.

If we were to roll a die one time, what are the odds in favor of rolling a 6? The probability of rolling a 6 is equal to $1/6$, and the probability of not rolling a 6 is equal to $5/6$, so the odds are 1:5. Conversely, the odds *against* rolling a 6 are 5:1.

We can also convert odds to probabilities, as shown in Formula 3.5. If the odds of event A are a:b, then the probability of event A is equal to $a/(a + b)$. For example, given the odds 2:5 in favor of event A, the probability of event A is equal to $2/(2 + 5) = 2/7$. The first number in the odds is the numerator in the probability formula, and the sum of the two parts of the odds is the denominator of the probability.

Formula 3.5 Converting odds to probability

$$\text{If odds of event A} = a{:}b, \text{ then } P(A) = \frac{a}{a + b}$$

3.11 CONDITIONAL PROBABILITY

For two events A and B, the probability of event A *given that event B has occurred* is denoted as $P(A|B)$. This is called the conditional probability, since B is a condition on which A depends. Conditional probability can be explained graphically. Let event A reside in a universe Ω that is divided into two parts, B and $\bar{B}$, as shown in Figure 3.8. By definition the area of the universe is equal to one.

Once we are told that event B has occurred, we can divide the universe to form Ω' as shown in Figure 3.9. Here, the probability of event A given event B is the ratio of the area of event A to the area of Ω', or event B.

The conditional probability $P(A|B)$ can be computed using Formula 3.6. Note that $P(A \text{ and } B) \le P(B)$.

Formula 3.6 Conditional probability

$$P(A|B) = \frac{P(A \cap B)}{P(B)} = \frac{P(A \text{ and } B)}{P(B)}$$

For example, if $P(A \text{ and } B) = 0.25$ and $P(B) = 0.40$, then

$$P(A|B) = \frac{P(A \text{ and } B)}{P(B)} = \frac{0.25}{0.40} = 0.625$$

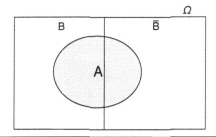

Figure 3.8 Universe with events A and B.

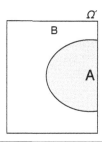

Figure 3.9 Universe with A given B.

Table 3.1   Defects found per production line.

	Defective	Nondefective	Total
Line 1	3	87	90
Line 2	10	75	85
Line 3	25	230	255
Line 4	7	63	70
Total	45	455	500

The data in Table 3.1 show the number of defects found in samples from different production lines.

Using Table 3.1 we can find the probability that a unit came from Line 2, given that it is defective. Define event A as Line 2 and event B as a defective unit. From the table, the probability of a unit being defective and from Line 2 equals 10/500. The probability of a defective unit is 45/500. Putting the information into the conditional formula gives:

$$P(A \mid B) = \frac{P(A \text{ and } B)}{P(B)} = \frac{10/500}{45/500} = 0.222$$

If we choose one of the 500 units at random and find it to be defective, then there is a 22.2% chance that the unit was produced on Line 2. We can also approach the problem using the divided universe concept. As soon as we are given the information that the unit is defective, we can solve the problem by dividing the universe and concentrating only on the defective column, as shown in Table 3.2. The proportion of Line 2 units in the defective column is 10/45 = 0.222.

Now, let's turn the question around: given that a unit is from Line 2, what is the probability that unit is defective? Recall that event A is defined as Line 2 and event B as a defective unit. Now, we solve $P(B \mid A)$:

$$P(B \mid A) = \frac{P(A \text{ and } B)}{P(A)} = \frac{10/500}{85/500} = 0.118$$

Note that this last example illustrates that $P(A \mid B)$ is not equivalent to $P(B \mid A)$. The numerators of both formulas are equal, but the denominators are not the same

Table 3.2   Reduced table, conditional on defectives.

	Defective
Line 1	3
Line 2	10
Line 3	25
Line 4	7
Total	45

since the probability is conditional on different events. Note that $P(A|B)$ means that if we choose a part and find it is defective, there is a 22.2% chance it came from Line 2. $P(B|A)$ means that if we choose a part from Line 2, there is an 11.8% chance it is defective. Mistaking $P(A|B)$ for $P(B|A)$ is an error in logic referred to as *transposing the conditional*.[5]

The conditional probability formula reduces to a simpler form when events A and B are independent. Recall that if two events are independent, the occurrence of one event does not influence the occurrence of the other, with the result that $P(A|B) = P(A)$ and $P(B|A) = P(B)$. If events A and B are independent, the conditional probability is as shown in Formula 3.7.

Formula 3.7 Conditional probability for independent events

$$P(A \mid B) = \frac{P(A \text{ and } B)}{P(B)} = \frac{P(A)P(B)}{P(B)} = P(A)$$

If two events A and B are *mutually exclusive*, then their conditional probability is equal to zero: $P(A|B) = P(B|A) = 0$ since $P(A \text{ and } B) = 0$.

3.12 MULTIPLICATION RULE

To calculate the intersection of two or more events, we use the *multiplication rule* shown in Formula 3.8. For events A and B, the multiplication rule states that the probability of events A and B occurring is the probability of event B given that event A has occurred times the probability of event A.

Formula 3.8 Multiplication rule for two events

$$P(A \cap B) = P(A \text{ and } B) = P(B|A)P(A)$$

$$P(A \cap B) = P(A \text{ and } B) = P(A|B)P(B)$$

We can use the multiplication rule to solve the socks in the drawer problem presented in Section 3.8 and shown in Figure 3.6. For example, consider the probability of choosing two white socks. Let event A be defined as choosing a white sock on the first draw, and event B as choosing a white sock on the second draw. The probability of two white socks is calculated as the probability of choosing a white sock on the first draw times the probability that the second draw is white, given that first was also white.

$$P(A \cap B) = P(A \text{ and } B) = P(A)P(B|A) = (6/10)*(5/9) = 1/3$$

If events A and B are independent, then the conditional probability of event A given event B is equal to the probability of event A, $P(A|B) = P(A)$, so the multiplication rule simplifies to Formula 3.9.

---

[5] The error of transposing the conditional often occurs in statistical hypothesis testing as well as in the courtroom. See, for example, http://scholarship.law.cornell.edu/cgi/viewcontent.cgi?article=1380&context=facpub for an interesting discussion on how juries treat DNA evidence.

Formula 3.9   Multiplication rule for two independent events

$$P(A \cap B) = P(A \text{ and } B) = P(A)P(B)$$

3.13 ADDITION RULE

The probability addition rule is used to calculate the probability of a union of two or more events. Because we won't always enumerate all the possible simple events for a scenario, we need a formula that will allow us to find probabilities for unions of events. The addition rule is shown in Formula 3.10.

Formula 3.10   Addition rule

$$P(A \cup B) = P(A \text{ or } B) = P(A) + P(B) - P(A \text{ and } B)$$

Note that the multiplication rule is used in the addition rule since we must calculate the intersection of events A and B. We subtract off the intersection of A and B to avoid double counting the simple event that satisfies both conditions of A and B.

If events A and B are independent, the addition rule can be written as shown in Formula 3.11.

Formula 3.11   Addition rule, independent events

$$P(A \cup B) = P(A \text{ or } B) = P(A) + P(B) - P(A)P(B)$$

If events A and B are mutually exclusive, their intersection is equal to zero. Therefore, the addition rule simplifies to Formula 3.12.

Formula 3.12   Addition rule, mutually exclusive events

$$P(A \cup B) = P(A \text{ or } B) = P(A) + P(B)$$

3.14 LAW OF TOTAL PROBABILITY AND BAYES' THEOREM

Bayes' theorem makes use of the *law of total probability*. Let the sample space Ω be divided into k disjoint outcomes for event B. Then the probability of another event, A, is equal to the weighted average of the conditional probabilities $P(A|B_i)$. Figure 3.10 illustrates an example with $k = 3$.

The law of total probability is shown in Formula 3.13.

Formula 3.13   Law of total probability

$$P(A) = P(A|B_1)P(B_1) + P(A|B_2)P(B_2) + \ldots + P(A|B_k)P(B_k)$$

$$P(A) = \sum_{i=1}^{k} P(A|B_i)P(B_i)$$

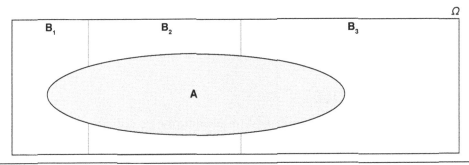

Figure 3.10   Schematic for law of total probability, $k = 3$.

In the simplest case, we have a partition of two parts, B and $\bar{\text{B}}$, and the law of total probability reduces to Formula 3.14.

Formula 3.14   Law of total probability, $k = 2$

$$P(A) = P(A|B)P(B) + P(A|\bar{B})P(\bar{B})$$

If we know the value of the conditional probability $P(A|B)$, how can we calculate $P(B|A)$? The Methodist minister and mathematician Thomas Bayes (1701–1761) developed the method to derive $P(B|A)$ from $P(A|B)$. This methodology was known as the Bayesian Heresy because it gave a way to predict the past from a future observation, a concept previously thought absurd.[6]

Bayes' theorem for $k = 2$ is shown in Formula 3.15.

Formula 3.15   Bayes' theorem, $k = 2$

$$P(B|A) = \frac{P(B)P(A|B)}{P(B)P(A|B) + P(\bar{B})P(A|\bar{B})} = \frac{P(B)P(A|B)}{P(A)}$$

The proof of the theorem uses the law of total probability:

$$P(B|A) = \frac{P(B)P(A|B)}{P(B)P(A|B) + P(\bar{B})P(A|\bar{B})}$$

$$= P(B)\frac{P(A|B)}{P(A)}$$

$$= P(B)\frac{P(A \cap B)}{P(A)P(B)}$$

$$= \frac{P(A \cap B)}{P(A)}$$

$$= P(B|A)$$

---

[6] For more information on the Bayesian Heresy read David Salsburg's book, *The Lady Tasting Tea: How Statistics Revolutionized Science in the Twentieth Century.*

Here is an example to illustrate the use of Bayes' theorem. At a regional medical center, 3.9% of the hospital's admissions are due to community acquired pneumonia. Hospital records show that the probability that a pneumonia patient is readmitted within 30 days of discharge is 18.1%. Readmission rates for all other diagnoses are 14.5%. Defining event A as readmission within 30 days of discharge and event B as a previous pneumonia diagnosis, we have:

$$P(A|B) = P(\text{Readmission} | \text{Pneumonia}) = 0.181$$

$$P(A|\overline{B}) = P(\text{Readmission} | \text{All other diagnoses}) = 0.145$$

Using this information, we can answer a completely different question: If a patient is readmitted within 30 days of discharge, what is the probability that he or she had been a pneumonia patient? This problem is an example of the Bayesian Heresy in which we predict the past given a future event. To solve, we must calculate $P(\text{Pneumonia} | \text{Readmission})$ or $P(B|A)$ even though we only have information on $P(A|B)$. Using Bayes' theorem, we can calculate:

$$P(B | A) = P(\text{Pneumonia} | \text{Readmission}) = \frac{P(B)P(A | B)}{P(B)P(A | B) + P(\overline{B})P(A | \overline{B})}$$

$$= \frac{0.039(0.181)}{0.039(0.181) + 0.961(0.145)} = 0.048$$

This result shows that although 18.1% of pneumonia patients are readmitted, there is only a 4.8% chance that a readmitted patient was previously hospitalized for pneumonia. Note that the terms $P(B)$ and $P(\overline{B})$ in the denominator add to one, but there is no such requirement for the terms $P(A|B)$ and $P(A|\overline{B})$. Use these facts to make sure you've constructed your formula correctly.

For a situation with k possible outcomes, $B_1, B_2, \ldots, B_k$, we can use the general form of Bayes' theorem shown in Formula 3.16.

Formula 3.16   General form of Bayes' theorem

$$P(B_1 | A) = \frac{P(B_1)P(A | B_1)}{\sum_{i=1}^{k} P(B_i)P(A | B_i)} = \frac{P(B)P(A | B)}{P(A)}$$

3.15 COUNTING EXAMPLES

The three problems in this section illustrate how counting principles, sampling, and the probability rules introduced earlier in this chapter can be used to solve quite interesting and complex problems. Here, the egg problem, the Lotto problem, and the birthday problem are introduced and their solutions are explained in detail.

3.15.1 The Egg Problem

Imagine that your local grocery store has a sale on large eggs, one dozen for 99 cents. You bring a carton home and realize that 5 of the 12 eggs are cracked (no wonder they were on sale!). Your spouse doesn't know about the cracked eggs and chooses three at random to make an omelet. What is the probability that exactly one of the three eggs chosen is cracked? We will use the concepts of classical probability, combinations, and sampling without replacement to solve.

In this type of problem, you are given a great deal of information about the population. First, you know how many are in the population—here, $N = 12$. Second, the population is separated into two distinct groups (cracked and not cracked), and the membership of those groups is known, $D = 5$ cracked eggs and $(N - D) = 7$ eggs not cracked. Next, you are told that a sample is taken from the population and how large the sample is. Here, it is $n = 3$ eggs chosen for the omelet.

The probability calculation consists of the number of ways of choosing exactly 1 cracked egg from a sample of 3 in the numerator, and the total number of ways 3 eggs can be chosen from 12 in the denominator. The numerator has two combination formulas because we have two distinct groups in the population (cracked and not cracked). The denominator contains one combination formula that tells us how many ways a sample of n can be chosen from N things.

$$\Pr(X = x) = \frac{\binom{D}{x}\binom{N-D}{n-x}}{\binom{N}{n}}$$

We have two groups in our population: 5 cracked and 7 uncracked eggs. Your spouse chose 3 of the dozen eggs for the omelet. Putting the numbers into the formula, we get:

$$\Pr(X = 1) = \frac{\binom{5}{1}\binom{7}{2}}{\binom{12}{3}}$$

Notice that the top numbers in the combinations in the numerator (5 and 7) add up to the top number in the combination in the denominator ($5 + 7 = 12$). Likewise, the bottom numbers in the numerator sum to the bottom number in the denominator ($1 + 2 = 3$). If you do that simple check you will get an egg problem correct every time. We see that there is close to a 50% chance that one cracked egg was used in the omelet.

$$\Pr(X = 1) = \frac{\binom{5}{1}\binom{7}{2}}{\binom{12}{3}} \approx \frac{\frac{5!}{1!\,(4!)} \times \frac{7!}{2!\,(5!)}}{\frac{12!}{3!\,(9!)}} = \frac{5 \times 21}{220} = 0.477$$

This type of problem, in which N, D, and n are given, is called a *hypergeometric* problem. The hypergeometric distribution is used often in quality inspection calculations and is presented in detail in Section 4.5.

3.15.2 The Lotto Problem

Like the player who uses a system for picking numbers introduced in Chapter 1, everyone dreams of winning the lottery and gaining financial independence. The author and philosopher Voltaire teamed up with a statistician to win more than a million francs in the 1728–1730 French lottery by buying up most of the tickets.[7] Nowadays, there are so many combinations for the Mega Millions game that it would take 28 years to fill in the bubbles on the paper forms to buy all the tickets.[8] For a more modest, single-ticket approach, what is the probability of winning the popular Mega Millions lottery?

When buying a ticket, a player chooses five numbers from 1 to 75 and then chooses one Mega Ball number from 1 to 15. There are nine ways to win, each with different odds and payouts, as shown in Table 3.3. We assume a simple $1 play with no "payout multiplier."

Can we calculate the odds reported in Table 3.3? To solve, we will use the concepts of classical probability, independent events, the multiplication rule, and the definition of odds.

We will calculate the odds for four of the nine entries (shaded in Table 3.3): matching five white balls and the Mega Ball, matching five white balls, matching four white balls and the Mega Ball, and matching zero white balls and the Mega Ball.

Table 3.3 Lottery winning combinations and odds.

Matching numbers	Cash prize	Odds of winning
5 white balls + Mega Ball	Jackpot!	1:258,890,849
5 white balls	$1,000,000	1:18,492,203
4 white balls + Mega Ball	$5,000	1:739,687
4 white balls	$500	1:52,834
3 white balls + Mega Ball	$50	1:10,719
3 white balls	$5	1:765
2 white balls + Mega Ball	$5	1:472
1 white ball + Mega Ball	$2	1:55
0 white balls + Mega Ball	$1	1:20

Source: Adapted from Mega Millions website, http://www.megamillions.com/how-to-play.

---

[7] To learn more, see the article on the Significance website: http://www.statslife.org.uk/history-of-stats-science/31-odd-statistical-snippet-of-the-week-voltaire-and-the-statistician-who-won-the-lottery-and-proved-that-the-earth-is-not-round.

[8] See the *Forbes* article: http://www.forbes.com/sites/joshbarro/2012/03/30/can-you-ever-guarantee-a-mega-millions-win/.

To find the odds of winning the jackpot, we first calculate the probability of matching all five white balls and the Mega Ball. There is one way to match all white balls, and $_{75}C_5$, or 75 choose 5 ways of selecting 5 numbers out of 75. Then, there is the probability of 1/15 of matching the Mega Ball. Multiplying the probabilities of these two independent events gives us:

$$P(\text{Win}) = \frac{1}{\binom{75}{5}} \times \frac{1}{15} = \frac{1}{258,890,850}$$

Then, the odds in favor of winning are calculated:

$$\text{Odds} = \frac{P(\text{Win})}{1 - P(\text{Win})} = \frac{\left(\dfrac{1}{258,890,850}\right)}{\left(\dfrac{258,890,849}{258,890,850}\right)} = 1{:}258,890,849$$

The probability of matching all five white balls but *not* the Mega Ball is found by using:

$$P(\text{Win}) = \frac{1}{\binom{75}{5}} \times \frac{14}{15} = \frac{1}{18,492,204}$$

The odds in favor of winning in this manner are:

$$\text{Odds} = \frac{P(\text{Win})}{1 - P(\text{Win})} = \frac{\left(\dfrac{1}{18,492,204}\right)}{\left(\dfrac{18,492,203}{18,492,204}\right)} = 1{:}18,492,203$$

These odds tell us it is 14 times more likely to win this $1,000,000 prize than it is to win the jackpot.

Next, let's find the probability of matching four white balls and the Mega Ball. Note that this is like the egg problem solved in Section 3.15.1. The 75 numbers are broken into two groups: the winning combination ($D = 5$) and the rest ($N - D$) = 70. We want four from the winning numbers and one from the rest.

$$P(\text{Win}) = \frac{\binom{5}{4}\binom{70}{1}}{\binom{75}{5}} \times \frac{1}{15} = \frac{1}{739,688}$$

The odds in favor of winning in this manner:

$$\text{Odds} = \frac{P(\text{Win})}{1 - P(\text{Win})} = \frac{\left(\dfrac{1}{739,688}\right)}{\left(\dfrac{739,687}{739,688}\right)} = 1{:}739,687$$

Finally, we can find the probability of matching zero white balls but matching the Mega Ball:

$$P(\text{Win}) = \frac{\binom{5}{0}\binom{70}{5}}{\binom{75}{5}} \times \frac{1}{15} = \frac{1}{21}$$

The odds in favor of winning this $1 prize are:

$$\text{Odds} = \frac{P(\text{Win})}{1 - P(\text{Win})} = \frac{\left(\dfrac{1}{21}\right)}{\left(\dfrac{20}{21}\right)} = 1{:}20$$

3.15.3 The Birthday Problem

According to author and professor of mathematics John Allen Paulos,[9] the innumerate in our society tend to attribute meaning to simple coincidences. For example, many people are amazed when, in a meeting of 10 people, two people share the same birth date (month and day, not year). "Wow, what are the chances?" they wonder aloud, and then attribute some great cosmic meaning to it all. Well, what are the chances? We will calculate them now using the concepts of classical probability, independent events, the multiplication rule, sampling without replacement, and the complement rule.

What is the probability that at least two people will have a birth date in common in a group of 10 people? This includes two or more people sharing a birth date in common, or having two or more sets of people having birth dates in common, and so on. There are a lot of different ways this could happen, so it is better to calculate the *complement* of these occurrences, which is the probability that all 10 people have distinct birth dates. We then can take this result and subtract it from one to get the probability of at least two birth dates in common.

Consider the first person in the room. He will have 365 possible allowable answers for his birth date (we are ignoring leap years here, for simplicity). After he tells you his birth date, the second person can only have one of 364 possible birth dates since we don't want any sharing of dates. The next will have 363 allowable answers, and so on.

$$\text{Pr(No shared birth dates)} \approx \frac{365 \times 364 \times 363 \times 362 \times 361 \times 360 \times 359 \times 358 \times 357 \times 356}{365^{10}}$$

The denominator denotes all the possible ways 10 people could have birth dates, without any restrictions. Each could have a choice of 365 dates.

---

[9] Paulos is a professor of mathematics at Temple University in Philadelphia, Pennsylvania. He is the author of many popular books on mathematical misconceptions, including *Innumeracy*, published in 2001.

Now, using the complement rule, we get

Pr(No shared birth dates) = 0.883

Pr(At least one shared birth date) = 1 − 0.883 = 0.117

There is about a 12% chance that there will be at least one matching birth date in any gathering of 10 people. That's not exactly a tiny chance, and certainly nothing to attribute to cosmic influence.

For determining the probability of at least one birth date match in a group of N people, we can use the general formula:

$$Pr(\text{At least 1 shared birth date}) = 1 - \left[\frac{365 \times (365 - 1) \times (365 - 2) \times \ldots \times (365 - (N - 1))}{365^N} \right]$$

3.16 CONDITIONAL PROBABILITY EXAMPLES

The following four problems require the use of conditional probability to solve. The first is a famous problem involving a game show, called the Monty Hall problem, and the second is the airline problem. The third, the spam problem, introduces the concepts of sensitivity and specificity of screening tests. The final example involves a phenomenon called Simpson's Paradox. In all cases, the solutions are explained in detail.

3.16.1 The Monty Hall Problem

The Monty Hall problem is a favorite of statisticians. This problem gained notoriety when Marilyn vos Savant answered it (correctly) in her "Ask Marilyn" column in *Parade* magazine. She promptly received patronizing letters from mathematics professors who dismissively informed her that her math and logic were wrong. She prevailed in the end, leaving many PhDs with egg on their faces and propelling the problem to its now classic status.[10]

Recall from your childhood watching the game show *Let's Make a Deal* with host Monty Hall. In the show, some contestant (usually dressed in an unflattering costume) is chosen from the audience. Let's call her Sally. Sally is presented with three doors. Behind one door is a new station wagon, and behind the other two are non-prizes, like a hog or a billy goat. Sally, clearly wanting the station wagon, chooses a door.

Then, in a cruel twist, Monty opens one of the doors that Sally has not chosen and reveals what is behind it. It is never the car; it's either the hog or the billy goat. Monty turns to Sally and asks whether she wants to switch her choice of door. The question then is to figure out the better strategy: Should Sally stick with her original choice, or should she switch doors? The stages of the game are shown in Figures 3.11, 3.12, and 3.13.

---

[10] To read more on the history of the Monty Hall problem, and the controversy Marilyn vos Savant created by answering it correctly, read "The Time Everyone 'Corrected' the World's Smartest Woman," http://priceonomics.com/the-time-everyone-corrected-the-worlds-smartest/.

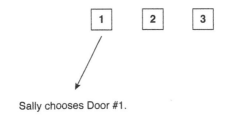

Figure 3.11   Monty Hall problem step 1.

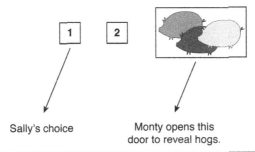

Figure 3.12   Monty Hall problem step 2.

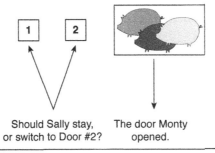

Figure 3.13   Monty Hall problem step 3.

A lot of people, PhD mathematicians included, think that at this point in the game it doesn't matter whether Sally switches, because the probability of choosing the correct door is 1/2, or 50%. Here is their logic: at first, Sally had a 1/3 chance of choosing the door with the car behind it. When Monty opened one of the losing doors, Sally was left with a choice between two doors. Therefore, there is now a 1 in 2 chance of selecting the correct door. It makes perfect sense. Except that it is wrong!

Since it is a small problem in terms of number of doors, we can solve it by enumeration, or writing out the outcomes for all the possible decisions Sally could make. We will need to calculate the probability of winning the station wagon if she stays with the original choice, and the probability of winning if she switches to the other door. In Table 3.4, with no loss of generality, let Door #1 be the winning door. Note that W = win and L = lose.

Table 3.4   Monty Hall enumeration of outcomes.

Original choice	Switch	Stay
Door #1 (car)	L	W
Door #2 (hog)	W	L
Door #3 (billy goat)	W	L

From inspecting Table 3.4, we can see that Sally will win two out of three times if she switches doors, and she will win only one out of three times if she stays. The conditional probability of winning given that she stays with the original door is $Pr(Win \mid Stay) = 1/3$ and the $Pr(Win \mid Switch) = 2/3$. Therefore, the optimal strategy is for Sally to always switch.

Why is this so? If Sally originally chose Door #1, the one with the station wagon, then Monty would open either Door #2 or #3 to reveal the farm animals. If she switched after this, she would switch to a losing door. If Sally originally chose Door #2, then Monty would have to open the only other losing door, Door #3. If Sally switched after this, she would choose the winning door, Door #1. The same is true if Sally originally chose Door #3. In other words, there is more of a chance of choosing the wrong door at the outset (2/3), so switching makes sense.

Marilyn vos Savant effectively explained the winning strategy to her detractors by posing the following question: What if, instead of three, there had been 1 million doors. Sally chooses one of them, and then Monty Hall opens up 999,998 of the remaining doors, leaving one. Would it make sense to switch?

3.16.2 The Airline Problem

At one time, I worked for a software company as a statistician, developing mathematical models to describe the relationship between pricing and customer behavior. I was on a project team that was trying to make a sale to a client, and some of the team had to fly to Ohio to make the pitch. The meeting went well, but it had run long, and the team missed the Friday afternoon flight back to Atlanta. I was in the home office when the guys called from the airline lounge. They were trying to figure out which flight to book back to Atlanta and wanted my advice as a statistician.

As the story went, the team lead, Kevin, had had his original morning flight to Ohio canceled. He was rebooked on another flight, and that airplane had to turn around and return to the airport due to an equipment problem. On the third try, he finally got to the client site for the meeting. Mulling this over in the lounge, the other team members thought it would be a good idea to book the same flight home as Kevin. Their logic was that the chances of Kevin getting another canceled or problem flight, after all his trouble that morning, were pretty small, and that any flight Kevin chose would most likely get back to Atlanta on time. They asked me my opinion. The situation reminded me of the joke about the skydiver who always carried a faulty backup parachute as insurance because he figured the chances of having two defective parachutes on a jump were practically zero.

I explained to the guys stuck in the airport that the probability of Kevin having a problem with his flight that evening changed depending on the time of day someone was making the prediction. If they had asked me in the morning to find the probability that Kevin would have a canceled flight, then a flight that had to turn around, and then a troublesome flight that evening, the probability would have been very, very small. But, since he had already had two of those incidents happen, and assuming that the flight status was independent and not due to continuing weather, then his trouble in the morning did not affect the probability that the next flight would be a problem. Hence, Pr(flight delay in evening | two delays in morning) = Pr(flight delay in evening) due to independence of the events. Kevin's evening flight had the same chance of being trouble-free as any other.

3.16.3 The Spam Problem

We all have been bothered by junk e-mails, or spam. Many companies have developed spam-filtering software to cut down on the amount of nuisance e-mail we all get. The problem with some of this filtering software is that it lets through some spam when it shouldn't, and, worse, it stops some legitimate e-mails from getting through to the intended recipient. How can we evaluate whether a spam-filtering program is effective? For this example, we will use a *contingency table* and the concepts of *sensitivity* and *specificity* to solve.

The screening software must do two things well. First, it must catch spam. Second, it must allow legitimate e-mails through. We can determine the extent to which the software does each task by calculating measures of sensitivity and specificity.

Sensitivity and specificity are used in the medical field to determine the efficacy of screening tests, for example. In the medical application, sensitivity is the probability of a positive test result given that there is disease (true positive). Specificity is the probability of a negative test result given that there is no disease (true negative). Both terms are conditional probabilities, as shown:

$$\text{Sensitivity} = P(\text{Test} + | \text{Disease})$$

$$\text{Specificity} = P(\text{Test} - | \text{No disease})$$

For the spam-filtering problem, having an e-mail filtered is considered a "positive test," and "disease" status can be classified as spam. In this case, sensitivity is the probability that an e-mail will be filtered out given that it is spam. Specificity is the probability that an e-mail will be passed through given that it is legitimate.

$$\text{Sensitivity} = P(\text{Filtered} | \text{Spam})$$

$$\text{Specificity} = P(\text{Passed through} | \text{Not spam})$$

A test was conducted to determine how well the software performed. The results of the software test are shown in the *contingency table* in Table 3.5.

Table 3.5   Contingency table for software performance.

	Spam	Passed through	Totals
Spam	110	15	125
Not spam	75	225	300
Totals	185	240	425

Based on the outcome of the test, the values of sensitivity and specificity are calculated as:

$$\text{Sensitivity} = P(\text{Filtered} \mid \text{Spam}) = 110/125 = 0.88$$

$$\text{Specificity} = P(\text{Passed through} \mid \text{Not spam}) = 225/300 = 0.75$$

Although the software finds and filters a commendable 88% of all spam, the specificity measure shows us it also filters out 25% of the good e-mail! It seems that a little more development work needs to be done to improve the specificity of the software.

3.16.4 The Simpson's Paradox Problem

Quality professionals make data-driven decisions and recommendations every day: data are charted, analyzed, plotted, and tabulated, all in order to assist in the decision-making process. Good data, well analyzed, make our lives easier. In some instances, however, the data can seem to turn on us by pointing to two contradictory statements at once. The data analysis may clearly point out that factor A is driving the response; at the same time, another analysis with the same data may just as clearly indicate that factor A has no effect on the response at all. How can both conclusions be true?

These head-scratching analysis results may be a sign that a statistical phenomenon known as *Simpson's Paradox*[11] is at play. Simpson's Paradox refers to a situation in which the conclusions we draw when data are presented in separate groups actually reverse when those groups are combined. In these cases, the quality professional has to have the proper tools to be a good data detective. Recognizing the hallmarks of Simpson's Paradox and discerning what mechanism is driving the response are the keys to unraveling the truth behind the data.

Suppose that you are the quality manager in a manufacturing facility, and an unexpected increase in defectives occurs over the course of two shifts. The line workers, quality inspectors, and engineers who have been working on the situation give a report with the summary data found in Table 3.6.

Doing some quick analysis, you confirm that the overall defect rate is 201/1800, or 11.2%. The defect rate on the first shift is 20/920, or 2.2%. The rate on the second

Table 3.6 Number defective by shift.

	Shift 1	Shift 2	Shift 3
Defective	20	181	201
Nondefective	900	699	1599
Total	920	880	1800
Percent defective	2.2%	20.6%	11.2%

---

[11] See E. H. Simpson, "The Interpretation of Interaction in Contingency Tables," *Journal of the Royal Statistical Society Series B* 13 (1951): 238–241.

shift is an even more alarming 181/880, or 20.6%. Your mind races as you brainstorm possible causes of the defective rate on second shift. You set up a meeting with the second-shift supervisor and engineer and plan to ask them in detail about what happened over the last shift.

After some more digging by your staff, you are given another report with the data found in Tables 3.7 and 3.8.

Taking out your calculator, you check the defective percentage by shift once more. For raw material from Supplier A, the defective rate for the first shift is 11/880, or 1.3%, a bit lower than in your previous analysis. This seems a little odd.

For the second shift, you calculate a defective rate of 1.3% as well. One point three percent! Wait a minute . . . second shift had a 20.6% defective rate and now it has the same rate as first shift? What happened to the huge quality disparity between shifts?

The second table gives no less puzzling results. Defective rates for *both* shifts in this table are 22.5%! This new set of tables seems to indicate that both shifts produced defectives at the same rate. The first analysis with the summary table clearly showed that the trouble was on second shift.

There is no error in the data or the analysis. You have stumbled upon Simpson's Paradox, a statistical phenomenon that occurs when the results calculated for separate groups suddenly change when the groups are combined into one table.

Understanding the Paradox

Let's look closely at Tables 3.7 and 3.8. Two suppliers are used for the raw material. The majority of product on the first shift was produced using material from Supplier A: 880 of the 920 products. Conversely, material from Supplier B was used for 800 of the 880 products produced on second shift. Looking at the defect

Table 3.7   Results for Supplier A (raw material).

	Shift 1	Shift 2	Shift 3
Defective	11	1	12
Nondefective	869	79	948
Total	880	80	960
Percent defective	1.3%	1.3%	1.3%

Table 3.8   Results for Supplier B (raw material).

	Shift 1	Shift 2	Shift 3
Defective	9	180	189
Nondefective	31	620	651
Total	40	800	840
Percent defective	22.5%	22.5%	22.5%

rates between suppliers, we see that product made using Supplier A material had a 12/960 = 1.25% defective rate, while that made using Supplier B material had a 189/840 = 22.5% defective rate.

As the tables show, the raw material shipment from Supplier B is the true cause of the defective products. But, because second shift made most of its product using this material, it seemed that the second shift *itself* was at fault when the data for both suppliers were combined into one table, as shown in Table 3.6.

In technical terms, defective rate and shift are *conditionally independent, given supplier*. This means that supplier is simultaneously related to both the shift and the defective rate. That is why looking at shift and number defective in the first table gave us the impression that second shift produced defectives at a higher rate: shift was an *indirect* measure of supplier in that case.

But, once we were given direct information about supplier (the real driver here), as in the second set of tables, knowing which shift made a product gave us no information about whether it was defective. These relationships are shown schematically in Figure 3.14.

"Fixing" the Paradox

The data in the three tables shown in the example were correct, and no analysis errors were made. The problem lay solely with the data. Because the faulty material from Supplier B was used disproportionately more in the second shift, supplier and shift became related variables. When information from both suppliers was combined across shifts, it incorrectly appeared that shift was the driver of the defects.

How can we avoid making faulty conclusions caused by Simpson's Paradox? A general piece of advice is to view data in their most granular form. Each time you roll up the data across a variable to create a summary table, your total sample increases, but you run the risk of combining data from a driver variable and hiding its effect. Therefore, make decisions using the lowest-level tables available. In our example, the lowest-level tables clearly (and correctly) showed that supplier was the driver of the defective parts.

Beware of Well-Behaved Data

If you recognize that you have an instance of Simpson's Paradox, you can easily make the right call by drawing conclusions from the lowest-level tables. A more

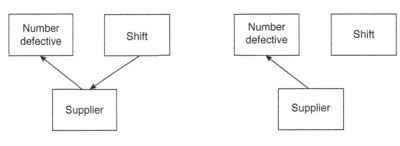

Figure 3.14   Schematic of relationships among variables.

common and insidious problem can exist when your data appear well behaved—no paradoxical results, just straightforward information. For example, what if only Table 3.6, which shows defectives versus shift, were made available to you? You would have drawn the wrong conclusion about defective rates on the second shift. The factor "supplier" would have been an unaccounted-for, *lurking variable*, and you would have based your decision on an indirect driver.

Or, what if Tables 3.7 and 3.8 were not broken down by the true driver of the defectives but by another incidental variable such as machine? The false shift effect would have remained.

It is wise to keep in mind that the variable that seems associated with your response in a summary table may actually be an indirect link and not the primary driver. A little more digging may be necessary to uncover the influential factor.

4

Discrete Probability Distributions

This chapter begins with an introduction to probability concepts for discrete random variables. After the term *discrete random variable* is defined, we continue by looking at the rules relating to discrete probability distributions. After this important groundwork is laid, seven well-known and very useful discrete probability distributions are then introduced: the discrete uniform, binomial, multinomial, hypergeometric, geometric, negative binomial (also known as the Pascal), and Poisson. For each distribution, the text presents and explains the probability mass function, gives the distributional parameters, and shows the formulas for calculating the expected values and variance of X. The shape of the distribution and how it changes based on the parameters is then illustrated. The text also gives real-world, quality-oriented situations in which the distribution can be applied. Related Microsoft Excel functions and worked examples are also given. A summary of the distributions presented is included at the end of the chapter.

4.1 PROBABILITY CONCEPTS FOR DISCRETE RANDOM VARIABLES

Recall from Chapter 3 that a random variable X can take on certain values based on the outcome of an experiment or procedure. For example, if we were to flip a coin, the outcome would be either a head or a tail. The random variable X for this procedure, then, can have outcomes described as {H, T}. If we were to throw a die, the random variable X could take on the values {1, 2, 3, 4, 5, 6}. The set of possible outcomes for X in these two cases is *finite*, meaning that there is a known number of outcomes of the procedure.

If we were to count the number of cars that pass a certain mile marker on a highway for one day, our possible outcomes could include no cars at all (unlikely, but not impossible), one, two, three, four, five, six, . . . We could go on and on. Where will this end? In this case, we don't have a specific stopping point for our possible outcomes. We describe the set of possible outcomes for this random variable as *countably infinite*. In other words, if we had enough time, we could count all the cars, but we don't know ahead of time how high we will go. Imagine trying to count all the grains of sand on a beach. In theory, we could count every grain, but we'd probably be late for dinner.

For both the finite and countably infinite cases, the random variable X is said to be *discrete*. The X can only take on certain values that can be written down directly, as in the coin and die examples, or it can take on counts, as in the car and sand examples.

4.1.1 Probability Mass Functions

The discrete random variable X can take on certain values based on probabilities. When tossing a coin, the possible outcomes of X are {H, T}. The probability of outcome H is 1/2, and the probability of outcome T is 1/2. Likewise, if X describes the outcome of a die toss, the outcomes {1, 2, 3, 4, 5, 6} all have a probability of occurrence equal to 1/6. We can define a *probability mass function* of a discrete random variable X, denoted $P(X)$, as the probabilities associated with each outcome of the procedure. For example, let X be the outcome of a coin toss. Then, the probability mass function is:

$$X = H, P(X) = 1/2$$

$$X = T, P(X) = 1/2$$

We can also put the probability mass function in a tabular form as shown in Table 4.1. The probability mass function for X = (outcome of a die toss) can be tabulated as shown in Table 4.2.

In order for a function to be classified as a *discrete probability mass function*, the probability of occurrence for each outcome must be between 0 and 1. This isn't too surprising, since this is the allowable range for probabilities. Also, the sum of the probabilities of all the possible outcomes of X must equal one. In other words, the

Table 4.1   Probability mass function of coin toss outcome.

X	$P(X)$
H	1/2
T	1/2

Table 4.2   Probability mass function of die toss outcome.

X	$P(X)$
1	1/6
2	1/6
3	1/6
4	1/6
5	1/6
6	1/6

Table 4.3 Probabilities for die toss.

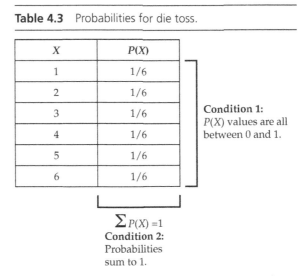

X	P(X)
1	1/6
2	1/6
3	1/6
4	1/6
5	1/6
6	1/6

Condition 1:
$P(X)$ values are all
between 0 and 1.

$$\sum P(X) = 1$$
Condition 2:
Probabilities
sum to 1.

probability of X equaling *something* must be equal to one, or certainty. If these two conditions are not satisfied, the function cannot be classified as a probability mass function. Table 4.3 shows that for the die toss example, both of these conditions are satisfied.

In addition to a table, we can plot the probability mass function on a graph, with the outcomes of the random variable X on the *x* axis and the probability plotted on the *y* axis. Figure 4.1 shows the probability plot of the die toss function. The bar chart emphasizes the discrete nature of X since the bars occur only at the numbers 1, 2, 3, 4, 5, and 6. Any value in between these numbers, such as X = 1.5, has a probability of occurrence equal to zero.

4.1.2 Expected Value, Variance, Skewness, and Kurtosis

The mean and the variance of a discrete variable X can be calculated using the probability distribution as shown in Formulas 4.1 and 4.2, respectively. The mean is also known as the expected value of X, expressed as $E(X)$.

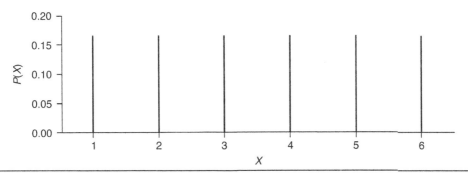

Figure 4.1 Probability mass function for die toss example.

Formula 4.1   Expected value of a discrete variable X

$$\mu_X = E(X) = \sum x \cdot P(x)$$

To calculate the expected value of X, take each value of X and multiply it by its respective probability, then add these results up. The mean can be thought of as the weighted average of X, with the probabilities serving as the weights. For example, the expected value of the die toss variable X is calculated using the formula, as shown. In this case, each value of $P(x)$ is equal to $1/6$. This distribution is an example of a *discrete uniform distribution*.

$$\mu_X = E(X) = \sum x \cdot P(x) = \sum x \cdot \left(\frac{1}{6}\right)$$

$$= 1 \times \left(\frac{1}{6}\right) + 2 \times \left(\frac{1}{6}\right) + 3 \times \left(\frac{1}{6}\right) + 4 \times \left(\frac{1}{6}\right) + 5 \times \left(\frac{1}{6}\right) + 6 \times \left(\frac{1}{6}\right)$$

$$= \left(\frac{1}{6}\right) \times 21 = 3.5$$

Formula 4.2   Variance of a discrete variable X

$$\sigma_X^2 = \text{Var}(X) = \sum [x^2 \cdot P(x)] - \mu^2$$

To calculate variance of X, we take each value of X and square it, multiply by the respective probability, and then add up the results. We then subtract off the squared mean. The variance of the die toss variable X can be calculated using:

$$\sigma_X^2 = \text{Var}(X) = \sum [x^2 \cdot P(x)] - \mu^2 = \sum \left[x^2 \cdot \left(\frac{1}{6}\right)\right] - \mu^2$$

$$= \left[1^2 \times \left(\frac{1}{6}\right) + 2^2 \times \left(\frac{1}{6}\right) + 3^2 \times \left(\frac{1}{6}\right) + 4^2 \times \left(\frac{1}{6}\right) + 5^2 \times \left(\frac{1}{6}\right) + 6^2 \times \left(\frac{1}{6}\right)\right] - \mu^2$$

$$= \left(\frac{1}{6}\right) \times 91 - 3.5^2 = 2.917$$

The standard deviation of the variable can be calculated by taking the square root of the variance as shown:

$$\sigma_X = \sqrt{2.917} = 1.708$$

The expected value and the variance of a distribution are also known as the first and second moments of the distribution. The third and fourth moments of a distribution are used in the measures of *skewness* and *kurtosis*, respectively. Skewness is a measure of symmetry of a distribution (or, rather, a lack of symmetry), and kurtosis is a measure of the height, or peakedness, of a distribution. As a point of reference, the skewness and kurtosis of a normal distribution are both equal to zero. The farther the skewness measure is from zero, the less symmetric the distribution. A negative skewness indicates that the distribution has a negative, or left, skew. A positive skewness value indicates a positive, or right, skew.

A negative kurtosis indicates that the distribution is flatter than a normal distribution, or platykurtic, whereas a positive kurtosis indicates that the distribution is more peaked than a normal distribution, or leptokurtic.

The Microsoft Excel functions =*skew()* and =*kurt()* can be used to calculate the skewness and kurtosis, respectively, of a data set.

Figure 4.2 shows distributions exhibiting, from left to right, positive skew, symmetry, and negative skew. Figure 4.3 gives an example of a platykurtic (flat) distribution and a leptokurtic (peaked) distribution.

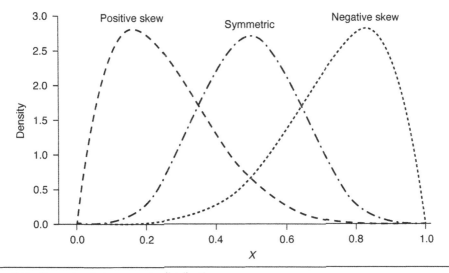

Figure 4.2   Example of skewness in distributions.

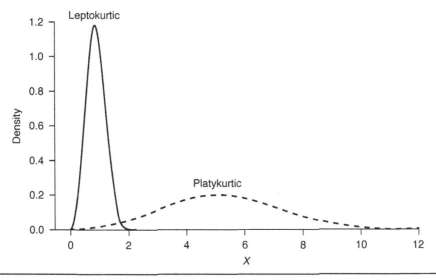

Figure 4.3   Examples of platykurtic and leptokurtic distributions.

4.1.3 Properties of the Expected Value and Variance

Expectation and variance can be calculated for single random variables as shown in Section 4.1.2, as well as for functions of a random variable involving constants and for functions of several random variables. Here are some properties of expectation and variance, presented without proof:

The expected value of a constant c is equal to c: $E(c) = c$

The expected value of a random variable X plus a constant is equal to the expected value of X plus c: $E(X + c) = E(X) + c$

The expectation of a constant multiplied by a random variable X is equal to the constant times the expected value of X: $E(cX) = cE(X)$

The expectation of the sum or difference of two random variables can be expressed as:

$$E(X_1 - X_2) = E(X_1) - E(X_2)$$
$$E(X_1 + X_2) = E(X_1) + E(X_2)$$

In general, the expectation of a linear combination of random variables $a_1X_1 + a_2X_2 + \ldots + a_nX_n$ is the linear combination of expectations:

$$E(a_1X_1 + a_2X_2 + \ldots + a_nX_n) = a_1E(X_1) + a_2E(X_2) + \ldots + a_nE(X_n)$$

The variance of a constant c is equal to zero: $\text{Var}(c) = 0$

The variance of a random variable X is expressed as

$$\text{Var}(X) = E(X^2) - [E(X)^2]$$

The variance of a random variable X plus a constant is equal to the variance of the random variable X: $\text{Var}(X + c) = \text{Var}(X)$

The variance of a random variable X multiplied by a constant is equal to the squared constant times the variance of X: $\text{Var}(cX) = c^2\text{Var}(X)$

Covariance is the measure of how well and in what direction two variables track each other. The covariance of two random variables X_1 and X_2 is expressed as:

$$\text{Cov}(X_1,X_2) = E(X_1X_2) - E(X_1)E(X_2)$$

The covariance of a constant times a random variable X_1 and a random variable X_2 is

$$\text{Cov}(aX_1,X_2) = a\text{Cov}(X_1,X_2)$$

The covariance of a random variable with itself is equal to its variance:

$$\text{Cov}(X_1,X_1) = \text{Var}(X_1)$$

The variance of the difference and sum of two random variables can be found using the following relationships:

$$\text{Var}(X_1 - X_2) = \text{Var}(X_1) + \text{Var}(X_2) - 2\text{Cov}(X_1,X_2)$$
$$\text{Var}(X_1 + X_2) = \text{Var}(X_1) + \text{Var}(X_2) + 2\text{Cov}(X_1,X_2)$$
$$\text{Var}(aX_1 - bX_2) = a^2\text{Var}(X_1) + b^2\text{Var}(X_2) - 2ab\text{Cov}(X_1,X_2)$$
$$\text{Var}(aX_1 + bX_2) = a^2\text{Var}(X_1) + b^2\text{Var}(X_2) + 2ab\text{Cov}(X_1,X_2)$$

In general, for random variables X_1 and X_2 the expectation of their product is

$$E(X_1X_2) = E(X_1)E(X_2) + (\text{Cov}(X_1,X_2))$$

If X_1 and X_2 are *independent*, then $E(X_1X_2) = E(X_1)E(X_2)$; thus,

$$\text{Cov}(X_1,X_2) = 0, \text{ if } X_1 \text{ and } X_2 \text{ independent}$$

Note that independence of two variables implies that their covariance is equal to zero, but a covariance equaling zero does not necessarily guarantee independence of two variables.

It follows from the preceding result that if X_1 and X_2 are *independent*, the expectation of a product of the random variables X_1 and X_2 is equal to the product of their expectations:

$$E(X_1X_2) = E(X_1)E(X_2), X_1 \text{ and } X_2 \text{ independent}$$

The variance of the difference and sum of two *independent* random variables thus becomes:

$$\text{Var}(X_1 - X_2) = \text{Var}(X_1) + \text{Var}(X_2) \text{ if } X_1 \text{ and } X_2 \text{ independent}$$
$$\text{Var}(X_1 + X_2) = \text{Var}(X_1) + \text{Var}(X_2) \text{ if } X_1 \text{ and } X_2 \text{ independent}$$

4.1.4 Cumulative Probability

We established in Section 4.1.1 that the sum of all probabilities in a probability mass function is equal to one. By adding a "cumulative" column, as shown in Table 4.4, we can see the probabilities accumulate over the values of X. More precisely, this cumulative column can be expressed as $\Pr(X \leq x)$, or the probability that the random variable X will equal or be less than some value x.

We can display the cumulative mass function graphically as well, as shown in Figure 4.4. Note that the discrete cumulative probability is a step function, in which jumps in the cumulative probability occur only at valid values of X.

A third requirement for a probability distribution function is that the cumulative probability must be monotonically increasing. In other words, as we move down the probability mass function table, the cumulative probability must be

Table 4.4 Probability mass function of die toss outcome.

X	$P(X)$	Cumulative, or $P(X \leq x)$
1	1/6	1/6
2	1/6	2/6
3	1/6	3/6
4	1/6	4/6
5	1/6	5/6
6	1/6	6/6

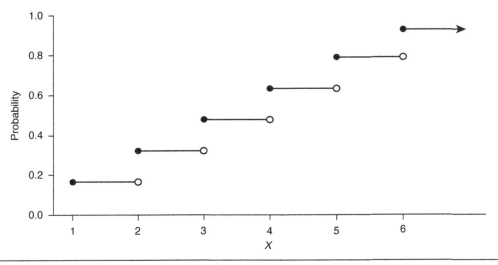

Figure 4.4 Cumulative mass function for die toss example.

either unchanged or increasing, but not decreasing. This third requirement is actually a consequence of the first, in which the probabilities must be between 0 and 1, and not negative. In sum, then, we can state the three requirements of a discrete probability distribution more formally:

1. The probability of X is between 0 and 1 for all possible values of x

2. Sum of $P(X) = 1$

3. $P(X \leq x)$ is monotonically increasing

Calculating cumulative probabilities for discrete random variables seems straightforward, but it is easy to get tripped up with the wording of a question. For example, consider these two questions for the die toss distribution:

1. What is the probability that X is at least 4?

2. What is the probability that X is less than 4?

In the first case, the calculation includes the probability that $X = 4$, $X = 5$, and $X = 6$. In the second case, the probability includes $X = 1$, $X = 2$, and $X = 3$. Table 4.5 lists commonly used phrases in probability statements and their correct interpretation, using the die toss example.

Another way to approach discrete probability problems is to write out the possible outcomes of X and then circle values that apply to the question. For example, for the *probability that X is at least 4*:

Here, we can see that the answer will include the probabilities that $X = 4$, $X = 5$, and $X = 6$.

Table 4.5 Interpretation of wording of probability questions (die toss example).

Find the probability that . . .	Interpretation	Calculation for die problem
X is *exactly* 4	Includes only $P(X = 4)$	$P(X = 4)$
X is *less than* 4	Does not include $P(X = 4)$	$P(X < 4) = P(X \leq 3) = 3/6$
X is *more than* 4	Does not include $P(X = 4)$	$P(X > 4) = P(X \geq 5) = 2/6$
X is *no less than* 4	Includes $P(X = 4)$	$P(X \geq 4) = 3/6$
X is *no more than* 4	Includes $P(X = 4)$	$P(X \leq 4) = 4/6$
X is *at least* 4	Includes $P(X = 4)$	$P(X \geq 4) = 3/6$
X is *at most* 4	Includes $P(X = 4)$	$P(X \leq 4) = 4/6$

4.2 THE DISCRETE UNIFORM DISTRIBUTION

Each of the possible outcomes of a discrete uniform distribution has an equal probability. A specific case of the discrete uniform distribution was introduced in Section 4.1.1, when describing the outcome of a die toss. The general form of the discrete uniform probability mass function is shown in Formula 4.3.

Formula 4.3   Discrete uniform probability mass function

$$p(x) = \frac{1}{b - a + 1}, \qquad x = \{a, a + 1, \ldots, b\}, b \geq a$$

The distribution parameters a and b are also the endpoints of the range of the random variable X.

The expected value and variance of X are shown in Formulas 4.4 and 4.5.

Formula 4.4   Expected value of discrete uniform distribution

$$E(X) = \frac{a + b}{2}$$

Formula 4.5   Variance of discrete uniform distribution

$$Var(X) = \frac{(b - a + 1)^2 - 1}{12}$$

The cumulative distribution function is shown in Formula 4.6.

Formula 4.6   Discrete uniform cumulative mass function

$$F(x) = \frac{\lfloor x - a + 1 \rfloor}{b - a + 1}, \qquad a \leq x \leq b$$

In Formula 4.6, the term $\lfloor x$ is a floor function denoting the largest integer less than or equal to x. For example, the floor of $x = 3.7$ is equal to 3. Formula 4.6 seems excessively fussy, but the expression allows us to calculate the cumulative probability for any x in the range $a \leq x \leq b$, and not just for the values for which $P(X)$ is nonzero.

4.3 THE BINOMIAL DISTRIBUTION

The binomial distribution is used when counting the number of defective units in a sample, and is the basis for the *np* and *p* statistical process control charts. The distribution is built from a series of independent *Bernoulli trials*. In a Bernoulli trial, there are only two possible outcomes, such as heads or tails, pass or fail, success or failure, or defective or non-defective. The probability of the outcome of interest is equal to p, and by the complement rule, the probability of the second outcome is equal to $(1 - p)$.

The binomial random variable X is the sum of the outcomes of a series of independent Bernoulli trials. For example, if we toss a coin three times, each toss is a Bernoulli trial. We can count the number of heads in the three trials, and this count, X, will then follow a binomial distribution.

Let the discrete random variable X equal the number of "successes" in n trials. Note that this definition of success is arbitrary and can be better described as the "outcome of interest." For example, we could just as well be counting the number of defectives in a sample as the number of good parts. The variable X will follow a binomial distribution if all of the following are satisfied:

1. There are a fixed number of trials, n

2. There are only two possible, mutually exclusive outcomes for each trial

3. Trials are independent

4. The probability of success p is constant from trial to trial

The binomial random variable has a discrete, finite number of possible outcomes.

4.3.1 Probability Mass Function

The probability mass function for the binomial variable X is shown in Formula 4.7.

> **Formula 4.7**   Binomial probability mass function
>
> $$P(X = x) = \binom{n}{x} p^x (1 - p)^{n-x}, \qquad x = 0, 1, \ldots, n$$

In Formula 4.7, the number of trials is n, the probability of "success" is p, and the number of successes in n trials is the random variable X. Converting the formula into plain English: "The probability that the random variable X equals some value x is equal to n choose x, times the probability of success to the x power, times the probability of failure to the n minus x power."

Note that the random variable can take on whole number values from a minimum of 0 to a maximum of n successes. In other words, if you flip a coin 10 times, you can't get a negative number of heads or 2.5 heads or 11 heads.

Let's pull the formula apart to make sense of it using a coin toss with $n = 3$ trials as an illustrative example. These trials, or tosses, are independent, meaning that the outcome of one trial does not influence the outcome of the next. Define X as the number of heads in three tosses. The probability of success p equals $1/2$, as does the probability of failure (tails). Let $X = 2$. What is the probability of getting exactly two heads in three tosses? We can enumerate the possibilities, as shown in Table 4.6.

We can see from the table of enumerated outcomes that there are three ways that two heads can occur in three trials, which is the combination $_3C_2$, and each of these ways has a probability of occurrence equal to $p^2(1 - p)$. Applying Formula 4.7, we can see the probability that $X = 2$ is equal to

$$P(X = 2) = \binom{n}{x} p^x (1 - p)^{n-x} = \binom{3}{2} \left(\frac{1}{2}\right)^2 \left(\frac{1}{2}\right)^1 = \frac{3}{8}$$

Before evaluating the binomial probability formula, do these "sanity checks" to make sure you are not making an error:

1. The sum of the probability of success p and the probability of failure $(1 - p)$ should equal 1

2. The number of successes x should not exceed the number of trials n

3. The exponents of p and $(1 - p)$ should sum to n

To find the cumulative probability using a binomial distribution, we use the summation operator, as shown in Formula 4.8. To find the probability that X will be equal to a value x or less, we sum the probabilities for the values 0 to x.

Formula 4.8 Binomial cumulative mass function

$$P(X \le x) = \sum_{x=0}^{x} \binom{n}{x} p^x (1 - p)^{n-x}; \quad x \in \{0, 1, 2, \dots, n\}$$

We can also use a table of cumulative binomial probabilities, provided in Appendix C. Based on n and p, we can find $\Pr(X \le x)$ in the interior of the table.

Table 4.6 Coin toss: ways that two heads in three trials can occur.

First trial	Second trial	Third trial	Probability of specific outcome
H	H	T	$p \times p \times (1 - p)$
H	T	H	$p \times (1 - p) \times p$
T	H	H	$(1 - p) \times p \times p$

4.3.2 Parameters, Expected Value, and Variance

The binomial distribution can be described using two parameters: n and p. (Note that these parameters are not represented by Greek letters, a fairly rare exception to the general rule.) By applying Formulas 4.1 and 4.2 for the expected value and variance of a discrete probability distribution, we can derive the equations for the mean and variance of the binomial random variable. Fortunately, we can save a lot of algebra and aggravation by using the results given in Formulas 4.9, 4.10, and 4.11.

Formula 4.9 Expected value of the binomial

$$\mu = E(X) = np$$

Formula 4.10 Variance of the binomial

$$\sigma^2 = \text{Var}(X) = np(1 - p)$$

Formula 4.11 Standard deviation of the binomial

$$\sigma = \sqrt{np(1 - p)}$$

If the parameter p is unknown, it can be estimated by dividing the number of successes by the number of trials, as shown in Formula 4.12. The quality of the estimate will improve as the number of trials increases. We read the term $\hat{p}$ as "p hat." Statisticians often use the hat symbol to signify that a parameter is estimated. Then the expected value, variance, and standard deviation of the random variable X can be estimated using Formulas 4.13, 4.14, and 4.15, respectively.

Formula 4.12 Estimator of p

$$\hat{p} = \frac{x}{n}$$

Formula 4.13 Mean estimator

$$\hat{\mu} = \hat{E}(X) = n\hat{p}$$

Formula 4.14 Variance estimator

$$\hat{\sigma}^2 = s^2 = \hat{\text{Var}}(X) = n\hat{p}(1 - \hat{p})$$

Formula 4.15 Standard deviation estimator

$$\hat{\sigma}^2 = s^2 = \sqrt{n\hat{p}(1 - \hat{p})}$$

4.3.3 Distribution Shape

The shape of the binomial distribution will change based on the number of trials n and the probability of success p. Figure 4.5 shows how the shape of the binomial distribution with $n = 10$ trials changes with p.

When the probability of success is relatively small, as shown in the first panel with $p = 0.10$, the mean of the distribution is $np = 1.00$ and the variance is $np(1 - p) = 0.90$. This distribution is skewed to the right. As the probability of success increases to 0.20, the mean and variance also increase, and the distribution looks less skewed. At $p = 0.50$, shown in the first panel in the second row, the mean is equal to 5.0, the center of the range of X, and the variance is at its highest at 2.5. The distribution at this point looks symmetric. Notice that the distribution begins to reduce in variance as p increases beyond 0.50 and also begins to skew to the left. In fact, the distributions in the first and last panels, and in the second and fifth panels have identical variances and are mirror images of each other. Table 4.7 shows the mean and variance of the distributions as p increases.

Figure 4.6 shows the shape of the distribution with $p = 0.25$ when n is increased from 5 to 40. The random variable in the binomial distribution in the first panel of Figure 4.6 can only take on the values $X = 0$ through $X = 5$. As shown in Table 4.8, the mean for the first distribution is $np = 1.25$ with a variance equal to 0.9375. As the number of trials increases, the number of possible values for X also increases. In addition, both the mean and variance of the distributions also increase with n. Note that the binomial distribution looks more and more symmetric as the number of trials increases.

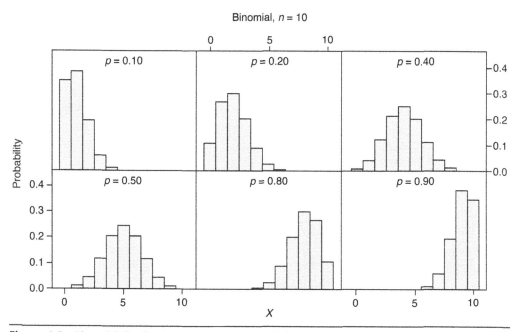

Figure 4.5   Binomial distributions: n constant, p varied.

Table 4.7 Mean and variance of binomial distribution for $n = 10$, various p.

p	Mean	Variance
0.10	1.00	0.90
0.20	2.00	1.60
0.40	4.00	2.40
0.50	5.00	2.50
0.80	8.00	1.60
0.90	9.00	0.90

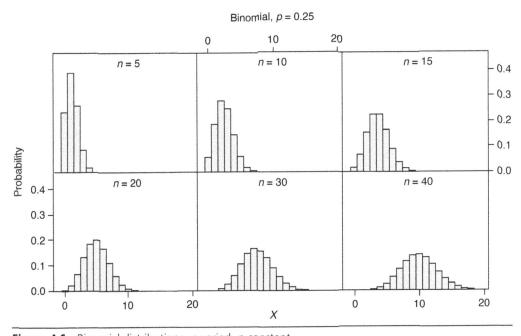

Figure 4.6 Binomial distributions: n varied, p constant.

Table 4.8 Mean and variance of binomial distribution for various n, $p = 0.25$.

n	Mean	Variance
5	1.25	0.9375
10	2.50	1.8750
15	3.75	2.8125
20	5.00	3.7500
30	7.50	5.6250
40	10.00	7.5000

4.3.4 Related Microsoft Excel Functions

Binomial probabilities can be calculated in Microsoft Excel[1] using the formula =*binom.dist()*. The function takes arguments for the number of successes, trials, the probability of success, and a cumulative logical flag, as shown in the dialog box in Figure 4.7. For example, for a binomial distribution with $n = 10$ and $p = 0.20$, we can find the probability that $X = 3$ by entering =*binom.dist(3,0.20,10,0)*.

If we wanted to know the probability that $X \leq 3$, we would turn on the cumulative flag in the formula by typing in the value 1 in the cumulative argument: =*binom.dist(3,0.20,10,1)*. Note that alternatively, the user can enter the word FALSE instead of the value 0 in the cumulative argument to calculate an exact probability, and the word TRUE in place of the value 1 to calculate a cumulative probability.

Sometimes we want to know what value of X will make a probability statement true. In this case, we use the inverse binomial function, =*binom.inv()*, shown in Figure 4.8. This can seem a bit tricky. The inverse function will return the

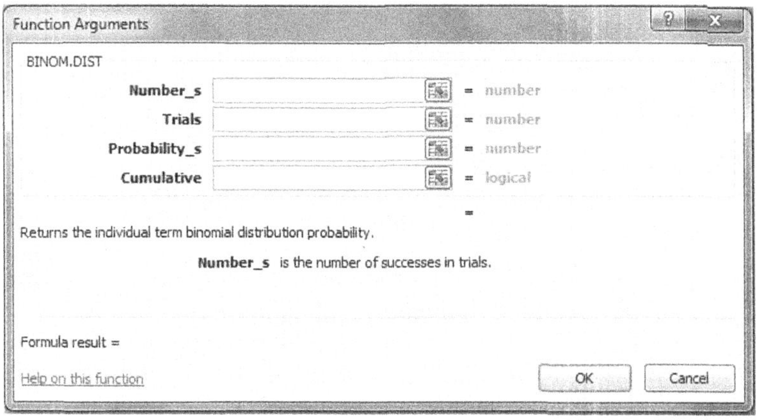

Figure 4.7   Microsoft Excel function =*binom.dist()*.

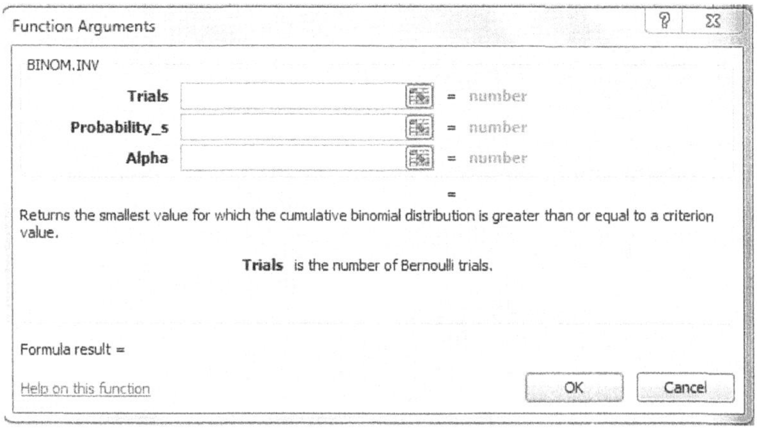

Figure 4.8   Microsoft Excel function =*binom.inv()*.

---

[1] Note that formulas are for Microsoft Excel 2010.

smallest value of X that makes the statement $\Pr(X \le x) = a$ true, given n, p, and a. For example, assume we have a binomial distribution with $n = 15$ and $p = 0.40$. What is the smallest value of X that makes the statement $\Pr(X \le x) = 0.80$ true? The Microsoft Excel function =*binom.inv (15,0.40,0.80)* returns $X = 8$. The probability that $X \le 7$ equals 0.787, which is too small to make the statement true, so we need to go up to $X = 8$ to satisfy the 0.80 criterion. In fact, $\Pr(X \le 8) = 0.905$. We cannot find an answer that will match our $a = 0.80$ exactly, because the values that X takes on are discrete.

4.3.5 Uses and Applications

The binomial distribution has applications in a broad range of industries. Consider the following scenarios:

- An improvement team in a hospital emergency department analyzes historical data to estimate the rate that patients leave without treatment (LWOT). This rate can then be used in the binomial formula to estimate the expected number of LWOTs on any given day, based on the number of patients in the waiting area.

- A bank manager can use the binomial distribution to estimate the number of the bank's current outstanding loans that will be paid back on time.

- A political pollster uses response data to estimate p, the proportion of voters that will cast their ballots for a particular candidate. He uses this estimate, along with a margin of error, to forecast the winner of the election.

- An injection molding company produces a plastic part. The customer requires that the length of the part be within a very tight tolerance. A fixture is designed to perform a go/no go test on the part dimension. Using the binomial distribution, a quality engineer can determine whether the process defective rate is remaining stable or increasing by tracking defectives with an np chart.

4.3.6 Binomial Connection to Statistical Process Control

The binomial distribution is the statistical basis for the np and p statistical process control charts. Based on historical data, the np chart is developed with a centerline equal to np and control limits equal to ± 3 standard deviations of the binomial variable X as shown in Formula 4.16. An operator takes a sample of size n each time period and plots the number of defective units found in the sample. The point should fall within the control limits if the binomial distribution of defectives has not changed. If a point falls above the upper control limit, it is a signal that the number of defectives is unusually high and that an assignable cause is acting on the process.

Formula 4.16   Control limits for np chart

$$\text{UCL} = \overline{np} + 3\sqrt{\overline{np}(1 - \overline{p})}$$

$$\text{Centerline} = \overline{np}$$

$$\text{LCL} = \overline{np} - 3\sqrt{\overline{np}(1 - \overline{p})}$$

The term $\overline{np}$ denotes the estimated mean number of defectives found in the samples of size n.

Likewise, a p chart tracks the percentage of defectives in a sample over time. The proportion defective in the sample is calculated by using p-hat $= x/n$. Using the rules of expectation and variance presented in Section 4.1.2, we can derive the mean and variance of the proportion defective p as shown in Formulas 4.17 and 4.18.

Formula 4.17 Expected value of p-hat

$$E(\hat{p}) = E\left(\frac{X}{n}\right) = \frac{1}{n}E(X) = \frac{np}{n} = p$$

Formula 4.18 Variance of p-hat

$$\text{Var}(\hat{p}) = \text{Var}\left(\frac{X}{n}\right) = \frac{1}{n^2}\text{Var}(X) = \frac{np(1-p)}{n^2} = \frac{p(1-p)}{n}$$

The expected value and variance of p-hat are used to calculate control limits for the p chart, as shown in Formula 4.19. Note that for a p chart, the sample sizes taken at each time period do not have to be equal. In these cases, the control limits are adjusted as n changes.

The plotted points should fall within the control limits if the distribution has not changed. The term $\overline{p}$ denotes the average proportion defective.

Formula 4.19 Control limits for p chart

$$\text{UCL} = \overline{p} + 3\sqrt{\frac{\overline{p}(1-\overline{p})}{n}}$$

$$\text{Centerline} = \overline{p}$$

$$\text{LCL} = \overline{p} - 3\sqrt{\frac{\overline{p}(1-\overline{p})}{n}}$$

$$\text{where } \overline{p} = \frac{\sum x}{\sum n}$$

4.4 THE MULTINOMIAL DISTRIBUTION

The multinomial distribution is an extension of the binomial in which independent trials can result in more than two mutually exclusive outcomes. Instead of defective and non-defective, we might be classifying parts into three, four, or more categories. For a set number of trials n, we then count the number of occurrences in each of the categories. Hence the multinomial random variable X_i is the sum of the successes for the *i*th category in *n* independent trials. The probability of success in the first category is p_1, for the second it is p_2, and so on. The sum of the probabilities across all the categories equals one.

In sum, for a multinomial random variable X

1. There are a fixed number of trials, *n*

2. There are *k* possible outcomes for each trial, each with probability p_k

3. The sum of the probabilities p_k from 1 to *k* will equal 1.0

4. Trials are independent

5. The probability of each outcome *k* is constant from trial to trial

The multinomial random variable has a discrete, finite number of possible outcomes.

4.4.1 Probability Mass Function

The probability mass function for the multinomial variable X is shown in Formula 4.20. Note that the binomial distribution is a special case of the multinomial when $k = 2$.

Formula 4.20   Multinomial probability mass function

$$P(X_1 = x_1, X_2 = x_2, \ldots, X_k = x_k) = \frac{n!}{x_1! \, x_2! \ldots x_k!} \, p_1^{x_1} p_2^{x_2} \ldots p_k^{x_k}$$

$$\text{where } \sum_{i=1}^{k} x_i = n, \ \sum_{i=1}^{k} p_i = 1.0$$

Let's use Formula 4.20 to solve a multinomial probability problem. A quality inspector inspects 10 products and categorizes them into one of four mutually exclusive grades: A, B, C, or D. The probability of Grade A is 0.55, Grade B is 0.20, Grade C is 0.10, and Grade D is 0.15. What is the probability that the sample of 10 products will have four products classified as Grade A, three as Grade B, one as Grade C, and two as Grade D?

$$P(X_1 = 4, X_2 = 3, X_3 = 1, X_4 = 2) = \frac{10!}{4! \, 3! \, 1! \, 2!} (0.55)^4 (0.20)^3 (0.10)^1 (0.15)^2 = 0.0208$$

Before evaluating the multinomial probability formula, do these "sanity checks" to make sure you are not making an error:

1. The sum of the outcomes in the denominator of the factorial term should equal *n*

2. The sum of the probabilities across outcomes should equal 1

3. The exponents of the probabilities should sum to *n*

4.4.2 Parameters, Expected Value, and Variance

The multinomial distribution can be described using the parameters n and p_1, $p_2, \ldots, p_k$. For each random variable X_i, we can calculate a mean, variance, and standard deviation using Formulas 4.21, 4.22, and 4.23, respectively. Note that each X_i in a multinomial distribution is a binomially distributed variable.

Formula 4.21   Expected value for a multinomial distribution

$$\mu_i = E(X_i) = np_i$$

Formula 4.22   Variance of a multinomial variable

$$\sigma_1^2 = \text{Var}(X_i) = np_i(1 - p_i)$$

Formula 4.23   Standard deviation of the multinomial

$$\sigma_i = \sqrt{np_i(1 - p_i)}$$

4.4.3 Uses and Applications

Examples of the use of the multinomial distribution follow:

- Using the multinomial distribution, an airline predicts the number of first class, business class, and coach class seats it will sell for an international flight.

- A resort hotel uses the multinomial distribution to estimate the number of guests coming from each of five midwestern states.

- The Small Business Association uses the multinomial distribution to predict the probability of default for 10 high-risk, 25 medium-risk, and 40 low-risk loan applicants.

- A political pollster uses survey response data to estimate p_i, the proportion of voters that will cast their ballots for each of five mayoral candidates in a Democratic primary. He uses this estimate, along with a margin of error, to forecast the probability of a runoff election.

- A quality engineer predicts the probability of returned parts due to four mutually exclusive failure modes.

4.5 THE HYPERGEOMETRIC DISTRIBUTION

The hypergeometric distribution can be thought of as the binomial distribution's more complicated cousin. Like the binomial, the hypergeometric distribution is used when counting the number of defective units in a sample, and is the basis of some ANSI Z1.4 sampling plans. Unlike the trials of the binomial, however, the trials of a hypergeometric are *not* independent. The probability of each trial is dependent on the outcomes of the trials before it. The difference between the binomial and hypergeometric distributions can be likened to the "socks in a drawer" problem described in Section 3.8.

In the binomial case, sampling from a small population is performed with replacement so that the probability of choosing a black sock remains constant, or in the case of sampling for quality, the population is considered to be so large relative to the sample size that the probability of success remains essentially constant, even without replacing samples.

In the hypergeometric case, we choose samples without replacement from a relatively small population, in which case the probability of a black sock changes from trial to trial. As we will see in Section 4.5.3, the hypergeometric distribution converges to a binomial when the ratio of the sample size n to the lot size N approaches zero. This ratio is called the *sampling fraction*.

The hypergeometric random variable X denotes the number of defectives (or any outcome of interest) found in a sample of size n from a lot size of N. For the hypergeometric distribution,

1. There are only two possible outcomes for each trial

2. The population size is denoted as N, and the population is finite

3. The sample size n is less than or equal to the population size N

4. There are D defectives (or any outcome of interest) in the population

5. There are $(N - D)$ non-defectives in the population

4.5.1 Probability Mass Function

The probability mass function for the hypergeometric variable X is shown in Formula 4.24.

Formula 4.24 Hypergeometric probability mass function

$$P(X = x) = \frac{\binom{D}{x}\binom{N-D}{n-x}}{\binom{N}{n}}, \qquad x \in \{max(0, n - (N - D)), \ldots, min(n, D)\}$$

In Formula 4.24, we find the probability of finding $X = x$ defectives in a sample of size n. The population is finite and equal to N. Within that population, we have D defectives and $N - D$ non-defectives. The numerator counts the number of ways we can choose x defectives and $(n - x)$ non-defectives from the population. The denominator counts the number of ways a sample of n can be chosen from a population of size N. Note that this is the same formula used to solve the egg problem in Section 3.15.1.

The hypergeometric random variable has a discrete, finite number of possible outcomes. Based on Formula 4.24, the range of the random variable may look very confusing. The extra complication stems from the fact that the range of possible defectives in a hypergeometric sample is limited by both the sample size and the number of defectives in the population. Let's see if we can unravel the meaning of the *min* and *max* formulas used.

The minimum number of defectives possible in a sample n is bounded by 0 or the value of $n - (N - D)$, whichever is larger. Note that the expression $n - (N - D)$ is the difference between the sample size n and the number of non-defective items in the population or lot $(N - D)$. For example, if the lot size $N = 10$ and the number of defectives $D = 8$, a sample of $n = 5$ will always contain at least three defective parts since there are only two non-defectives in the entire lot. Hence, the minimum feasible X is calculated by $max(0, n - (N - D)) = max(0, 5 - (10 - 8))$ is equal to 3 in this case. If instead $N = 10$ and $D = 2$, then the sample of $n = 5$ could feasibly contain 0 defectives since $max(0, 5 - (10 - 2)) = 0$.

The maximum number of defectives in a sample is limited by the sample size n or the number of defectives in the population D, whichever is smaller. For example, if our lot size is 10 units and there are $D = 6$ defectives in the population, a sample of $n = 3$ units can return 0, 1, 2, or 3 defectives, hence limited by the sample size. If our sample is $n = 8$, then the sample can contain 0, 1, 2, 3, 4, 5, or 6 defectives, in this case limited by the number of defective units D in the population. Table 4.9 displays the allowable values of X for $N = 5$ for differing numbers of defectives and sample sizes.

Let's use Formula 4.24 to find the following hypergeometric probabilities. For $N = 10$, $D = 6$, and $n = 5$, find $P(X = 5)$:

$$P(X = 5) = \frac{\binom{D}{x}\binom{N-D}{n-x}}{\binom{N}{n}} = \frac{\binom{6}{5}\binom{4}{0}}{\binom{10}{5}}$$

For $N = 10$, $D = 6$, and $n = 7$, find $P(X = 5)$:

$$P(X = 5) = \frac{\binom{D}{x}\binom{N-D}{n-x}}{\binom{N}{n}} = \frac{\binom{6}{5}\binom{4}{2}}{\binom{10}{7}}$$

Before evaluating the hypergeometric probability formula, do these "sanity checks" to make sure you are not making an error:

1. The sum of the values for D and $N - D$ should equal the value of N in the denominator

2. The sum of the values of x and $n - x$ should equal the value of n in the denominator

To find the cumulative probability using a hypergeometric distribution, we use the summation operator, as shown in Formula 4.25. To find the probability that X will be equal to a value x or less, we sum the probabilities for the values 0 to x.

Formula 4.25 Hypergeometric cumulative mass function

$$P(X \le x) = \sum_{x=0}^{x} \frac{\binom{D}{x}\binom{N-D}{n-x}}{\binom{N}{n}}, \qquad x \in \{max(0, n - (N - D)), \ldots, min(n, D)\}$$

Table 4.9 Allowable *X* values for hypergeometric distribution with *N* = 5.

n	D	$N-D$	Allowable values of X					
5	5	0						5
5	4	1					4	
5	3	2				3		
5	2	3			2			
5	1	4		1				
4	5	0					4	
4	4	1				3	4	
4	3	2			2	3		
4	2	3		1	2			
4	1	4	0	1				
3	5	0				3		
3	4	1			2	3		
3	3	2		1	2	3		
3	2	3	0	1	2			
3	1	4	0	1				
2	5	0			2			
2	4	1		1	2			
2	3	2	0	1	2			
2	2	3	0	1	2			
2	1	4	0	1				
1	5	0		1				
1	4	1	0	1				
1	3	2	0	1				
1	2	3	0	1				
1	1	4	0	1				

4.5.2 Parameters, Expected Value, and Variance

The hypergeometric distribution can be described using three parameters: *N*, *D*, and *n*. (Note that these parameters are not represented by Greek letters, an exception to the general rule.) The expected value, variance, and standard deviation of the hypergeometric distribution are shown in Formulas 4.26, 4.27, and 4.28, respectively.

Formula 4.26 Expected value of the hypergeometric

$$\mu = E(X) = n\frac{D}{N}$$

Formula 4.27 Variance of the hypergeometric

$$\sigma^2 = \text{Var}(X) = n\frac{D}{N}\left(1 - \frac{D}{N}\right)\left(\frac{N-n}{N-1}\right)$$

Formula 4.28 Standard deviation of the hypergeometric

$$\sigma = \sqrt{n\frac{D}{N}\left(1 - \frac{D}{N}\right)\left(\frac{N-n}{N-1}\right)}$$

4.5.3 Distribution Shape

The shape of the hypergeometric distribution will change based on the number of trials n for any given N, also called the sampling proportion, and the number defectives in the population D. Figure 4.9 shows how the shape of the hypergeometric distribution with population size $N = 100$ and the number of defectives $D = 20$ changes as the sampling proportion increases.

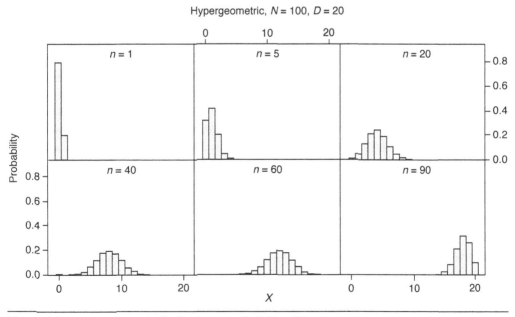

Figure 4.9 Hypergeometric distribution: n varied, N and D constant.

As shown in the first panel with $n = 1$ and $N = 100$, the only possible values for x are equal to 0 and 1. Here the sampling proportion is small, equal to 1%. As n increases, the sampling proportion also increases, meaning that sampling without replacement will increasingly affect the probability of success from trial to trial. Note the limiting factors in the range of x in play here as well. For $n = 5$, the only possible values for x are equal to 0, 1, 2, 3, 4, and 5. As n increases relative to the number of defectives, the minimum x will increase in value and top out at 20. For $n = 90$, the minimum number of defectives is 10.

As shown in Figure 4.10, the shape of the hypergeometric distribution changes as the population increases. In fact, as population size N increases and the sampling fraction n/N decreases, the hypergeometric distribution approaches the binomial distribution. If the sample size n is very small relative to the population size N, then sampling without replacement will not change the probability of success significantly.

For example, if there are 6 white socks and 4 black socks in a drawer, choosing a white sock on the first trial changes the probability of choosing a white sock on the second trial from $6/10 = 0.60$ to $5/9 = 0.556$. However, if there are 6,000 white socks and 4,000 black socks, the probability changes from $6,000/10,000 = 0.60$ to $5,999/9,999 = 0.5999$.

4.5.4 Related Microsoft Excel Function

Hypergeometric probabilities can be calculated in Microsoft Excel using the formula *=hypergeom.dist()*. The function takes arguments for the number of defectives in the sample (Sample_s), the sample size (Number_Sample), the number of defectives in the population (Population_s), the population size (Number_Population), and a cumulative logical flag, as shown in the dialog box in Figure 4.11.

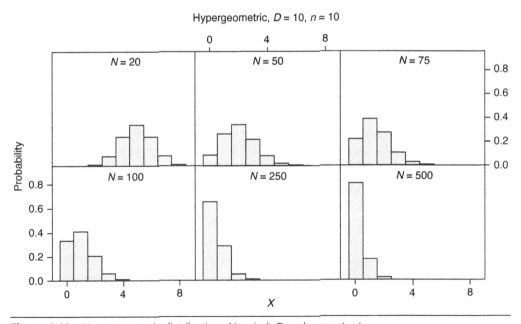

Figure 4.10   Hypergeometric distribution: N varied, D and n constant.

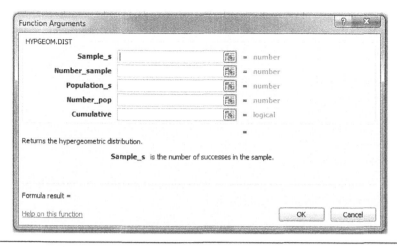

Figure 4.11 Microsoft Excel function =*hypergeom.dist()*.

For example, for a hypergeometric distribution with $N = 100$ and $D = 25$ and a sample size $n = 15$, we can find the probability that $X = 3$ by entering =*hypergeom. dist(3,15,25,100)*.

If we wanted to know the probability that $X \leq 3$, we would turn on the cumulative flag in the formula by typing in the value 1 in the cumulative argument: =*hypergeom.dist(3,15,25,100,1)*.

4.5.5 Uses and Applications

The hypergeometric distribution has many applications in industry, as shown by the following example scenarios:

- A quality engineer uses the hypergeometric distribution to develop a sampling plan for small lots with a historic percent defective equal to 0.02.

- The hypergeometric distribution is used to design an incoming material inspection plan that rejects a lot based on the number of defectives found in the sample.

4.6 THE GEOMETRIC AND NEGATIVE BINOMIAL DISTRIBUTIONS

The geometric and negative binomial distributions are related, with the geometric being a specific case of the negative binomial. The geometric random variable X is commonly defined as the number of independent samples taken before the *first* success is encountered. For example, we can sample from a lot of product until we encounter the first defective unit, and then record the number of samples tested before that first defective unit was found.

The negative binomial, also known as the Pascal distribution, is the general case of the geometric, in which the random variable X is the number of trials until the rth success. The name *negative binomial* has legitimate, albeit arcane, mathematical roots, but most people find it rather misleading.[2] The uninitiated might even be falsely led to think the distribution somehow generates negative probabilities of the binomial distribution.

Both the negative binomial and geometric distributions share features with the binomial distribution. Like the binomial, there are only two mutually exclusive outcomes to every trial, these trials are independent, and the probability of success is constant from trial to trial. However, unlike the binomial case, we are not taking a set number of samples and counting defective units. Rather, the number of defectives we find is determined a priori, and it is the *number of samples n* that is the random variable.

4.6.1 Probability Mass Function

The probability mass function for the geometric variable X is shown in Formula 4.29. Here, the random variable X is defined as the number of failures before the first success. The cumulative distribution appears in Formula 4.30.

Formula 4.29   Geometric probability mass function

$$P(X = x) = p(1-p)^x, \qquad x \in \{0, 1, 2, \ldots\}$$

Formula 4.30   Cumulative distribution function

$$F(X) = P(X \le x) = 1 - (1-p)^{x+1}, \qquad x \in \{0, 1, 2, \ldots\}$$

In Formula 4.29, we see that the probability of finding the first success on any particular sample implies that all the previous samples were in fact failures. Since trials are independent, we can multiply these x number of failure probabilities to get $(1-p)^x$. Finally, the probability of achieving success on the $(x + 1)$st trial is equal to p.

Using Formula 4.29, we can calculate the probability of having 10 non-defectives before we find our first defective unit. Here, a defective unit is considered a "success." Let $p \approx$ the probability of a defective = 0.03. Then,

$$P(X = 10) = (0.03)(1 - 0.03)^{10}$$

There is another parameterization of the geometric distribution that is widely used. The idea is quite similar, but in the alternate version we define our random variable X as the total number of trials to the first success, *counting the trial in which the success was encountered*. Either version of the probability mass function will give the same result. The user must take care to understand the definition of the random variable; namely, are you including the trial with the success in your count? The alternate probability mass function and cumulative density function are shown in Formulas 4.31 and 4.32, respectively.

---

[2] To learn more, refer to https://www.encyclopediaofmath.org/index.php/Negative_binomial_distribution.

Formula 4.31   Geometric probability mass function, alternate form

$$P(X = x) = p(1 - p)^{x-1}, \qquad x \in \{1, 2, \dots\}$$

Formula 4.32   Geometric cumulative distribution function, alternate form

$$F(X) = P(X \le x) = 1 - (1 - p)^x, \qquad x \in \{1, 2, \dots\}$$

Note that the lower bound for X in the alternate version is 1 since we are counting total trials until the first success.

Using Formula 4.31, we can revisit our previous example. We can calculate the probability of having 10 non-defectives before we find our first defective unit with the probability of a defective = 0.03. Here, X is defined as a total of 11 trials.

$$P(X = 11) = (0.03)(1 - 0.03)^{10}$$

As promised, the result is the same.

4.6.2 Expected Value and Variance of the Geometric Distribution

The expected value and variance of the geometric distribution can be calculated from its parameters, as shown in Formulas 4.33 and 4.34. Note that this is the expected value and variance for the form of the distribution shown in Formula 4.29. The random variable X is the number of failures before the first success.

Formula 4.33   Expected value of geometric distribution

$$E(X) = \frac{(1 - p)}{p}$$

Formula 4.34   Variance of geometric distribution

$$\text{Var}(X) = \frac{(1 - p)}{p^2}$$

The expected value and variance of the alternate form of the distribution shown in Formula 4.31, in which we count the total number of trials including the first success, are shown in Formulas 4.35 and 4.36, respectively.

Formula 4.35   Expected value of alternate form of geometric distribution

$$E(X) = \frac{1}{p}$$

Formula 4.36   Variance of alternate form of geometric distribution

$$\mathrm{Var}(X) = \frac{(1-p)}{p^2}$$

Note that the variance of each of the forms of the geometric distribution is the same.

4.6.3 Memoryless Property of the Geometric Distribution

The geometric distribution is the only discrete probability distribution that possesses the *memoryless property*. Like its continuous cousin, the exponential distribution (see Section 5.10), the geometric distribution "forgets" how long we have been performing trials. Much like Bill Murray in the movie *Groundhog Day*, we get to start fresh at the beginning of each trial. For example, if we have already performed t trials without a success, this in no way influences the probability that we will have to perform at least s more trials until our goal is reached. More formally, we can write a conditional probability statement to explain this memoryless property, as shown in Formula 4.37.

Formula 4.37   Memoryless property of geometric distribution

$$P(X > (t + s) \mid X > t) = P(X > s)$$

In other words, it doesn't matter if you've already had t failures; the probability of having to run at least s more trials until the first success is the same. This memoryless principle provides the evidence against the so-called *gambler's fallacy*, in which a gambler continues to plug quarters into the same slot machine thinking the machine is due to win.

Let's use some numbers to get a better grasp of this memoryless property. The following geometric probability statements indicate that it doesn't matter if we currently have 3 or 30 or 300 failures; the probability of having to run at least 4 more trials until the first success is the same:

$$P(X > (4 + 3 = 7) \mid X > 3) = P(X > 4)$$

$$P(X > (4 + 30 = 34) \mid X > 30) = P(X > 4)$$

$$P(X > (4 + 300 = 304) \mid X > 300) = P(X > 4)$$

4.6.4 Negative Binomial Distribution

The formula for the negative binomial, or Pascal, distribution allows us to find the probability of the rth success occurring on the xth trial, with probability of success equal to p. The probability mass and cumulative distribution functions appear in Formulas 4.38 and 4.39, respectively. The rationale of the formula is that if, say, the fourth success occurs on the tenth trial, there were exactly three successes in the first nine trials. We use the combination $_9C_3$ to determine how many ways that could happen. Then, we multiply $_9C_3$ by the probability of exactly four successes and six failures. Note that as with the geometric distribution, there are alternate versions of the negative binomial formula as well, but they are not presented here.

Formula 4.38   Negative binomial, or Pascal, probability mass function

$$P(X = x) = \binom{x-1}{r-1} p^r (1-p)^{x-r}, \qquad x \in (r, r+1, \dots)$$

Formula 4.39   Negative binomial cumulative distribution function

$$F(X) = P(X \le x) = \sum_{x=r}^{x} \binom{x-1}{r-1} p^r (1-p)^{x-r}, \qquad x \in (r, r+1, \dots)$$

Note that this formula will collapse into the geometric probability mass function when $r = 1$, as shown:

$$P(X = x) = \binom{x-1}{0} p^1 (1-p)^{x-1} = p(1-p)^{x-1}$$

The expected value and variance of the negative binomial distribution are shown in Formulas 4.40 and 4.41, respectively.

Formula 4.40   Expected value of negative binomial distribution

$$E(X) = \frac{r}{p}$$

Formula 4.41   Variance of negative binomial distribution

$$\text{Var}(X) = \frac{r(1-p)}{p^2}$$

4.6.5 Related Microsoft Excel Functions

Geometric and negative binomial probabilities can be calculated in Microsoft Excel using the formula *=negbinom.dist()*. The function takes arguments for the number of failures (Number_f), the number of successes (Number_s), the probability of success (Probability_s), and a cumulative logical flag, as shown in the dialog box in Figure 4.12. For example, for a geometric distribution with $p = 0.30$, we can find the probability that there will be $x = 4$ failures before the first success by entering *=negbinom.dist(4,1,0.30,0)*.

Note that the Microsoft Excel function matches the form of Formula 4.29 for the geometric distribution. If we wanted to know the probability that $x \le 4$, we would turn on the cumulative flag in the formula by typing in the value 1 in the cumulative argument: *=negbinom.dist(4,1,0.30,1)*.

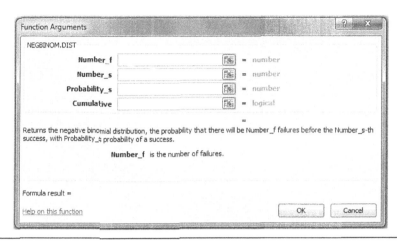

Figure 4.12 Microsoft Excel function =*negbinom.dist()*.

The more general negative binomial distribution would have a value other than 1 for the number of successes. For example, for a probability of success equal to 0.40, we can find the probability that the third success will happen on the fifth trial by entering =*negbinom.dist(2,3,0.40,0)*.

4.6.6 Uses and Applications

The geometric and negative binomial distributions are useful in determining how many units will be processed before the desired outcome is achieved. For example:

- A quality engineer uses the geometric distribution to determine the average number of units that must be tested before the first defective is found.

- A sports statistician determines the probability that the World Series will go to seven games based on the negative binomial distribution.

4.7 THE POISSON DISTRIBUTION

The discrete distributions covered so far have all been related, since in each case we performed trials and counted successes in one way or another. The Poisson distribution, in contrast, seems to be a bit of a fish out of water (that's a statistician's poor excuse for a joke).

The Poisson is used when counting the number of arrivals in a certain time period, or when counting the number of defects in a sampling unit of product. In the first case, the Poisson distribution is used in queuing applications. For example, we might want to determine the probability of X or more arrivals at a bank during a certain time period in order to staff the teller windows at the right level. Disney uses the Poisson distribution and other queuing theory techniques extensively in its theme parks. The techniques give the parks the ability to give guests an estimated wait time for the Pirates of the Caribbean ride, or to figure out how many switchbacks to put in a ride's waiting line to give guests the illusion of forward progress.

The second application of the Poisson distribution allows quality practitioners to determine the probability of X defects per sampling unit. For example, an automobile manufacturer may sample three car hoods per hour and count the total number of paint defects. These defects could include any number of occurrences of dirt, runs, sags, overspray, under spray, or orange peel defects. This type of data collection is in sharp contrast to that used for the binomial family of distributions, in which a unit is classified as either defective or non-defective, or go/no go.

The Poisson distribution has the following requirements:

1. The random variable X is defined as the number of occurrences of an event over some interval. This interval can be a time interval, or it can be interpreted as a sampling unit.

2. The occurrences are random.

3. The occurrences are independent of each other.

4. The probability of occurrence is constant across the interval of interest.

For the arrivals case, these requirements state that our random variable is the number of arrivals per time period (hour, shift, week, and so on). The arrivals occur randomly, and each arrival is independent of the others, meaning that one arrival doesn't influence the occurrence of the next arrival, for example. Last, if we are measuring arrivals per hour, the probability of an arrival occurring in, say, minute 15 is the same as the probability of an arrival in minute 59.

For the defect count case, our random variable is the number of defects in the sampling unit, whether that is 1 car hood or 10 car hoods. The defects are assumed to occur at random and are independent of each other. And, the probability of a defect on the right corner of the hood is the same as the probability of a defect occurring in the center of the hood, and so on.

4.7.1 Probability Mass Function

The probability mass function of the Poisson is shown in Formula 4.42,

Formula 4.42   Poisson probability mass function

$$P(X = x) = \frac{e^{-\mu}\mu^x}{x!}, \qquad x = 0, 1, 2, \ldots$$

where μ is the sole parameter. Note that some texts use the Greek letter λ to denote the mean of the Poisson distribution. The range of the random variable X has no upper bound.

This formula certainly looks different from the other formulas we have seen so far. You might be wondering what "e" stands for. The term e denotes a specific *irrational number*, or one with a never-ending set of places after the decimal point, similar to how the term π is a quick way to denote 3.14159 . . . . In addition, both π and e fit into the rarified class of transcendental numbers since they are both irrational and non-algebraic, meaning that they are not solutions to a nonzero polynomial equation with rational coefficients. Impress your friends this weekend with that little factoid!

The term *e* is a result of the following infinite sum:

$$\sum_{i=0}^{\infty} \frac{1}{i!} = \frac{1}{0!} + \frac{1}{1!} + \frac{1}{2!} + \frac{1}{3!} + \frac{1}{4!} + \ldots e \cong 2.71828$$

When performing calculations for the Poisson distribution on a calculator, it is important to use the *e* key instead of approximating by typing in just a few digits of the number, such as 2.72. If you don't use the *e* key, your result is likely to have quite a bit of rounding error.

To illustrate this point, let's find the probability that the number of occurrences *X* equals 15, given *m* = 20, first by correctly using the *e* key, and then by incorrectly using the approximation $e \approx 2.72$.

Correct method: Using *e* key on calculator:

$$P(X = 15) = \frac{e^{-20}20^{15}}{15!} = 0.0516$$

Incorrect method: Using $e \approx 2.72$.

$$P(X = 15) = \frac{(2.72)^{-20}20^{15}}{15!} = 0.0510$$

Depending on the application, the difference in the second result could have a major unwanted impact. Poisson probabilities $P(X = x)$ for various values of μ are tabulated in Appendix D.

The cumulative mass function is shown in Formula 4.43.

Formula 4.43   Poisson cumulative mass function

$$P(X \le x) = \sum_{x=0}^{x} \frac{e^{-\mu}\mu^x}{x!}, \qquad x \in \{0, 1, 2, \ldots\}$$

We can also use a table of cumulative Poisson probabilities, provided in Appendix E. Based on μ we can find $P(X \le x)$ in the interior of the table.

4.7.2 Parameters, Expected Value, and Variance

The Poisson distribution is unusual in that it has only one parameter, μ. Both the mean and the variance of the Poisson are equal to μ. See Formulas 4.44, 4.45, and 4.46.

Formula 4.44   Expected value of the Poisson

$$\mu = E(X) = \mu$$

Formula 4.45   Variance of the Poisson

$$\sigma^2 = Var(X) = \mu$$

Formula 4.46 Standard deviation of the Poisson

$$\sigma = \sqrt{\mu}$$

If the parameter μ is not known, it can be estimated by calculating the average number of observed occurrences over several intervals. The estimators for the Poisson parameters are shown in Formulas 4.47–4.49.

Formula 4.47 Poisson distribution mean estimator

$$\hat{\mu} = \hat{E}(X) = \bar{X}$$

Formula 4.48 Poisson distribution variance estimator

$$\hat{\sigma}^2 = \hat{Var}(X) = \bar{X}$$

Formula 4.49 Poisson distribution standard deviation estimator

$$\hat{\sigma} = \sqrt{\bar{X}}$$

4.7.3 Distribution Shape

As the mean of the Poisson distribution increases, the spread, or standard deviation, increases by the square root of the mean. The shapes of Poisson distributions for various values of μ are shown in Figure 4.13.

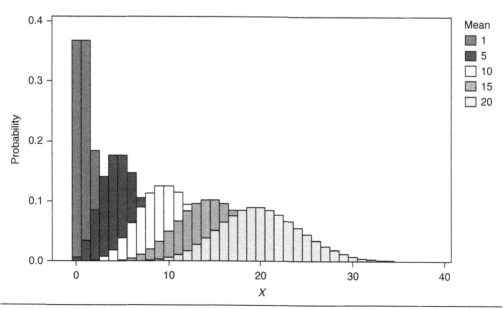

Figure 4.13 Shape of the Poisson distribution, varying μ.

4.7.4 Poisson Approximation to Binomial

The Poisson distribution can be used to approximate the binomial distribution using $\mu = np$ if the sample size n is large and the probability of success p is small. More specifically, the Poisson can be used to estimate a binomial probability when $n \geq 100$ and $np \leq 10$. Figure 4.14 shows the similarities between the binomial and Poisson distributions when $n = 100$ and $np = 10$.

4.7.5 Related Microsoft Excel Functions

The probabilities for a Poisson random variable can be calculated in Microsoft Excel using the formula *=poisson.dist()*. The function takes arguments for the number of events X, the distribution mean, and a cumulative logical flag, as shown in the dialog box in Figure 4.15. For example, for a Poisson distribution with $\mu = 9.5$, we can find the probability that there will be $x = 7$ events by entering *=poisson.dist(7,9.5,0)*.

   If we wanted to know the probability that $X \leq 7$, we would turn on the cumulative flag in the formula by typing in the value 1 in the cumulative argument: *=poisson.dist(7,9.5,1)*.

4.7.6 Uses and Applications

The Poisson distribution is used extensively in simulation to model arrivals and is used in quality control to model the number of defects per unit. For example:

* To determine staffing levels, an engineer uses the Poisson distribution to model the number of customers arriving at a bank during lunch hour, or the number of shoppers waiting to check out at the grocery store on a Saturday.

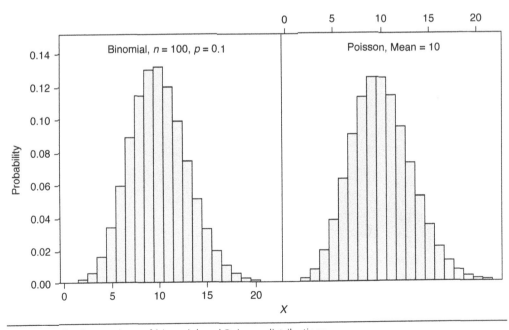

Figure 4.14   Comparison of binomial and Poisson distributions.

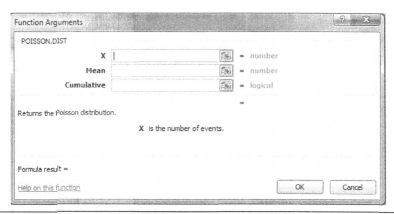

Figure 4.15   Microsoft Excel function =*poisson.dist()*.

- To determine the timing of a traffic light, a traffic study uses the Poisson distribution to model the number of cars passing through a particular intersection.

- To track the number of surface defects in stainless steel panels, a quality engineer creates a statistical process control chart based on the Poisson distribution.

4.7.7 Poisson Connection to Statistical Process Control

The Poisson distribution is the underpinning of the c and u charts in statistical process control. The c chart tracks the number of defects found per unit when sample size is constant over time. The u chart tracks defects per unit when sample size is variable. Formulas 4.50 and 4.51 give the calculations for the control limits for the c and u charts, respectively.

Formula 4.50   Control limits for c chart

$$\text{UCL} = \bar{c} + 3\sqrt{\bar{c}}$$
$$\text{Centerline} = \bar{c}$$
$$\text{LCL} = \bar{c} - 3\sqrt{\bar{c}}$$

Formula 4.51   Control limits for u chart

$$\text{UCL} = \bar{u} + 3\sqrt{\frac{\bar{u}}{n}}$$
$$\text{Centerline} = \bar{u}$$
$$\text{LCL} = \bar{u} - 3\sqrt{\frac{\bar{u}}{n}}$$

4.8 SUMMARY OF DISCRETE PROBABILITY DISTRIBUTIONS

The table on page 80 provides a summarization of important details on the distributions covered in this chapter.

Distribution	Parameters	Density function	Domain of X	Expected value and variance	Special note
Discrete uniform	a, b $b \geq a$	$p(x) = \dfrac{1}{b-a+1}$	$x = \{a, a+1, \ldots, b\}$	$E(X) = \dfrac{a+b}{2}$ $\mathrm{Var}(X) = \dfrac{(b-a+1)^2 - 1}{12}$	
Binomial	n, p	$P(X = x) = \binom{n}{x} p^x (1-p)^{n-x}$	$x = \{0, 1, \ldots, n\}$	$\mu = E(X) = np$ $\sigma^2 = \mathrm{Var}(X) = np(1-p)$	Used for p and np charts
Multinomial	$n,$ $p_1, p_2, \ldots, p_k$	$P(X_1 = x_1, X_2 = x_2, \ldots, X_k = x_k) =$ $\dfrac{n!}{x_1! x_2! \ldots x_k!} p_1^{x_1} p_2^{x_2} \ldots p_k^{x_k}$	$\displaystyle\sum_{i=1}^{k} x_i = n, x_i \geq 0$	$\mu_i = np_i$ $\sigma_i^2 = np_i(1-p_i)$	
Hypergeometric	N, D, n	$P(X = x) = \dfrac{\binom{D}{x}\binom{N-D}{n-x}}{\binom{N}{n}}$	$x \in \{\max(0, n-(N-D)), \ldots, \min(n, D)\}$	$\mu = E(X) = n\dfrac{D}{N}$ $\sigma^2 = n\dfrac{D}{N}\left(1 - \dfrac{D}{N}\right)\left(\dfrac{N-n}{N-1}\right)$	
Geometric	p	$P(X = x) = p^x(1-p)^x$	$x \in \{0, 1, 2, \ldots\}$	$E(X) = \dfrac{(1-p)}{p}$ $\mathrm{Var}(X) = \dfrac{(1-p)}{p^2}$	Memoryless property
Negative binomial, Pascal	p, r	$P(X = x) = \binom{x-1}{r-1} p^r (1-p)^{x-r}$	$x \in (r, r+1, \ldots)$	$E(X) = \dfrac{r(1-p)}{p}$ $\mathrm{Var}(X) = \dfrac{r(1-p)}{p^2}$	
Poisson	μ	$P(X = x) = \dfrac{e^{-\mu}\mu^x}{x!}$	$x = 0, 1, 2, \ldots$	$\mu = E(X) = \mu$ $\sigma^2 = \mathrm{Var}(X) = \mu$	Used for c and u charts

5

Continuous Probability Distributions

In this chapter the term *continuous random variable* is defined and the rules relating to continuous probability distributions are explained. Three important probability theorems are then presented: the law of large numbers, Markov's inequality, and Chebyshev's theorem. Fifteen useful continuous probability distributions are then introduced: the uniform, triangular, normal, standard normal, Student's *t*, gamma, chi-square, exponential, Erlang, Weibull, Rayleigh, *F*, beta, lognormal, and Cauchy.

For each distribution in the chapter, the probability density function is presented along with the distributional parameters. The cumulative distribution function is also presented when a closed form exists. The effect of the parameters on the location, scale, and shape of the distribution is also shown. Formulas for calculating the expected value and variance of each distribution are given. Related Microsoft Excel functions and worked examples are also presented. The text also gives real-world situations in which the distribution can be applied.

5.1 PROBABILITY CONCEPTS FOR CONTINUOUS RANDOM VARIABLES

In Chapter 4, discrete random variables and their distributions were introduced. There, the random variable X had a finite set of possible values, or a countably infinite set of values. In contrast, a *continuous random variable* can take on an infinite set of values. For example, the continuous variable X may take on any value in the range [1, 2], which would include the values 1.24, 1.6654, and an infinite number of other possibilities. Unlike counts, continuous variables are generally measured using an instrument, such as a ruler for length, a scale for weight, or a thermometer for temperature.

5.1.1 Continuous Probability Distributions

In order for a mathematical formula to be considered a continuous probability distribution function, three requirements must be met. These are presented a bit differently than the ones we studied in Section 4.1.4 for discrete distributions:

1. The random variable x must be continuous

2. $f(x) \geq 0$ *for all* x

3. $\int_x f(x)dx = 1$ (the integral of $f(x)$ evaluated over the range of x equals 1)

"Hey, what's all this integration stuff?" For continuous probability distributions, probability is found using the area under the curve, not the height of the curve. Area is found by integration, as you might recall from a Calculus II course. If you can't or won't recall Calculus II, that's OK, because we won't be evaluating integrals in this text.

With the discrete random variables in Chapter 4, there was a specific probability associated with each value of x, denoted as $p(x)$. For continuous random variables, the probability density function $f(x)$ does not give a probability for a given x. Instead, probability is defined as the area under the curve that $f(x)$ defines. *The probability that x exactly equals a certain value is zero since there is no area at a point.* Therefore, we talk about the probability that a continuous variable x is less than or greater than a certain value.

What do these three rules for continuous distributions imply? Rule 2 requires that the density function always give a value greater than or equal to zero. How does this affect probability? This requirement ensures that the cumulative distribution function is always going to increase or at least stay the same as x increases. For example, given that the random variable x has the following density function:

$$f(x) = 2x, 0 \leq x \leq 1$$

we can draw the graph shown in Figure 5.1. Notice that the density function $f(x)$ is always positive and that it can take on values greater than one. Obviously, $f(x)$ is not representing probability; it is the area underneath $f(x)$ that gives probability.

Now let's take a look at some areas. The probability that x is less than 0.50 can be shown as the area under $f(x)$ from $x = 0$ to $x = 0.5$, as shown in Figure 5.2.

The area we shade in as we move to the right on the x axis is increasing. The probability that x is between 0 and 0.50 is greater than the probability that x is

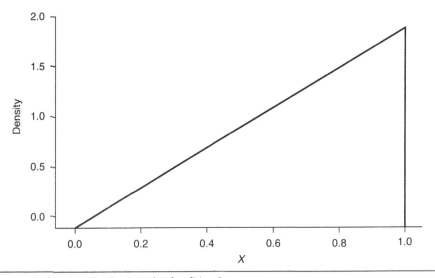

Figure 5.1   Probability distribution plot for $f(x) = 2x$.

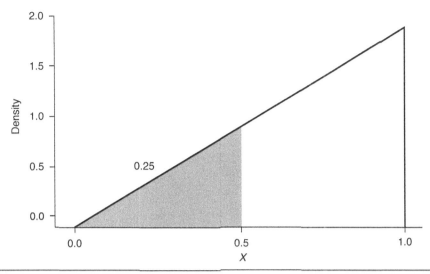

Figure 5.2 Area under the curve for $f(x) = 2x$.

between 0 and 0.25; the probability that x is between 0 and 0.75 is greater than the probability that x is between 0 and 0.50, and so on. This monotonically increasing cumulative probability is a consequence of Rule 2.

The total area under the curve across the range of x is equal to one. We don't need to know calculus to get the result in this case. Recognizing that the area is triangular, we can take

$$\text{Area} = \tfrac{1}{2}bh$$
$$= \tfrac{1}{2}(1.0)(2.0)$$
$$= 1$$

This result satisfies Rule 3.

We can also see that the cumulative probability is monotonically increasing by looking directly at the *cumulative distribution function*. The cumulative distribution function, denoted as $F(x)$, gives the probability that the random variable X is less than or equal to some value x, or $\Pr(X \leq x)$. The cumulative distribution function for a continuous probability distribution takes the general form:

$$\Pr(X \leq x) = F(x) = \int_{-\infty}^{x} f(x)dx$$

For some distributions, the integral results in a closed-form solution that can be used to calculate cumulative probabilities. In the case of the normal, standard normal, Student's t, chi-square, F, beta, and lognormal distributions, however, no closed-form formula exists. Instead, we must use tabulated cumulative probabilities. Honestly, that is just as well, since it is easier to look up a number in a table than to apply a formula.

Returning to our example probability distribution, we can derive the cumulative distribution function and use it to calculate the cumulative probability for any x.

$$f(x) = 2x, 0 \le x \le 1$$

$$\Pr(X \le x) = F(x) = \int_0^x 2x\,dx = x^2$$

Hence, the cumulative distribution function is:

$$F(x) = \begin{cases} 0, & x < 0 \\ x^2, & 0 \le x \le 1 \\ 1, & x > 0 \end{cases}$$

We see from the graph of the cumulative distribution function in Figure 5.3 that $F(x)$ is monotonically increasing with x. The probability that X is less than or equal to any value x can be calculated using $F(X)$ or read directly from the graph. For example, $F(0.8) = 0.64$.

A probability density function is fully described by its parameters. These parameters can be classified as affecting the location, scale, or shape of the distribution. Location parameters affect where the distribution will lie along the x axis. Changing a location parameter will shift the distribution along the x axis. Scale parameters affect the breadth of the distribution along the x axis, and shape parameters affect the form of the distribution, such as its skewness. Among the three, a change in the shape parameter will have the most impact on the appearance of the distribution.

5.1.2 Expectation and Variance of Continuous Random Variables

Recall from Chapter 4 that the mean of the discrete random variable X can be calculated by multiplying each possible value of X by its probability and then

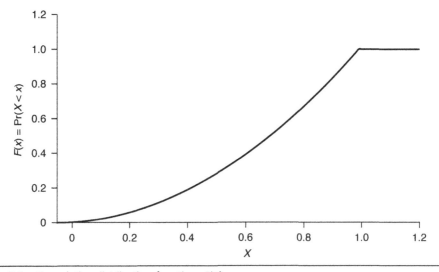

Figure 5.3   Cumulative distribution function, $F(X)$.

summing up. The variance of the discrete random variable X can be calculated by squaring each X and multiplying by the corresponding probability, summing up, and then subtracting the squared mean. For continuous variables, we follow this same procedure, except that we integrate instead of add.

The formulas for finding the expectation and variance of a continuous random variable are as follows:

$$\mu = \int_x xf(x)dx$$

$$\sigma^2 = \int_x (x - \mu)^2 f(x)dx$$
$$= \int_x (x)^2 f(x)dx - \mu^2$$

We will not use integration in this text, but sometimes it is just nice to know where things come from. Now that we've admired the formulas, we can move on. Each of the 15 continuous distributions in the text has a closed-form solution for the expected value and variance, except for the Cauchy distribution, in which both the mean and variance are undefined.

5.2 USEFUL PROBABILITY THEOREMS

There are several useful probability theorems, and three are presented in this section without proof: the law of large numbers, Markov's inequality, and Chebyshev's inequality.

5.2.1 The Law of Large Numbers

The law of large numbers and its proof were developed by Jakob Bernoulli and published posthumously in 1713. Later, the strong law of large numbers was developed and subsequently proven. As a result, Bernoulli's original law became known as the weak law of large numbers. To the layperson, the differences between the two laws are not very meaningful. Both laws state that as we take more and more independent samples to estimate a probability or a parameter of a distribution, the estimate tends to approach the actual probability or parameter. In other words, more data produces better estimates.

5.2.2 Markov's Inequality

Let X be a nonnegative random variable with an expected value μ. Markov's inequality gives an upper bound on the probability that X is greater than some positive value a. We can express the upper bound using Formula 5.1.

Formula 5.1 Markov's inequality

$$\Pr(X \geq a) \leq \frac{\mu}{a}, \qquad \text{for } a > 0$$

This theorem will hold for *any* distribution of X, which is quite remarkable. We do not need to know the distribution of the random variable, only its mean, to produce a rough guess about the probability that X exceeds a particular value.

For example, let X be the weights of shipments received at a loading dock, with the mean of X equal to 200 pounds. The distribution of X is unknown. Using Markov's inequality, we can state that no more than 50% of the shipments will exceed 400 pounds.

$$\Pr(X \geq 400) \leq \frac{200}{400}$$

5.2.3 Chebyshev's Inequality

Chebyshev's inequality is a corollary of the more general Markov's inequality. Chebyshev gives a lower bound on the proportion of a distribution that lies within k standard deviations of the mean. As with Markov, the theorem holds true for any distribution. Formula 5.2 shows the lower-bound calculation.

Formula 5.2 Chebyshev's inequality

$$\Pr(\mu - k\sigma \leq X \leq \mu + k\sigma) \geq 1 - \frac{1}{k^2}, \qquad \text{for } k > 0$$

The theorem provides useful insights when $k > 1$. For example, for $k = 2$, the inequality indicates that for *any* distribution, at least 75% of the population will lie within two standard deviations of the mean. Table 5.1 gives various values of k and the corresponding Chebyshev lower bounds.

Table 5.1 Chebyshev lower bounds for various k.

Number of standard deviations from mean, k	Percentage of distribution lying within ±k standard deviations of the mean is at least
1.0	0
$\sqrt{2}$	50
1.5	55.56
2.0	75
2.5	84
3.0	88.89
4.0	93.75

5.3 THE UNIFORM DISTRIBUTION

One of the most basic and useful continuous probability distributions is the uniform distribution. It is an intrinsic part of data generation in simulation.

5.3.1 Probability Density Function

The density function for a uniform distribution has two parameters, a and b, which are also the endpoints for the range of X. The parameter a is a location parameter, and the difference $(b - a)$ is a scale parameter. The functional form is shown in Formula 5.3.

Formula 5.3   Probability density function of uniform distribution

$$f(x) = \frac{1}{(b - a)}, \qquad a \leq x \leq b \text{ and } b > a$$

The expected value and variance of X are functions of the parameters a and b and are calculated using Formulas 5.4 and 5.5, respectively.

Formula 5.4   Expected value of uniform distribution

$$E(X) = \frac{a + b}{2}$$

Formula 5.5   Variance of uniform distribution

$$\text{Var}(X) = \frac{(b - a)^2}{12}$$

The uniform distribution has a rectangular shape, so it is straightforward to calculate probabilities. The cumulative distribution function of the uniform distribution is shown in Formula 5.6.

Formula 5.6   Cumulative distribution function of uniform distribution

$$F(x) = \begin{cases} 0, & x < a \\ \dfrac{x - a}{(b - a)}, & a \leq x \leq b \\ 1, & x > b \end{cases}$$

5.3.2 Distribution Shape

The uniform distribution has zero slope, as shown in Figure 5.4.

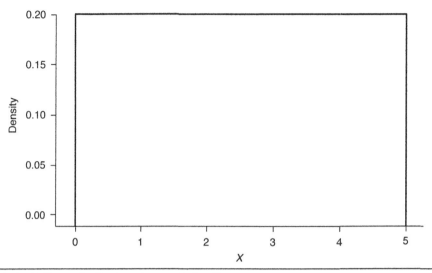

Figure 5.4   Uniform distribution plot: *a* = 0, *b* = 5.

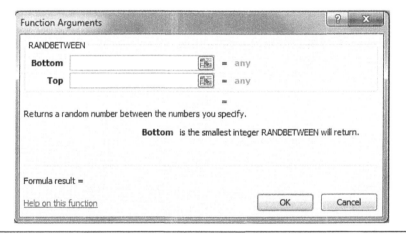

Figure 5.5   Microsoft Excel function =*randbetween()*.

5.3.3 Related Microsoft Excel Function

To generate an observation from a uniform distribution with endpoints [*a*, *b*], we can use the Microsoft Excel function =*randbetween(a,b)*, as shown in Figure 5.5.

5.4 THE TRIANGULAR DISTRIBUTION

The triangular distribution has three parameters, *a*, *b*, and *m*, with *a* < *m* < *b*. The parameter *a* is a location parameter, *(b – a)* is a scale parameter, and *m* is a shape parameter. As with the uniform distribution, *a* and *b* refer to the endpoints of the range of *x*, with *a* < *b*. The parameter *m* gives the mode, or peak, of the distribution.

5.4.1 Probability Density Function

The probability density function of the triangular distribution is shown in Formula 5.7.

Formula 5.7 Triangular probability density function

$$f(x) = \begin{cases} \dfrac{2(x-a)}{(b-a)(m-a)}, & a \le x \le m \\ \dfrac{2(b-x)}{(b-a)(b-m)}, & m < x \le b \\ 0, & \text{otherwise} \end{cases}$$

The expected value and variance of the triangular random variable X are given by Formulas 5.8 and 5.9, respectively.

Formula 5.8 Expected value of triangular distribution

$$E(X) = \frac{a+b+m}{3}$$

Formula 5.9 Variance of triangular distribution

$$Var(X) = \frac{a^2 + b^2 + m^2 - ab - am - bm}{18}$$

The cumulative distribution function of the triangular distribution is shown in Formula 5.10.

Formula 5.10 Cumulative distribution function of triangular distribution

$$F(x) = \begin{cases} 0, & x < a \\ \dfrac{(x-a)^2}{(b-a)(m-a)}, & a \le x \le m \\ 1 - \dfrac{(b-x)^2}{(b-a)(b-m)}, & m < x \le b \\ 1, & x > b \end{cases}$$

5.4.2 Distribution Shape

The mode of the triangular distribution occurs at $x = m$. The distribution is right-skewed if $(m-a) < (b-m)$, is left-skewed if $(m-a) > (b-m)$, and is symmetric if $m = \dfrac{(a+b)}{2}$. The shape of the triangular distribution for various values of m is shown in Figure 5.6.

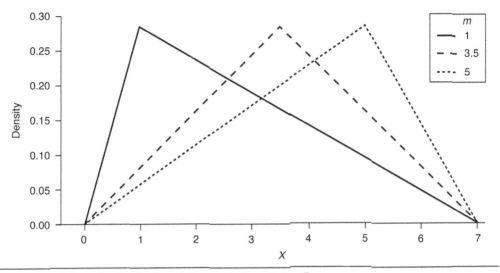

Figure 5.6 Triangular distribution plot: *m* varied, *a* = 0, *b* = 7.

5.5 THE NORMAL DISTRIBUTION

Perhaps the best known of all statistical distributions is the normal, or Gaussian, distribution. The normal distribution is part of the exponential family of distributions, which also includes the gamma, Erlang, chi-square, exponential, Rayleigh, and Weibull distributions, among others.

5.5.1 Probability Density Function

The normal distribution has two parameters, μ, a location parameter, and σ, a scale parameter. Notation for a normally distributed random variable X is $X \sim N(\mu, \sigma^2)$. The parameter μ can take on any value, but σ must be positive. The normal probability density function is shown in Formula 5.11.

Formula 5.11 Normal probability density function

$$f(x) = \frac{1}{\sqrt{2\pi\sigma^2}} e^{\frac{-(x-\mu)^2}{2\sigma^2}}, \quad -\infty < x < \infty$$

This function produces the characteristic bell-shaped curve that we have all seen, an example of which is shown in Figure 5.7.

Figure 5.8 shows that changing μ moves the center of the distribution along the x axis, while increasing σ makes the distribution more spread out. Note that the normal distribution is always symmetric. Both its skewness and kurtosis are equal to zero.

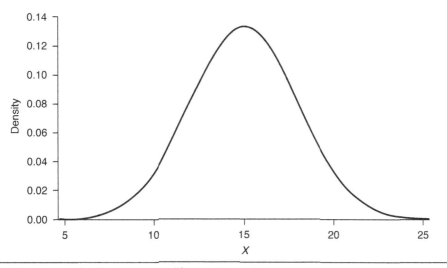

Figure 5.7 Normal distribution curve with $\mu = 15$, $\sigma = 3$.

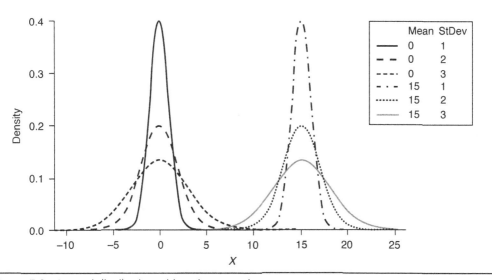

Figure 5.8 Normal distribution with various μ and σ.

The expected value of a normally distributed variable X is equal to μ, and the variance is equal to σ^2, as shown in Formulas 5.12 and 5.13, respectively.

Formula 5.12 Expected value of normal distribution

$$E(X) = \mu$$

Formula 5.13 Variance of normal distribution

$$\text{Var}(X) = \sigma^2$$

5.5.2 Parameter Estimators

Let $x_1, x_2, \ldots, x_n$ be a random sample from a normal distribution with mean μ and standard deviation σ. We can estimate the distribution parameters using the statistics $\overline{X}$ and s for μ and σ, respectively, as shown in Formulas 5.14 and 5.15. To estimate the variance σ^2, we use the sample variance, s^2. An alternate form of the sample standard deviation formula is shown in Formula 5.16. This form is often used for manual calculations.

Formula 5.14   Mean estimator for normal distribution

$$\overline{X} = \frac{\sum_{i=1}^{n} x_i}{n}$$

Formula 5.15   Standard deviation estimator for normal distribution

$$s = \sqrt{\frac{\sum_{i=1}^{n} (x_i - \overline{x})^2}{n-1}}$$

Formula 5.16   Calculation formula for s

$$s = \sqrt{\frac{\sum_{i=1}^{n} x_i^2 - n\overline{x}^2}{n-1}}$$

Notice that the estimated standard deviation shown in Formulas 5.15 and 5.16 has $(n-1)$ in its denominator. This quantity is called the *degrees of freedom*, and it reflects the size of the sample, less any restrictions placed on that sample. How is the restriction determined? In this instance, the restriction stems from using the mean estimator $\overline{x}$ in the calculation. Based on the formula for the sample mean, the quantity $n\overline{x}$ is equal to the sum of the n data points in the sample. Hence, the total has already been determined. For example, let the sum of the sample equal 10. If we have a sample of size 2, the sum would be

$$x_1 + x_2 = 10$$

How many choices do we have for x_1 in this equation? The data point x_1 could be equal to 3 or 17 or –324.6, and so on. There are an infinite number of possibilities for x_1, meaning that we have complete freedom for this variable. However, as soon as we assign a number for x_1, x_2 is automatically determined since it must make the sum equal to 10. For two variables, then, we have one degree of freedom.

For a sample size of three:

$$x_1 + x_2 + x_3 = 10$$

The points x_1 and x_2 can take on any values, but once these are chosen, x_3 is also automatically determined. Therefore, for a sample size of three, we have one restricted variable and two degrees of freedom.

In general, for a sum of n data points with a known total, there are (n – 1) degrees of freedom.

5.5.3 The Central Limit Theorem

One of the most important and useful theorems in all of statistics is the central limit theorem. It is invoked when we perform hypothesis testing, linear regression, analysis of variance, design of experiments, and control charting. Simply stated, the central limit theorem (CLT) is as follows:

If the random variable X has a mean μ and variance σ^2, and we take n independent samples from the distribution, then the sum of the x's will approximately follow a normal distribution with mean $= n\mu$ and variance $= n\sigma^2$.

A few comments are in order. First, the reason why the CLT is so terrific is that the underlying distribution of X can be *anything*. As long as we take enough independent samples and add them up, the resulting sum will become approximately normal with a known mean and variance. Stated another way, we can start with any distribution, and then through sampling and summing, we can turn it into a normal distribution.

Second, the distribution of the sum of the X's is *approximately* normal, and this approximation will improve as n increases. If the underlying distribution of X is fairly symmetric, the approximation looks better faster as n increases. For very skewed distributions, it takes more samples in the sum to look normal. In general, using a sample of 30 for the calculations should make even the sums of the most skewed distributions look normal. Recognize that this is just a guideline and that there is nothing particularly magic about the number 30.

Many texts present the CLT in terms of the sample average. If we take n independent samples and then calculate their average, the sampling distribution of $\overline{X}$ will be approximately normal with mean μ and variance equal to $\dfrac{\sigma^2}{n}$.

For example, let X be a random variable with mean 100, variance equal to 225, and a standard deviation of 15. If we take independent samples of $n = 9$, then the resulting distribution of averages will approximately follow a normal distribution with mean 100, variance equal to 25, and standard deviation equal to 5. Note that the distribution of the averages is less variable than the distribution of the individuals. The distribution of the averages will become less and less variable as we increase the sample size used to calculate the averages. See Figure 5.9.

A more general presentation of the CLT states that *any* linear combination of independent samples from the distribution of X will approach a normal distribution. For example, we can take random, independent samples of $n = 3$ and calculate $y = x_1 + 2x_2 + 3x_3$. The resulting random variable Y will follow an approximate normal distribution with mean $= 6\mu$ and variance $= 14\sigma^2$. Recall from Section 4.1.3

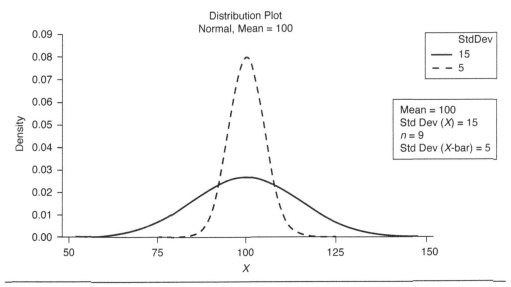

Figure 5.9 Sampling distribution of X-bar.

that we can calculate the expectation and variance of a linear combination of random variables by using:

$$E(Y) = \mu \sum_{i=1}^{n} a_i$$

$$E(Y) = E(x_1 + 2x_2 + 3x_3) = \mu + 2\mu + 3\mu = 6\mu$$

And, due to independence,

$$\text{Var}(Y) = \sigma^2 \sum_{i=1}^{n} a_i^2$$

$$\text{Var}(Y) = \text{Var}(x_1 + 2x_2 + 3x_3) = \sigma^2 + 4\sigma^2 + 9\sigma^2 = 14\sigma^2$$

5.5.4 Normal Probability Plots

Many statistical hypothesis tests require that the data follow a normal distribution. The CLT is pivotal in turning non-normal data into approximately normal averages or sums, but only if we have enough samples for the calculation. How can we tell whether our data are normally distributed? One method is to create a normal probability plot of the data to see how well they fit a normal distribution.

An example normal probability plot is shown in Figure 5.10. The *y* axis of the plot represents percentiles of the normal distribution. The scale is created so that a perfect normal distribution would fall on the diagonal line drawn on the graph. The extent to which our actual data points follow this line tells us how well the data fit a normal distribution.

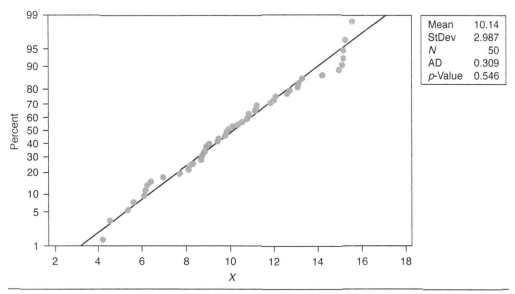

Figure 5.10   Example normal probability plot.

Many texts tell analysts to apply a "fat pencil test": If we can cover up the data points by laying a fat pencil on the diagonal line, our data are most likely normal. I've never been a fan of the fat pencil test. Who has fat pencils handy? Instead, we have a statistical test and p value that we can use. The probability plot shown provides the value of the Anderson-Darling (AD) statistic as well as the p value for the hypotheses H_0: Data follow a normal distribution versus H_1: Data do not follow a normal distribution. If the data set is normal, we *will not* reject H_0. A p value greater than 0.05 indicates that there is no significant evidence against our assumption of normality. Much cleaner than the fat pencil test and easier to justify in a meeting. In Figure 5.10, the p value is 0.546, indicating that the normal assumption is not disputed by the data.

Figure 5.11 shows a normal probability plot for a symmetric, but heavy-tailed, distribution. We see that there are data points farther out in the tails of the distribution than would be expected from a normal distribution. The p value of the AD test, $p = 0.017$, shows us that we do not have a normal distribution.

Figure 5.12 shows the normal probability plot for a right-skewed distribution. We see that the data do not include any negative values, since the points do not start until the zero point on the x axis. The cumulative probability builds very quickly, meaning that there are many data points near zero. The buildup then slows down, indicating that the distribution tails off as we move to the right. Once again, based on the p value, we reject H_0 and claim the data are not from a normal distribution.

5.5.5 Normal Approximations

Several discrete and continuous distributions can be well approximated by the normal distribution under certain conditions. For example, if X follows a binomial distribution with a large n such that $np \geq 5$ and $n(1-p) \geq 5$, we can use the normal

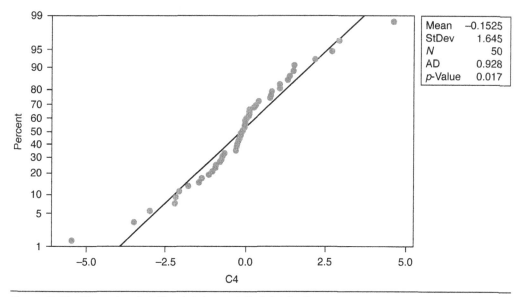

Figure 5.11   Normal probability plot, heavy-tailed distribution.

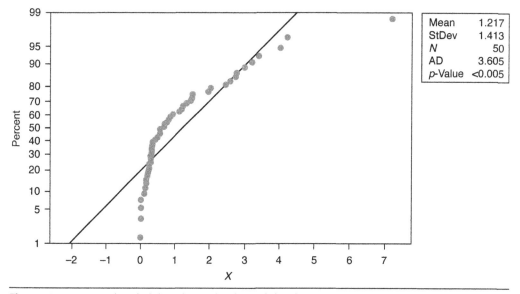

Figure 5.12   Normal probability plot, right-skewed distribution.

distribution to approximate the binomial probabilities. In the binomial case, we use a normal distribution with a mean equal to np and standard deviation equal to the square root of $np(1 - p)$. The conditions necessary for the normal approximation of the binomial, Poisson, Student's t, gamma, and m-Erlang distributions are shown in Table 5.2.

In the binomial and Poisson cases, we are using a continuous distribution to approximate probabilities from a discrete distribution. We must use a *continuity*

Table 5.2   Normal approximations for certain distributions.

Distribution, parameters	Conditions for normal approximation
Binomial (n, p)	If $np \geq 5$, and $n(1 - p) \geq 5$, use normal with $\mu = np$ and $\sigma = \sqrt{np(1 - p)}$.
	Use continuity correction.
	Approximation improves as n increases.
Poisson (μ)	If $\mu > 5$, use normal with $\mu = \mu$ and $\sigma = \sqrt{\mu}$.
	Use continuity correction.
	Approximation improves as μ increases.
Student's t $(n - 1)$	If $n > 31$, use normal with $\mu = 0$ and $\sigma = 1$.
	Approximation improves as n increases.
Gamma (α, β)	If $\alpha > 30$, use normal with $\mu = \alpha\beta$ and $\sigma = \sqrt{\alpha\beta}$.
	Approximation improves as α increases.
m-Erlang (m, β)	If $m > 30$, use normal with $\mu = m\beta$ and $\sigma = \sqrt{m\beta}$.
	Approximation improves as m increases.

correction in the calculations to account for the difference between the continuous and discrete scales.

For example, let $X \sim$ Bin(20, 0.40). The value of np is 8 and $np(1 - p)$ is 12, so the criteria for using a normal approximation are met. We can use a normal distribution with mean equal to $np = 8$ and standard deviation equal to $\sqrt{20(0.40)0.60}$ to approximate the binomial probabilities. To find $P(X \leq 5)$, we add the continuity correction and solve Pr(X < 5.5) using the normal. How good is our approximation? The binomial distribution gives us Pr(X $\leq$ 5) = 0.1256 and the normal approximation Pr(X < 5.5) yields 0.1269. The approximation will improve as n increases.

Table 5.3 shows the continuity corrections necessary when using the normal distribution to approximate probabilities from a discrete distribution.

Table 5.3   Continuity corrections for discrete distributions.

Discrete probability statement	Statement for normal approximation with continuity correction
Pr(X = x)	Pr(x − 0.5 < X < x + 0.5)
Pr(X < x)	Pr(X < x − 0.5)
Pr(X ≤ x)	Pr(X < x + 0.5)
Pr(X > x)	Pr(X > x + 0.5)
Pr (X ≥ x)	Pr(X > x − 0.5)

5.5.6 Related Microsoft Excel Functions

There are two useful Microsoft Excel functions for the normal distribution. The first is =*norm.dist()*, shown in Figure 5.13, which takes on arguments for X, the mean, the standard deviation, and a cumulative flag. To find the value of the normal distribution density function at a certain point X, we use 0 for the cumulative flag. Be aware that this result is only the height of the normal curve at a point x and is not a probability. To find the probability that the normal random variable X is less than or equal to some value x, we use 1 for the cumulative flag. For example, let X follow a normal distribution with mean 5.0 and standard deviation equal to 2.0. To find the height of the normal density function at the point $x = 3.5$, we use =*normdist(3.5,5.0,2.0,0)*.

However, to find the probability that X is less than or equal to 3.5, we place a 1 in the cumulative argument: =*normdist(3.5,5.0,2.0,1)*. The latter application is much more common.

The second Microsoft Excel function is =*norm.inv()*, shown in Figure 5.14. Given a probability, the function returns the value of x that solves $\Pr(X < x) = p$. For example, given a normal distribution with mean equal to 5.0 and standard

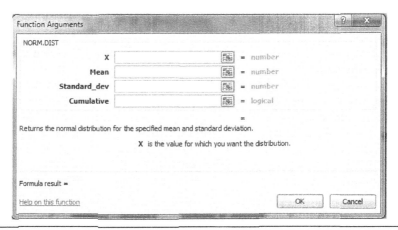

Figure 5.13   Microsoft Excel function =*norm.dist()*.

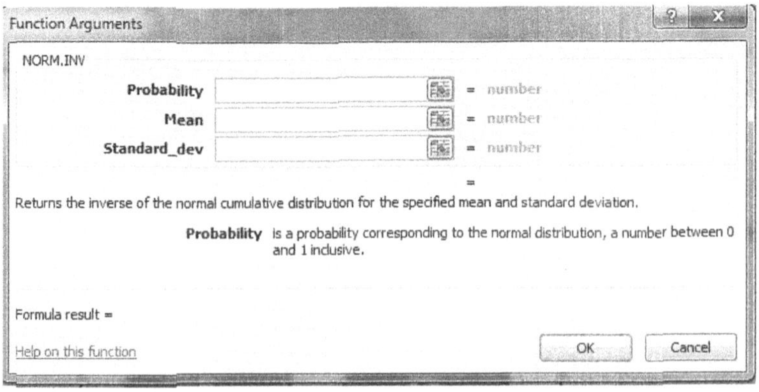

Figure 5.14   Microsoft Excel function =*norm.inv()*.

deviation equal to 2.0, what value of X corresponds to the 75th percentile of the distribution? In other words, what value of X will make the statement $\Pr(X < x) = 0.75$ true? To solve, we use $=norm.inv(0.75,5.0,2.0)$.

5.5.7 Uses and Applications

It is hard to overestimate the importance of the normal distribution in statistical analysis. The quality applications of the normal distribution are vast. Consider the following scenarios:

- A design engineer uses the normal distribution to develop tolerances for a new metal part.

- A Six Sigma Black Belt uses the normal distribution to estimate the proportion of units that will fall out of specification if the current process mean shifts by 1.5 standard deviations.

- A quality engineer uses the normal distribution to calculate the capability of a process to report to the customer.

- An R&D engineer uses the normal distribution to test whether a new design has significantly reduced the average weight of an aerospace component.

- An emergency department uses the normal distribution to estimate a patient's length of stay.

- A mortgage lender uses the normal distribution to estimate the time it will take to close a customer's loan.

- A machine operator uses the normal distribution to track the average and range of strength readings of a welded assembly using an X-bar R chart.

5.5.8 Normal Connection to Statistical Process Control

Walter Shewhart drew the first statistical process control chart, at the Westinghouse plant in Hawthorne, Illinois, in 1924.[1] His X chart was based on normal distribution theory and was a technique to monitor the distribution of a process variable. The chart signaled when the process mean or variance changed over time, indicating that the process was not stable or that a special cause of variation was acting on the process.

Today, the X (individuals) and MR (moving range), X-bar and R (range), and X-bar and S (standard deviation) charts all use the normal distribution as the basis for the control limits. Since the normal distribution is fully described by two parameters, μ and σ, we must simultaneously track the mean as well as the variability of the process to ensure that the distribution of outputs is stable.

If a quality characteristic of a manufactured unit, such as weight, follows a normal distribution, then we can take a single sample at regular time intervals and plot the value of the weights on an X control chart. The control limits will correspond to the ±3 sigma limits of the process weight distribution. In theory,

---

[1] Read more about Shewhart and his contributions at http://asq.org/about-asq/who-we-are/bio_shewhart.html.

99.73% of all weights will fall within these limits. A point falling outside the control limits is most likely an outlier, indicating that the distribution has changed. We then investigate the cause of the outlier and make process adjustments to bring the process back into control.

In order to track the variability of the process, we construct a moving range (MR) chart by plotting the absolute differences between pairs of consecutive data points. Formulas 5.17 and 5.18 show the calculations for the control limits for the X-MR chart. The values for d_2, D_3, and D_4 are based on subgroup size and can be found in the table in Appendix F.

Formula 5.17 Control limits for X chart (use $n = 2$ for subgroup size)

$$UCL = \bar{X} + 3\frac{\overline{MR}}{d_2} = \bar{X} + 3\frac{\overline{MR}}{1.128}$$

$$Centerline = \bar{X}$$

$$LCL = \bar{X} - 3\frac{\overline{MR}}{d_2} = \bar{X} - 3\frac{\overline{MR}}{1.128}$$

Formula 5.18 Control limits for MR chart (use $n = 2$ as subgroup size)

$$UCL = D_4\overline{MR} = 3.267\overline{MR}$$

$$Centerline = MR$$

$$LCL = D_3\overline{MR} = 0$$

If we instead take a sample, or subgroup, of $n > 1$ units per time period, we can construct an X-bar R chart or X-bar S chart to track the distribution of the process output. In general, an X-bar R chart is used for subgroup sizes of 8 or less, and an X-bar S chart is used for larger subgroup sizes. The range statistic can become unreliable for large subgroup sizes since it uses the extremes of the sample in its calculation, and hence is very sensitive to outliers. The calculations for the control limits for X-bar R and X-bar S charts are shown in Formulas 5.19–5.22. The values A_2, A_3, B_3, B_4, D_3, and D_4 are based on sample size and can be found in Appendix F.

Formula 5.19 Control limits for the X-bar chart using R

$$UCL = \bar{\bar{X}} + A_2\bar{R}$$

$$Centerline = \bar{\bar{X}}$$

$$LCL = \bar{\bar{X}} - A_2\bar{R}$$

Formula 5.20   Control limits for R chart

$$UCL = D_4\bar{R}$$

$$Centerline = \bar{R}$$

$$LCL = D_3\bar{R}$$

Formula 5.21   Control limits for the X-bar chart using S

$$UCL = \bar{\bar{X}} + A_3\bar{S}$$

$$Centerline = \bar{\bar{X}}$$

$$LCL = \bar{\bar{X}} - A_3\bar{S}$$

Formula 5.22   Control limits for S chart

$$UCL = B_4\bar{S}$$

$$Centerline = \bar{S}$$

$$LCL = B_3\bar{S}$$

5.6 THE STANDARD NORMAL DISTRIBUTION

If X is normally distributed with mean μ and variance σ^2, we can standardize X to have a mean equal to zero and a variance equal to one by computing what is known as a Z score. See Formula 5.23. By using the Z transformation, we can calculate the relative location of a normally distributed data point x: the point x is $|Z|$ standard deviations away from the mean. A negative Z indicates that the point is below the mean, while a positive Z tells us the point is above the mean.

Formula 5.23   Z score

$$Z = \frac{X - \mu}{\sigma}$$

5.6.1 Probability Density Function

The random variable Z follows a standard normal distribution with $E(Z) = 0$ and $\text{Var}(Z) = 1$, written as $Z \sim N(0,1)$. The probability density function is thus simplified as shown in Formula 5.24.

Formula 5.24 Probability density of standard normal distribution

$$f(z) = \frac{1}{\sqrt{2\pi}} e^{\frac{-z^2}{2}}, \quad -\infty < z < \infty$$

5.6.2 Areas under the Curve

The graph of the standard normal probability density is shown in Figure 5.15. It is centered at the mean, which is equal to zero, and has a standard deviation equal to one.

Recall from Section 5.1 that for continuous distributions, probabilities are calculated as areas under the curve. The normal and standard normal distributions do not have a closed-form solution for the area under the curve, so we rely on tabulated values that have been integrated numerically to find probabilities. To determine a probability for a normal distribution with mean μ and variance σ^2, we first convert X to a standard normal distribution, $Z \sim N(0,1)$. Then we can use a cumulative standard normal table based on the Z scale to find probabilities. Why standardize X to Z? If we didn't, there would have to be a separate table of probabilities for every possible combination of μ and σ^2 (an infinite number of tables).

For all normal distributions, the probability of the random variable X lying within one standard deviation of the mean is 0.6827. The probability is 0.9545 that

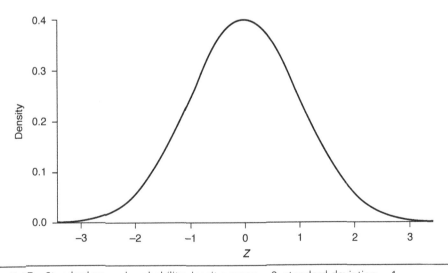

Figure 5.15 Standard normal probability density: mean = 0, standard deviation = 1.

X is within two standard deviations of the mean, and 0.9973 that X is within three standard deviations of the mean. These probabilities are shown as areas under the curve in Figures 5.16, 5.17, and 5.18, respectively.

5.6.3 Using the Cumulative Standard Normal Table

The standard normal table in Appendix G gives the probability that the random variable Z is equal to or less than some value a. Note that for continuous distributions there is no probability associated with a single point. Therefore, the statements $\Pr(Z \le a)$ and $\Pr(Z < a)$ are equivalent since $\Pr(Z = a) = 0$.

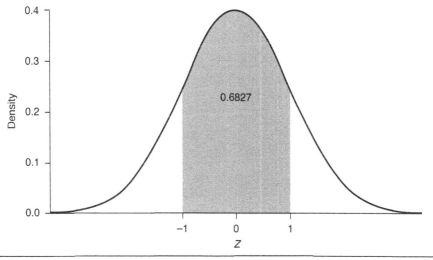

Figure 5.16 Area under the standard normal curve, ± one standard deviation from the mean: mean = 0, standard deviation = 1

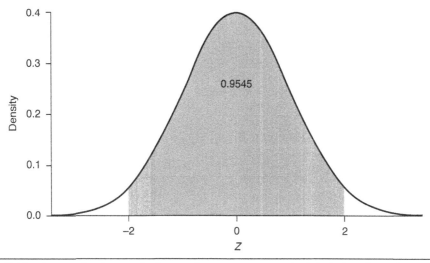

Figure 5.17 Area under the standard normal curve, ± two standard deviations from the mean: mean = 0, standard deviation = 1.

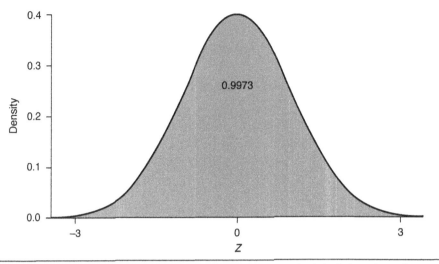

Figure 5.18 Area under the standard normal curve, ± three standard deviations from the mean: mean = 0, standard deviation = 1.

Let $X \sim N(10, 4)$. If we want to know the probability that X is less than the value 12.1, we first convert to the Z scale:

$$Z = \frac{(X - \mu)}{\sigma} = \frac{(12.1 - 10)}{2} = 1.05$$

A portion of the cumulative standard normal table is shown in Table 5.4. To find $Pr(Z \leq 1.05)$,[2] we look up the value 1.05 and read off the corresponding probability from the interior of the table. The value $Z = 1.05$ is found by using the first column to find 1.0 and then looking across the top of the table to find the hundredths place 0.05. The corresponding value 0.8531 is the probability that Z is less than or equal to 1.05.

Finding the Probability That Z Is Greater Than the Value a

If we want to find the probability that Z is *greater than* some value a, we can make use of the complement rule. Using the table, we can find the probability that Z is *less than a*, and then subtract the result from 1. For example, to find $Pr(Z > 1.05)$, we use the table and the complement to find $1 - Pr(Z \leq 1.05) = (1 - 0.8531) = 0.1469$, as shown graphically in Figure 5.19.

Finding the Probability That Z Is between Two Values

The probability that Z is within an interval can be solved by first sketching the normal curve and shading in the area of interest. The sketch makes it clear what values need to be looked up and what needs to be done with them.

---

[2] An alternate notation for $Pr(Z \leq z)$ is the more succinct $\phi(z)$, read as "fee of z." You may see this format in statistics texts and journal articles.

Table 5.4 Cumulative probabilities of the standard normal distribution, partial table.

z	0.00	0.01	0.02	0.03	0.04	0.05	0.06	0.07	0.08	0.09
0.0	0.5000	0.5040	0.5080	0.5120	0.5160	0.5199	0.5239	0.5279	0.5319	0.5359
0.1	0.5398	0.5438	0.5478	0.5517	0.5557	0.5596	0.5636	0.5675	0.5714	0.5753
0.2	0.5793	0.5832	0.5871	0.5910	0.5948	0.5987	0.6026	0.6064	0.6103	0.6141
0.3	0.6179	0.6217	0.6255	0.6293	0.6331	0.6368	0.6406	0.6443	0.6480	0.6517
0.4	0.6554	0.6591	0.6628	0.6664	0.6700	0.6736	0.6772	0.6808	0.6844	0.6879
0.5	0.6915	0.6950	0.6985	0.7019	0.7054	0.7088	0.7123	0.7157	0.7190	0.7224
0.6	0.7257	0.7291	0.7324	0.7357	0.7389	0.7422	0.7454	0.7486	0.7517	0.7549
0.7	0.7580	0.7611	0.7642	0.7673	0.7704	0.7734	0.7764	0.7794	0.7823	0.7852
0.8	0.7881	0.7910	0.7939	0.7967	0.7995	0.8023	0.8051	0.8078	0.8106	0.8133
0.9	0.8159	0.8186	0.8212	0.8238	0.8264	0.8289	0.8315	0.8340	0.8365	0.8389
1.0	0.8413	0.8438	0.8461	0.8485	0.8508	0.8531	0.8554	0.8577	0.8599	0.8621

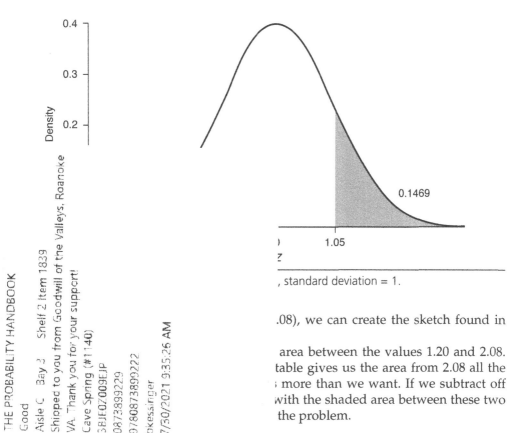

, standard deviation = 1.

.08), we can create the sketch found in

area between the values 1.20 and 2.08. table gives us the area from 2.08 all the ; more than we want. If we subtract off with the shaded area between these two the problem.

$(Z < 1.20) = 0.9812 - 0.8849 = 0.0963$

ι a Negative Value

:red on zero, which means half its values normal tables do not include entries for

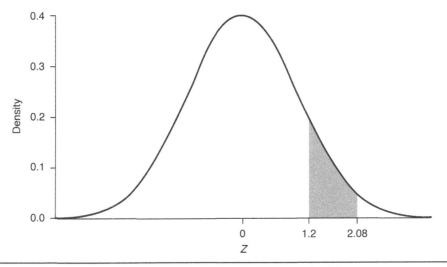

Figure 5.20 Distribution plot: Pr(1.20 < Z < 2.08), mean = 0, standard deviation = 1.

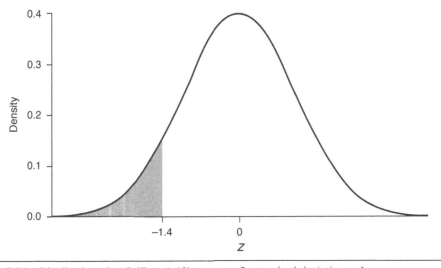

Figure 5.21 Distribution plot: Pr(Z < −1.40), mean = 0, standard deviation = 1.

negative Z values, so we instead use the symmetry of the normal distribution to solve for probabilities involving negative values. Once again, sketching is a vital step in understanding what area we are seeking. For example, if we need to find $P(Z < -1.40)$, we can create a sketch similar to Figure 5.21.

Using symmetry, we recognize that the area below −1.4 is equal to the area above +1.4, as shown in Figure 5.22. Therefore, $Pr(Z < -1.40) = Pr(Z > 1.40) = 1 - Pr(Z < 1.40) = 1 - 0.9192 = 0.0808$.

Finding the Probability That Z Is Greater Than a Negative Value

To find the probability that Z is greater than a negative value, we sketch and use symmetry to find the equivalent statement for a positive Z value. For example, to find $Pr(Z > -1.88)$, we first sketch as in Figure 5.23.

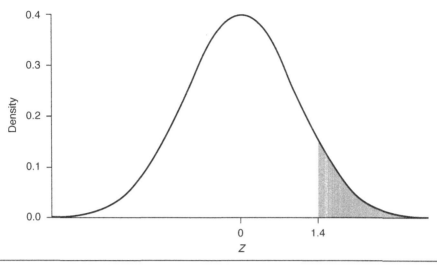

Figure 5.22 Distribution plot: Pr(Z > 1.4), mean = 0, standard deviation = 1.

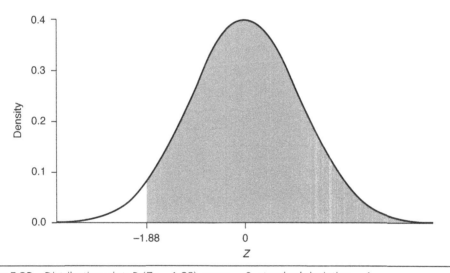

Figure 5.23 Distribution plot: Pr(Z > –1.88), mean = 0, standard deviation = 1.

Recognizing the symmetry of the standard normal, we can draw Figure 5.24. This leads us to conclude that Pr(Z > –1.88) = Pr(Z < 1.88) = 0.9699.

Finding the Probability That **Z** *Is between Two Negative Values*

To find the probability that Z lies in an interval bounded by two negative values, we can sketch and find the equivalent statement that uses positive values. For example, to find Pr(–2.34 < Z < –0.42), we use the sketches in Figures 5.25 and 5.26 and write:

$$Pr(-2.34 < Z < -0.42) = Pr(0.42 < Z < 2.34) = Pr(Z < 2.34) - Pr(Z < 0.42) =$$
$$0.9904 - 0.6628 = 0.3276$$

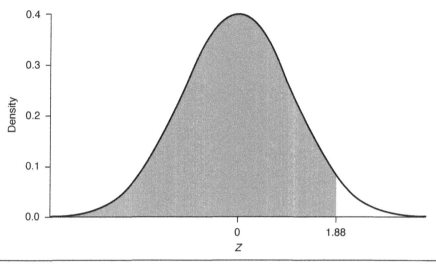

Figure 5.24 Distribution plot: Pr(Z < 1.88), mean = 0, standard deviation = 1.

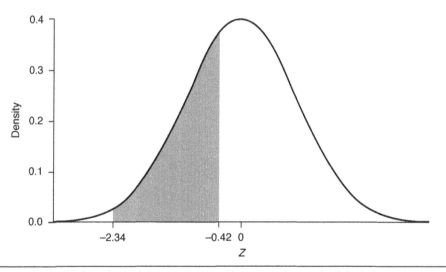

Figure 5.25 Distribution plot: Pr(–2.34 < Z < –0.42), mean = 0, standard deviation = 1.

Finding the Probability That Z Is between a Negative and a Positive Value

Finding the probability that Z is between a negative value and a positive value is the most challenging in terms of using the cumulative standard normal table. Sketching is a lifesaver. To find Pr(–1.00 < Z < 1.55), we have the sketch in Figure 5.27.

We see that we need to find the probability that Z is less than 1.55 and then subtract off the area that is below Z = –1.00. We have already established that Pr(Z < –a) = 1 – Pr(Z < a).

$$\text{Pr}(Z < 1.55) - \text{Pr}(Z < -1.00) = \text{Pr}(Z < 1.55) - (1 - \text{Pr}(Z < 1.00)) = 0.9394 - (1 - 0.8413) = 0.7807$$

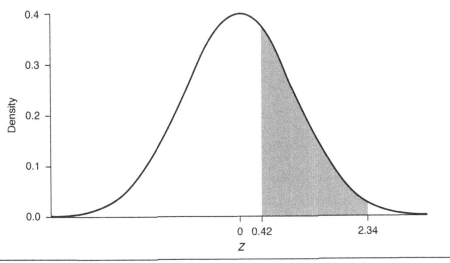

Figure 5.26   Distribution plot: Pr(0.42 < Z < 2.34), mean = 0, standard deviation = 1.

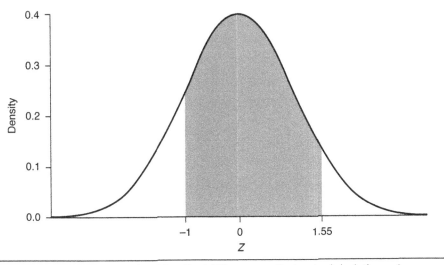

Figure 5.27   Distribution plot: Pr(−1.00 < Z < 1.55), mean = 0, standard deviation = 1.

Determining Z = a, Given a Probability

In the examples and exercises in the last section, we were given a value *a* and asked to find the probability that Z was less than *a*. What if we are given the probability and asked to find *a*? We need to, in effect, read the Z table inside out to find this answer. For example:

   If Pr(Z < *a*) = 0.9868, find *a*.

Here it really helps to draw a sketch and shade in the area. The first thing we need to determine is whether the value *a* is negative or positive. By drawing the normal curve, we see that the value *a* must be positive since the probability that Z is less than the value *a* is more than 0.50. We can look directly in the table in Appendix G and find 0.9868 in the interior, then read over and up to find the a value. Here, a equals 2.22.

Next let's find $\Pr(Z < a) = 0.0708$. A quick sketch shows that a must be negative since the $\Pr(Z < a)$ is less than 0.50. To use the table, we first write the probability statement in terms of the positive a value:

$$1 - \Pr(Z < +a) = 0.0708$$

We now find the value a corresponding to $(1 - 0.0708) = 0.9292$, which is 1.47. Therefore, our solution is $\Pr(Z < -1.47) = 0.0708$.

Linear Interpolation for Probability Tables

What if, when solving for a, we can't find the exact probability in the interior of the table? In effect, the answer a is actually between two Z values. In these cases, we use *linear interpolation* to solve for a.

For example, if we need to solve the following statement for a:

$$\Pr(Z < a) = 0.9378$$

Since 0.9378 is greater than 0.50, we know that the value a is positive. Look for the value 0.9378 in the interior of the cumulative standard normal table. There is no exact match in the table, but two values are close:

a	$\Pr(Z < a) = p$
1.53	0.9370
1.54	0.9382

The value a lies between the values 1.53 and 1.54. Using linear interpolation, we first find the slope m between the two points in the table:

$$m = \frac{\Delta y}{\Delta x} = \frac{\Delta a}{\Delta p} = \frac{a_2 - a_1}{p_2 - p_1} = \frac{(1.54 - 1.53)}{(0.9382 - 0.9370)} = \frac{0.01}{0.0012}$$

Next, we find how far the probability of interest is from the smaller probability value we have found in the table. Based on our problem, the probability of interest is 0.9378.

$$p - p_1 = (0.9378 - 0.9370) = 0.0008$$

Putting things together, we can find a:

$$a = a_1 + (p - p_1)m$$

$$= 1.53 + (0.0008)\left(\frac{0.01}{0.0012}\right)$$

$$= 1.5367$$

5.6.4 Related Microsoft Excel Functions

There are two Microsoft Excel functions specifically for the standard normal distribution. In addition, the more general Microsoft Excel functions for the normal distribution can also be used (see Section 5.5.6). The first standard normal formula is =*norm.s.dist()* and it takes on arguments for Z and a cumulative flag, as shown in Figure 5.28. To find the value of the standard normal distribution density function at a certain point z, we use 0 for the cumulative flag. Be aware that this result is only the height of the standard normal curve at a point and is not a probability. To find the probability that the random variable Z is less than or equal to some value *a*, we use 1 for the cumulative flag. For example, let Z follow a standard normal distribution. To find the height of the standard normal density function at the point Z = 1.5, we use =*norm.s.dist(1.5, 0)*.

However, to find the probability that Z is less than or equal to 1.5, $Pr(Z < 1.5)$, we place a 1 in the cumulative argument: =*norm.s.dist(1.5, 1)*. The latter application is much more common.

The second Microsoft Excel function is =*norm.s.inv()*, which, given a probability, returns the value of *a* that solves $Pr(Z < a) = p$. The function has only one argument, the value of the probability. For example, to find $Pr(Z < a) = 0.35$, we enter =*norm.s.inv(0.35)*. See Figure 5.29.

Note that this method of finding *a* given a probability is more accurate than using the linear interpolation method described in Section 5.6.3.

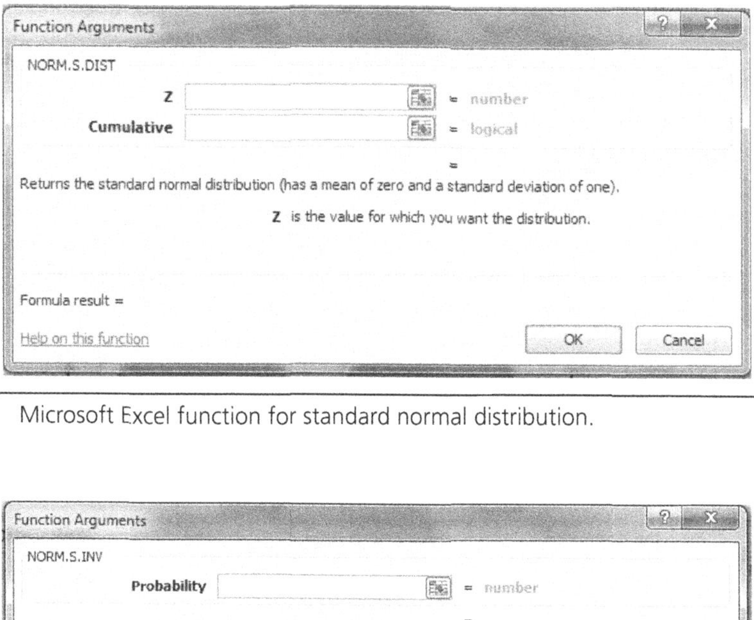

Figure 5.28 Microsoft Excel function for standard normal distribution.

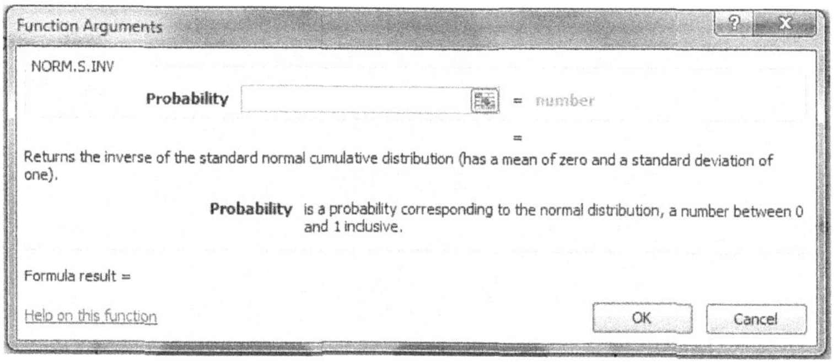

Figure 5.29 Microsoft Excel function for inverse probability.

5.6.5 Uses and Applications

The standard normal distribution is used extensively in hypothesis testing for means and proportions. For example:

- A supplier quality engineer uses the standard normal distribution to determine how many standard deviations a process distribution has shifted.

- A Master Black Belt uses the standard normal distribution to determine how many employees she must survey in order to achieve a particular margin of error.

- A production engineer uses the standard normal distribution to test whether the mean weight of plastic parts has increased after a change in materials.

- A machine operator uses the standard normal distribution to determine whether a part dimension is unusually high.

- A statistician uses the standard normal distribution to calculate the alpha and beta risk for a new control chart.

5.7 STUDENT'S *t* DISTRIBUTION

William Gossett was a brilliant mathematician who eventually became chief statistician at Guinness Brewing. In order to protect its trade secrets, Guinness prohibited employees from publishing research papers. Gossett was eventually allowed to publish his paper on the distribution of small samples, but only if he used a pseudonym. Hence, Gossett's paper appeared under the pseudonym of "Student" in Karl Pearson's journal *Biometrika* in 1908.[3] Although Pearson did not appreciate the usefulness of the *t* distribution, R. A. Fisher recognized its merits and started using the *t* test for small samples and in regression analysis testing. Throughout his life, Gossett continued to publish under the pseudonym Student. Gossett was known to be easy to work with and quite humble, which must have helped him maintain friendships with both Pearson and Fisher, two giants in the statistical field who despised each other.[4]

5.7.1 Probability Density Function

Student's *t* random variable *X* is composed of the ratio

$$X = \frac{Z}{\sqrt{V/r}}$$

---

[3] Gossett's original paper can be read at http://www.york.ac.uk/depts/maths/histstat/student.pdf.

[4] The history of statistics tends to read like a soap opera at times. See *The Lady Tasting Tea: How Statistics Revolutionized Science in the Twentieth Century* by David Salsburg for more insights.

where Z and V are independent and $Z \sim N(0,1)$ and V follows a chi-square distribution as described in Section 5.9, $V \sim \chi^2(r)$. Substituting in the expressions $Z = (X - \mu)/\sigma$ and $V = rs^2/\sigma^2$, found in Sections 5.6.1 and 5.9.1, respectively, into the previous equation yields the relationship in Formula 5.25.

Formula 5.25   Student's t random variable

$$X = \frac{(X - \mu)/\sigma}{\sqrt{rs^2/r\sigma^2}} = \frac{(X - \mu)}{s}$$

Student's t distribution has a single parameter, r, or degrees of freedom. The value of r is based on the sample size n, where $r = (n - 1)$. The distribution function is shown in Formula 5.26.

Formula 5.26   Probability density of Student's t distribution

$$f(x) = \frac{\Gamma\left(\frac{r+1}{2}\right)}{\sqrt{\pi r}\, \Gamma\left(\frac{r}{2}\right)\left(1 + \frac{x^2}{r}\right)^{\frac{r+1}{2}}}, \quad -\infty < x < \infty$$

The term $\Gamma(\alpha)$ is the gamma function. The gamma function is an integral, but for any positive integer n, the function simplifies to $\Gamma(n) = (n - 1)!$. For example, $\Gamma(4) = (4 - 1)! = 6$. Note also that $\Gamma\left(\frac{1}{2}\right) = \sqrt{\pi}$. The expected value and variance of Student's t distribution are shown in Formulas 5.27 and 5.28, respectively.

Formula 5.27   Expected value of Student's t distribution

$$E(X) = 0$$

Formula 5.28   Variance of Student's t distribution

$$\text{Var}(X) = \frac{r}{r - 2}, \quad r > 2$$

5.7.2 Distribution Shape

Student's t distribution is centered at $\mu = 0$ and is symmetric around its mean. The distribution resembles the bell shape of the normal distribution, but with heavier tails. The distribution becomes more and more like a normal distribution as the degrees of freedom increase. Figure 5.30 shows the difference between Student's t distribution with one degree of freedom and the standard normal distribution.[5]

---

[5] Student's t distribution with one degree of freedom is also the Cauchy distribution, as shown in 5.15.1.

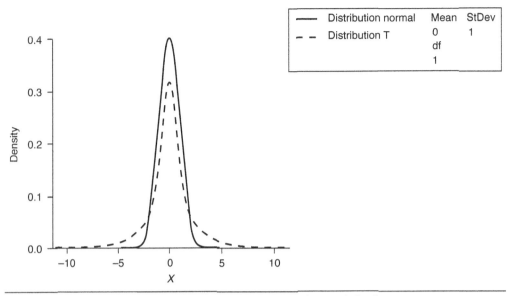

Figure 5.30 Comparison between Student's *t* and standard normal distributions.

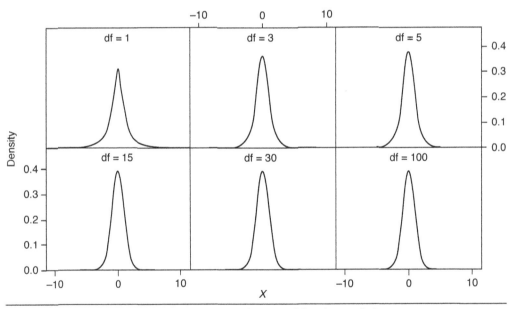

Figure 5.31 Shape of Student's *t* distribution, degrees of freedom varied.

Figure 5.31 shows how the shape of Student's *t* distribution becomes more "normal" as the degrees of freedom, and hence the sample size, increase.

5.7.3 Using Student's *t* Table

We use Student's *t* table to find the *t* values associated with various cumulative probabilities. An excerpt from the table found in Appendix H is shown in Table 5.5. In this table, the degrees of freedom are in the first column. Each row corresponds

Table 5.5 Excerpt from Student's t table.

Degrees of freedom	Area in upper tail				
	0.005	0.01	0.025	0.05	0.10
	Area in two tails				
	0.01	0.02	0.05	0.10	0.20
1	63.657	31.821	12.706	6.314	3.078
2	9.925	6.965	4.303	2.920	1.886
3	5.841	4.541	3.182	2.353	1.638
4	4.604	3.747	2.776	2.132	1.533
5	4.032	3.365	2.571	2.015	1.476

to a different value for degrees of freedom, which constitutes a separate distribution. The table columns map to different one-tailed and two-tailed probabilities. The one-tailed probability is for the upper tail, in which $\Pr(X > x)$, and the two-tailed probability is $\Pr(X < -x) + \Pr(X > x)$. The interior of the table gives the value of Student's t associated with the given degrees of freedom and cumulative probabilities. For example, given Student's t distribution with four degrees of freedom, the value associated with an upper tail probability of 0.05 is equal to 2.132.

5.7.4 Related Microsoft Excel Functions

There are many Microsoft Excel functions associated with Student's t distribution. The first is $=t.dist()$, shown in Figure 5.32. To find the value of the probability density function associated with a particular X and value for degrees of freedom, enter 0 in the cumulative argument. To find $P(X < x)$, enter 1 in the cumulative argument.

The function $=t.dist.2t()$, shown in Figure 5.33, returns the sum of probability $P(X < -x)$ and $P(X > x)$.

Given a probability and value for degrees of freedom, the function $=t.inv()$ returns the associated X value, as shown in Figure 5.34.

The function $=t.inv.2t()$ returns the X associated with the two-tailed probability entered, as shown in Figure 5.35.

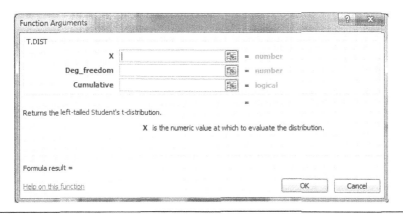

Figure 5.32 Microsoft Excel function $=t.dist()$.

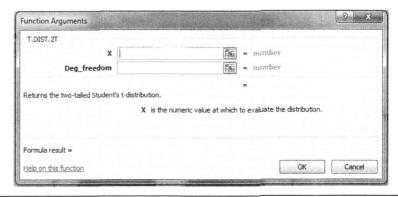

Figure 5.33 Microsoft Excel function =*t.dist.2t()*.

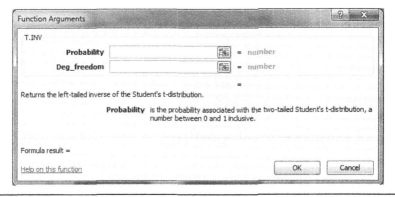

Figure 5.34 Microsoft Excel function =*t.inv()*.

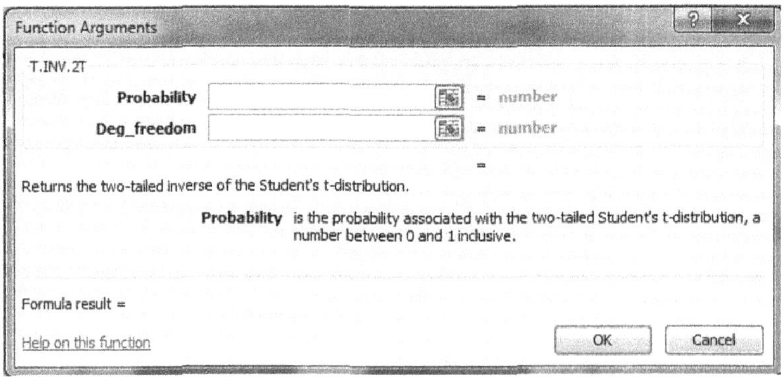

Figure 5.35 Microsoft Excel function =*t.inv.2t()*.

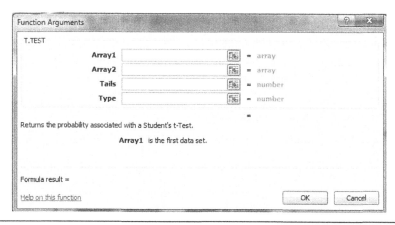

Figure 5.36 Microsoft Excel function =*t.test()*.

Finally, the function =*t.test()* can be used to perform a *t* test of means. The data arrays corresponding to each group are entered in the first two arguments, as shown in Figure 5.36. Then, the analyst specifies whether the test is one-tailed or two-tailed. The type of test is entered in the last argument, where 1 = paired *t* test, 2 = two-sample *t* test with equal variance, and 3 = two-sample *t* test with unequal variance (also known as the Behrens-Fisher problem). The function will return a *p* value for the test specified.

5.7.5 Uses and Applications

If the underlying distribution of a population being sampled is normal, but we do not know the value of the parameter σ, we can use Student's *t* distribution to model the data. Since we are estimating σ (via *s*) from our sample of size *n*, Student's *t* distribution takes this uncertainty into account by producing a bell-shaped distribution with more weight in the tails than a normal distribution. As our sample size increases, the tails increasingly resemble those of a standard normal distribution. Some statistics texts advise that an analyst can use the *Z* distribution in this situation if *n* > 30. However, since the critical values of Student's *t* distribution are available in tables and easily accessible through software packages, an analyst would be better served to use Student's *t* for large sample sizes as well.

Examples of the use of Student's *t* distribution include the following:

- A quality manager uses Student's *t* distribution to determine whether the mean burst strength of paper packages exceeds the minimum standard.

- A Six Sigma Green Belt uses Student's *t* distribution to test whether there is a difference in mean porosity for two different membrane designs.

- A quality engineer uses a paired *t* test to evaluate the effectiveness of a new training program by analyzing the mean improvement in test scores before and after training.

- A Six Sigma Black Belt uses Student's *t* distribution to determine whether an independent variable in a regression model is a significant predictor of the response.

5.8 THE GAMMA DISTRIBUTION

The gamma distribution is useful in modeling service times in queuing problems. It is a bit of a chameleon distribution, since in specific cases it becomes the exponential, chi-square, Rayleigh, and Erlang distributions, among others.

5.8.1 Probability Density Function

The probability density function of the gamma distribution is shown in Formula 5.29.

Formula 5.29 Probability density of gamma distribution

$$f(x) = \frac{x^{\alpha-1}e^{-x/\beta}}{\Gamma(\alpha)\beta^{\alpha}}, \quad x > 0$$

As explained in Section 5.7.1, the term $\Gamma(\alpha)$ is the *gamma function*. The gamma function is an integral, but for any positive integer n, the function simplifies to $\Gamma(n) = (n-1)!$. For example, $\Gamma(4) = (4-1)! = 6$. Note also that $\Gamma\left(\frac{1}{2}\right) = \sqrt{\pi}$.

The gamma probability distribution function has two parameters, the shape parameter α and the scale parameter β. If α is an integer, then the cumulative distribution function has the closed form shown in Formula 5.30.

Formula 5.30 Cumulative distribution function of gamma distribution

$$F(x) = 1 - e^{-x/\beta} \sum_{k=0}^{\alpha-1} \frac{(x/\beta)^k}{k!}, \quad x > 0$$

Formulas 5.31 and 5.32 show the expected value and variance, respectively, of the gamma distribution.

Formula 5.31 Expected value of gamma distribution

$$E(X) = \alpha\beta$$

Formula 5.32 Variance of gamma distribution

$$\text{Var}(X) = \alpha\beta^2$$

5.8.2 Distribution Shape

Figures 5.37 and 5.38 show the shape of the gamma distribution for various values of α and β.

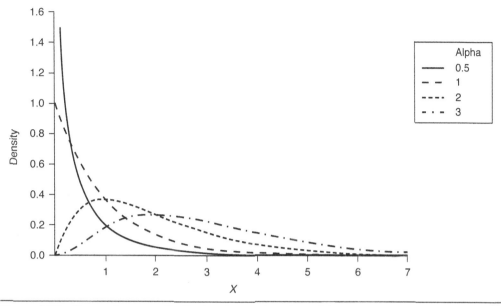

Figure 5.37 Shape of gamma distribution: beta = 1, various alpha.

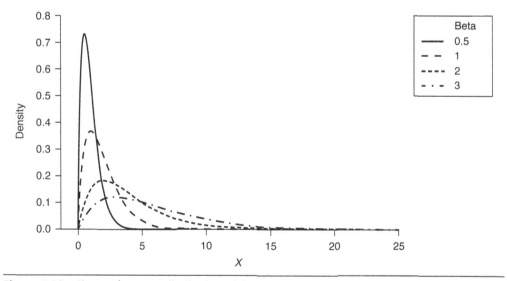

Figure 5.38 Shape of gamma distribution: alpha = 2, various beta.

5.8.3 Related Microsoft Excel Functions

Two Microsoft Excel functions can be used for the gamma distribution. The first is =*gamma.dist()*, found in Figure 5.39, which gives the value of the gamma probability density function at a point x when 0 is entered in the cumulative argument. To find $Pr(X < x)$, enter 1 for the cumulative argument.

Given a cumulative probability, the Microsoft Excel function =*gamma.inv()* will return the associated x value, as shown in Figure 5.40.

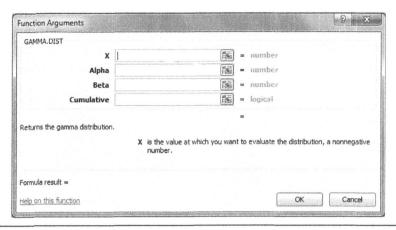

Figure 5.39   Microsoft Excel function =*gamma.dist()*.

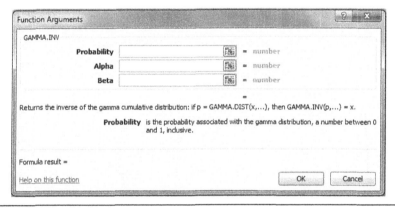

Figure 5.40   Microsoft Excel function =*gamma.inv()*.

5.8.4 Uses and Applications

The gamma function is used in simulation and reliability applications. For example:

- A quality engineer uses the gamma distribution to model service times for help desk calls for an IT call center simulation.

- A production engineer uses the gamma distribution to model the time between machine breakdowns.

- A reliability engineer uses the gamma distribution to estimate the mean time between unit failures.

- An engineer at an amusement park uses the gamma distribution to model guests' time in queue for the new roller coaster.

5.9 CHI-SQUARE DISTRIBUTION

The chi-square (pronounced *kai-square*) sampling distribution is a workhorse in statistical analysis. It is used to perform parametric tests on the variance of a normal distribution, and in nonparametric tests of independence for contingency tables, goodness-of-fit tests, and many specialty applications such as the Mantel-Haenszel test for independence measured over time.[6]

5.9.1 Probability Density Function

The chi-square distribution is a special case of the gamma distribution with $\alpha = r/2$ and $\beta = 2$. The term r is the degrees of freedom for the chi-square distribution. The chi-square random variable X is a function of the sample variance of the normal distribution, s^2, as shown in Formula 5.33. The term $(n-1)s^2/\sigma^2$ follows a chi-square distribution with $r = (n-1)$ degrees of freedom:

Formula 5.33   Chi-square random variable

$$\frac{(n-1)s^2}{\sigma^2} \sim \chi^2(n-1)$$

The probability density function of the chi-square distribution is shown in Formula 5.34.

Formula 5.34   Probability density of chi-square distribution

$$f(x) = \frac{x^{\left(\frac{r}{2}-1\right)}e^{-x/2}}{\Gamma\left(\frac{r}{2}\right)2^{\left(\frac{r}{2}\right)}}, \quad x > 0$$

The expected value and variance of the chi-square distribution are displayed in Formulas 5.35 and 5.36, respectively.

Formula 5.35   Expected value of chi-square distribution

$$E(X) = r$$

Formula 5.36   Variance of chi-square distribution

$$\mathrm{Var}(X) = 2r$$

---

[6] Refer to http://www.biostathandbook.com/cmh.html for an interesting explanation of the Mantel-Haenszel test involving ponies and pink leg warmers.

The cumulative probabilities $\Pr(X < a)$ of the chi-square distribution are customarily determined by a chi-square table. The chi-square table in Appendix I gives the chi-square values x associated with the *upper tail* probability, or $\Pr(X \geq x)$. An excerpt is shown in Table 5.6. The rows of the table correspond to the degrees of freedom, r. The columns of the table show various upper tail values. The interior of the table gives the chi-square value corresponding to the upper tail area listed in the column. For example, for a chi-square distribution with four degrees of freedom, the value that corresponds to an upper tail area of 0.05 is 9.488, such that $\Pr(\chi^2 \geq 9.488) = 0.05$ and $\Pr(\chi^2 < 9.488) = 0.95$.

5.9.2 Distribution Shape

The chi-square distribution becomes more symmetric and more disperse as r increases. The shape of the distribution for various values of r is shown in Figure 5.41.

Table 5.6 Excerpt from chi-square table.

Degrees of freedom, r	Upper Tail Probability									
	0.995	0.99	0.975	0.95	0.9	0.1	0.05	0.025	0.01	0.005
1	3.93E-05	0.0002	0.001	0.004	0.016	2.706	3.841	5.024	6.635	7.879
2	0.01	0.02	0.051	0.103	0.211	4.605	5.991	7.378	9.21	10.597
3	0.072	0.115	0.216	0.352	0.584	6.251	7.815	9.348	11.345	12.838
4	0.207	0.297	0.484	0.711	1.064	7.779	9.488	11.143	13.277	14.86
5	0.412	0.554	0.831	1.145	1.61	9.236	11.07	12.833	15.086	16.75

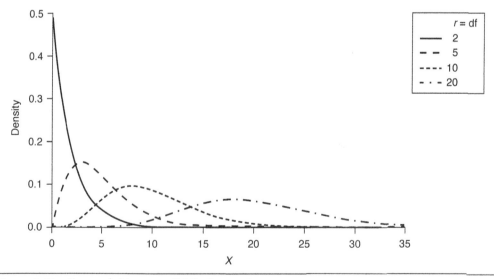

Figure 5.41 Shape of chi-square distribution, various r.

5.9.3 Cochran's Theorem

Cochran's theorem relates the sum of squared samples from a normal distribution to a chi-square distribution. If the random variable Z follows a standard normal distribution, then Z^2 follows a $\chi^2(1)$ distribution. The sum of n squared independent Z's follows a $\chi^2(n)$ distribution. In general, if we have a random sample x_1, $x_2, \ldots, x_n$ from a normal distribution with mean equal to 0 and known variance σ^2, $N(0, \sigma2)$, the sum of the squared observations divided by σ^2 is distributed as χ^2 with n degrees of freedom. Cochran's theorem is used as the rationale for the partitioning of variances in the analysis of variance, or ANOVA.

5.9.4 Related Microsoft Excel Functions

There are four Microsoft Excel functions related to the chi-square distribution. The function =$chisq.dist()$, shown in Figure 5.42, takes arguments for x, degrees of freedom, and a cumulative flag. Entering 0 in the cumulative flag argument returns the value of the chi-square probability density distribution. Turning the cumulative flag on by entering 1 returns cumulative probability $\Pr(X < x)$. To find $P(X > x)$, use =$chisq.dist.rt()$, as shown in Figure 5.43.

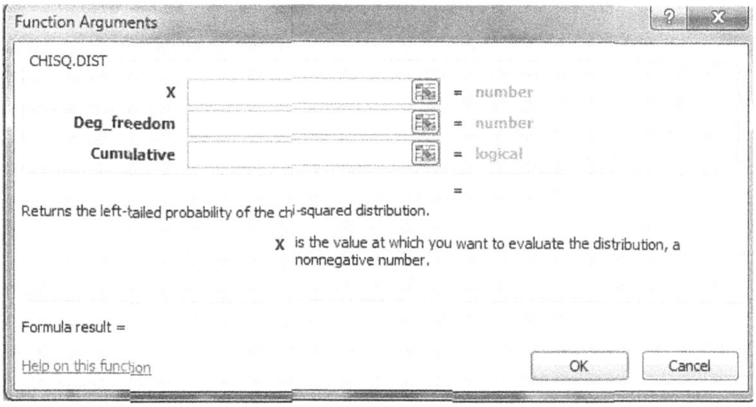

Figure 5.42   Microsoft Excel function =$chisq.dist()$.

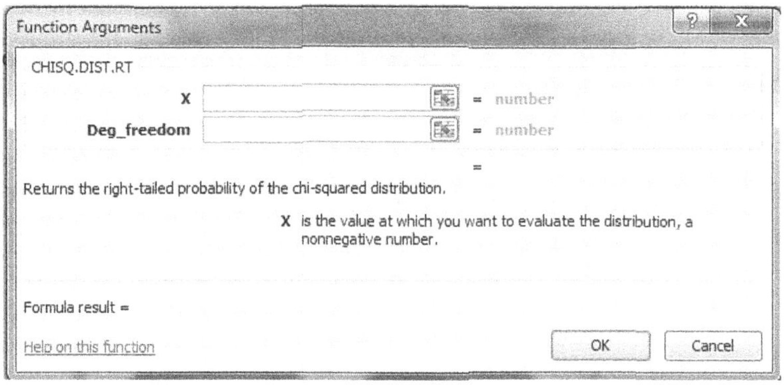

Figure 5.43   Microsoft Excel function =$chisq.dist.rt()$.

The function =*chisq.inv()*, found in Figure 5.44, returns the chi-square value associated with the left-tail probability entered. The function =*chisq.inv.rt()*, shown in Figure 5.45, returns the chi-square value associated with the right-tail probability specified.

5.9.5 Uses and Applications

The chi-square distribution is used in many types of hypothesis tests. For example:

- A biostatistician uses the chi-square distribution to determine whether there is a relationship between melanoma and smoking.

- An engineer uses the chi-square distribution to test whether the variance in a part's dimension is less than the published industry standard.

- A college administrator uses the chi-square distribution to determine whether there is a relationship between student gender and choice of college major.

- A quality engineer uses a chi-square goodness-of-fit test to determine whether a data set follows a uniform distribution.

- A marketing analyst uses the chi-square distribution to test whether the frequencies of specific defect types differ across shifts.

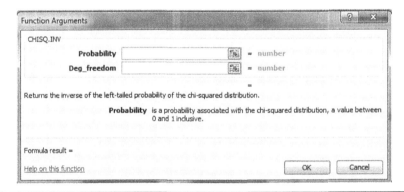

Figure 5.44 Microsoft Excel function =*chisq.inv()*.

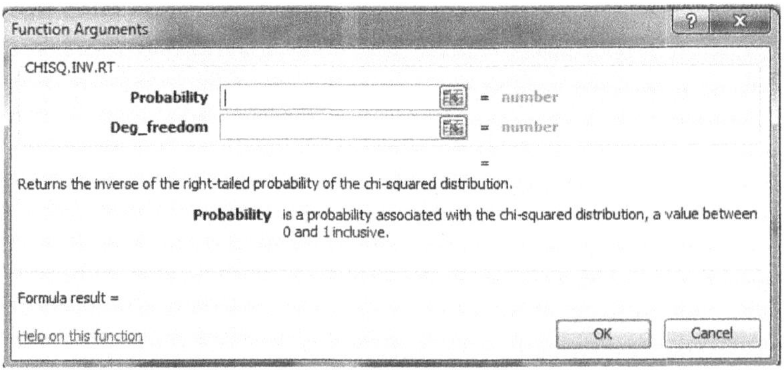

Figure 5.45 Microsoft Excel function =*chisq.inv.rt()*.

5.10 THE EXPONENTIAL DISTRIBUTION

The exponential distribution is used extensively in simulation and in reliability. It is unusual in that it is the only continuous probability distribution that has the memoryless property.

5.10.1 Probability Density Function

Another special case of the gamma (α, β) distribution is the exponential distribution. The exponential distribution is a gamma with $\alpha = 1$. Therefore, the exponential distribution has only one parameter β, the scale parameter.

The exponential probability density function is shown in Formula 5.37.

Formula 5.37 Probability density function of exponential distribution

$$f(x) = \frac{1}{\beta} e^{-x/\beta}, \qquad x > 0, \qquad \beta > 0$$

The expected value and variance of the distribution are shown in Formulas 5.38 and 5.39, respectively.

Formula 5.38 Expected value of exponential distribution

$$E(X) = \beta$$

Formula 5.39 Variance of exponential distribution

$$Var(X) = \beta^2$$

Note that the exponential distribution is sometimes parameterized using $\theta = \frac{1}{\beta}$. This probability density function for the alternate form of the distribution is shown in Formula 5.40.

Formula 5.40 Alternate form for probability density function of exponential distribution

$$f(x) = \theta e^{-\theta x}, \qquad x > 0, \qquad \theta > 0$$

The expectation and variance are denoted in Formulas 5.41 and 5.42, respectively.

Formula 5.41 Expected value of exponential, alternate form

$$E(X) = \frac{1}{\theta}$$

Formula 5.42 Variance of the exponential distribution, alternate form

$$Var(X) = \frac{1}{\theta^2}$$

The cumulative distribution function of the exponential distribution is a closed form, as shown in Formulas 5.43 and 5.44.

Formula 5.43 Cumulative distribution function of exponential distribution

$$F(x) = 1 - e^{-x/\beta}, \qquad x > 0$$

Formula 5.44 Cumulative distribution function of exponential distribution, alternate form

$$F(x) = 1 - e^{-\theta x}, \qquad x > 0$$

5.10.2 Distribution Shape

The exponential distribution is right-skewed. The slope of the distribution flattens as β increases. The y-intercept of the density function is equal to $1/\beta$. Figure 5.46 shows the shape of the exponential function for various values of β.

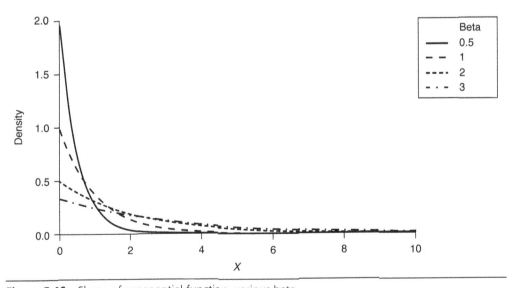

Figure 5.46 Shape of exponential function, various beta.

5.10.3 Memoryless Property of Exponential Distribution

The exponential distribution, like its discrete cousin the geometric distribution, exhibits the memoryless property, presented in Section 4.6.3. The memoryless property states that $P(X > (t + s) \mid X > t) = P(X > s)$.

$$P(X > t) = 1 - F(t) = e^{-x/\beta}$$

$$P(X > (t + s) \mid X > t) = P(X > s)$$

$$P(X > (t + s) \mid X > t) = \frac{e^{-(t+s)/\beta}}{e^{-t/\beta}} = e^{-s/\beta}$$

The memoryless property implies that the probability that a unit will remain working for time $t + s$, given that it has already lasted to time t, is equal simply to the probability that the unit operates for time s.

Looked at another way, the probability that a unit will remain operational for an incremental time s is the same no matter how long it has been previously operational, expressed as t. It doesn't matter if a lightbulb has been burning for 10 hours or 1000 hours; the probability that it will burn for 2 hours more is the same.

5.10.4 The Erlang Distribution

The sum of m independent exponential (β) random variables will follow a gamma (m, β) distribution. This distribution is also known as an m-Erlang (β) distribution. The expected value and variance of the m-Erlang distribution are shown in Formulas 5.45 and 5.46, respectively.

Formula 5.45 Expected value of m-Erlang distribution

$$E(X) = m\beta$$

Formula 5.46 Variance of m-Erlang distribution

$$\mathrm{Var}(X) = m\beta^2$$

5.10.5 Related Microsoft Excel Functions

There is one Microsoft Excel function associated with the exponential function, as shown in Figure 5.47. The function =*expon.dist()* uses the alternate version of the exponential distribution. The argument λ is $(1/\beta)$. To find the value of the exponential probability density function at a value x, enter 0 in the cumulative argument. To find $\Pr(X < x)$, enter 1 in the cumulative argument.

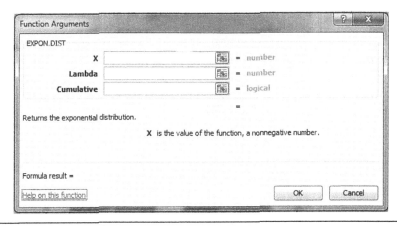

Figure 5.47   Microsoft Excel function =*expon.dist()*.

5.10.6 Uses and Applications

The exponential distribution is widely used in simulation and reliability. For example:

- A Six Sigma Black Belt uses the exponential distribution to model wait times in a Monte Carlo simulation of patient flow through a hospital emergency department.

- A reliability engineer uses the exponential distribution to calculate the probability that an electric component will function for more than 100 hours.

5.10.7 Exponential Connection to Reliability

When we calculate *reliability*, we are finding the probability that a system or an individual unit will still be working at time *t*, such as the probability that a switch will be functioning 100 hours from now. We can more formally define the term *reliability* as the probability that the *time to failure* of a system or unit will be greater than or equal to a time *t*. If *X* is a random variable representing the time to failure of the system or unit, then reliability at time *t* can be expressed as:

$$R(t) = \Pr(X \geq t)$$

We can use the complement rule and the cumulative distribution function to find reliability by calculating:

$$R(t) = 1 - \Pr(X < t) = 1 - F(t)$$

When the failure time *X* follows an exponential distribution, then reliability can be written as shown in Formula 5.47.

Formula 5.47   Exponential reliability function

$$R(t) = 1 - F(t) = 1 - (1 - e^{-t/\beta}) = e^{-t/\beta}$$

For example, if a unit has a failure time X that follows an exponential distribution with $\beta = 3$, then the reliability of the unit at time 5 is calculated as:

$$R(t) = 1 - F(t) = e^{-5/3} = 0.189$$

If there are k independent units working in series, what is the probability that the system will fail at time t? If any one or more units in a series fail, the system will fail. For the system to work, all units must be functioning. Using exponential failure times, the complement rule, and the multiplication rule for independent events, we get:

$$P(\text{system fails}) = 1 - P(\text{system works}) = 1 - R_1(t)R_2(t) \ldots R_k(t)$$

$$= 1 - \prod_{i=1}^{k} R_i(t) = 1 - \prod_{i=1}^{k} e^{-t/\beta_i} = 1 - e^{\Sigma(-t/\beta_i)}$$

Note here that the exponents of e can be summed. For example, $e^a e^b = e^{(a+b)}$.

If we have four units arranged in series, as shown in Figure 5.48, each with independent exponential failure times with parameter $\beta = 6$, the reliability of the system at time $t = 2$ is calculated

$$= R(\text{system}) = \prod_{i=1}^{k} R_i(t) = \prod_{i=1}^{4} e^{-t/\beta_i} = e^{\Sigma(-2/6)} = e^{(-4/3)} = 0.2636$$

The probability of systems failure at time $t = 2$, then, is $1 - 0.2636 = 0.7634$.

As discussed in Section 5.10.3, the memoryless property of the exponential distribution produces the result that, given that a unit has lasted until time t, the reliability at time $(t + s)$ is simply equal to the reliability at time s. For example, given that a unit has lasted 100 hours, its reliability at time 120 is equal to $R(20)$.

For exponentially distributed failure times, the *mean time to failure* (MTTF) is the expected value of the distribution, β. The reliability of a unit at $t = \text{MTTF}$ is equal to $e^{-1} = 0.3679$.

The failure, or hazard, rate of a unit or system $\lambda(t)$ is the ratio of the distribution of the time to failure and the reliability distribution. For the exponential distribution, the hazard rate is constant over time, as shown in Formula 5.48.

Formula 5.48 Exponential distribution hazard function

$$\lambda(t) = \frac{f(t)}{R(t)} = \frac{\beta e^{-t/\beta}}{e^{-t/\beta}} = \beta$$

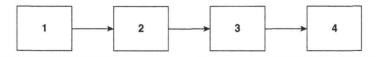

Figure 5.48 Four independent units arranged in series.

5.11 THE WEIBULL DISTRIBUTION

The Weibull distribution was developed by a Swedish engineer, Waloddi Weibull, who popularized its use in modeling metallurgic failures.[7] This distribution is most famously applied in the failure rate bathtub curve, as shown in Figure 5.49, in which three separate Weibull functions are plotted over time. The first is called the burn-in or infant mortality rate, in which the failure rate is high and then falls off quickly over a short period of time. The middle segment is the constant failure rate, followed by the wear-out period of rapidly increasing failures.

5.11.1 Probability Density Function

The Weibull distribution has a shape parameter, α, and a scale parameter, β. The parameter β is also known as the characteristic life. The probability density function is shown in Formula 5.49. Note that there are other, equivalent versions of the Weibull probability density function.

> **Formula 5.49**   Weibull probability density function
>
> $$f(x) = \alpha\beta^{-\alpha}x^{\alpha-1}e^{-(x/\beta)^{\alpha}}, \qquad x > 0, \alpha > 0, \beta > 0$$

The cumulative distribution function has a closed form, as shown in Formula 5.50.

> **Formula 5.50**   Weibull cumulative distribution function
>
> $$F(x) = 1 - e^{-(x/\beta)^{\alpha}}, \qquad x > 0$$

The expected value and variance of the Weibull distribution are shown in Formulas 5.51 and 5.52, respectively.

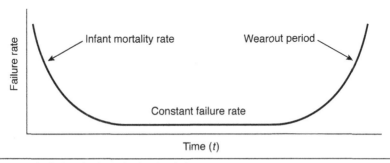

Figure 5.49   Weibull distribution "bathtub" failure rate curve.

---

[7] Read Robert Abernathy's biography of Weibull at http://www.barringer1.com/weibull_bio.htm.

Formula 5.51   Expected value of Weibull distribution

$$E(x) = \beta\Gamma\left(1 + \frac{1}{\alpha}\right)$$

Formula 5.52   Variance of the Weibull distribution

$$\text{Var}(x) = \beta^2\left\{\Gamma\left(1 + \frac{2}{\alpha}\right) - \Gamma^2\left(1 + \frac{1}{\alpha}\right)\right\}$$

Recall that $\Gamma(x)$ is the gamma function, which reduces to $(x - 1)!$ if x is an integer.

5.11.2 Distribution Shape

For alpha between 1 and 3, the Weibull distribution is skewed. For alpha > 3, the distribution becomes more symmetric. Note that if $\alpha = 1$, the Weibull becomes the exponential (β). The shape of the Weibull distribution for various values of alpha and beta is shown in Figure 5.50.

5.11.3 The Rayleigh Distribution

The Rayleigh distribution is a special case of the Weibull distribution with $\alpha = 2$. The Rayleigh has a parameter k that is equal to ($\beta^2/2$) in terms of the Weibull parameter. The probability density function of the Rayleigh is shown in Formula 5.53.

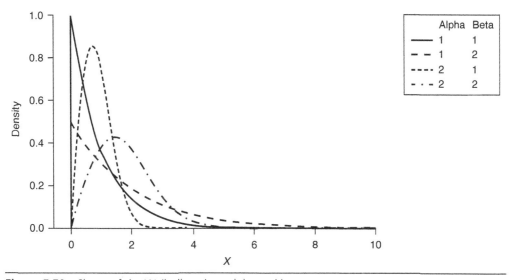

Figure 5.50   Shape of the Weibull, various alpha and beta.

Formula 5.53   Rayleigh probability density function

$$f(x) = \frac{1}{k} x e^{-(x^2/2k)}, \qquad x > 0, \qquad k > 0$$

The cumulative distribution function has a closed form as shown in Formula 5.54.

Formula 5.54   Rayleigh cumulative distribution function

$$F(x) = 1 - e^{-(x^2/2k)}, \qquad x > 0$$

The expected value and variance of the Rayleigh distribution are shown in Formulas 5.55 and 5.56, respectively.

Formula 5.55   Expected value of Rayleigh distribution

$$E(x) = \sqrt{\frac{k\pi}{2}}$$

Formula 5.56   Variance of the Rayleigh distribution

$$Var(x) = \frac{k(4 - \pi)}{2}$$

5.11.4 Related Microsoft Excel Function

The one Microsoft Excel function related to the Weibull distribution is =*weibull.dist()*, as shown in the dialog box in Figure 5.51. The function takes arguments for

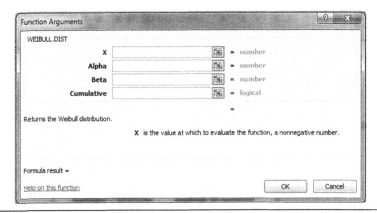

Figure 5.51   Microsoft Excel function =*weibull.dist()*.

X, alpha, and beta, along with a cumulative flag. To find the value of the Weibull (α, β) function at $X = x$, we enter 0 for the cumulative flag. To find $\Pr(X < x)$ we turn the cumulative flag on by entering 1 for that argument.

5.11.5 Uses and Applications

The Weibull distribution is used extensively in reliability calculations. For example:

- A quality engineer uses the Weibull distribution to model the reliability of a unit that has an increasing hazard rate over time.

- A reliability engineer uses the Weibull distribution to find the probability of failure of a system experiencing its infant mortality phase.

- A Six Sigma Black Belt uses the Weibull distribution to estimate the characteristic life of a switch assembly.

5.11.6 Weibull Connection to Reliability

The Weibull distribution is well suited for modeling the reliability of systems since it can be used to model decreasing, constant, or increasing hazard rates depending on choice of parameters.

The reliability function for the Weibull distribution takes the form shown in Formula 5.57.

Formula 5.57   Weibull reliability function

$$R(t) = e^{-(t/\beta)^{\alpha}}, \qquad t > 0$$

The failure, or hazard, rate, $\lambda(t)$, is shown in Formula 5.58.

Formula 5.58   Weibull hazard function

$$\lambda(t) = \alpha\beta^{-\alpha}t^{\alpha-1}, \qquad t > 0$$

If the parameter α is less than 1, the hazard function is decreasing over time, as in an infant mortality phase. If $\alpha = 1$, the Weibull hazard rate is not dependent on time, resulting in a constant hazard rate equivalent to that of the exponential distrbution. An α greater than 1 results in an increasing hazard rate over time, appropriate for modeling wear-out periods. The slope of the hazard function decreases as β increases.

When time to failure $t = \beta$, the cumulative time to failure function is equal to 0.632, regardless of the value of alpha. The probability of a component failing on or before time β is equal to 0.632. The relationship is illustrated in Figure 5.52.

$$F(X \le \beta) = 1 - e^{-(1)\alpha} = 0.632$$

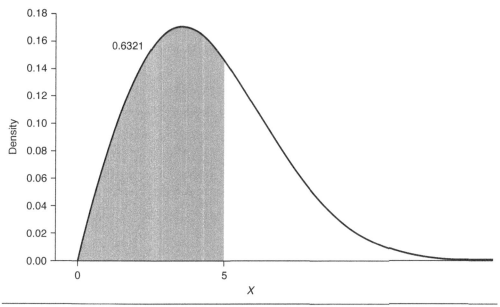

Figure 5.52   Distribution plot: $Pr(T < t)$ at $t =$ beta (alpha = 2, beta = 5).

5.12 THE *F* DISTRIBUTION

The *F* distribution was developed by George Snedecor, who named it in honor of the statistician R. A. Fisher. It is a sampling distribution used for testing the equality of two variances from normal populations. The *F* distribution is also used in the analysis of variance (ANOVA) to test the equality of means. In ANOVA, the *F* statistic compares the magnitude of the *between sample* variation with that of the *within sample* variation.

5.12.1 Probability Density Function

Let the random variable *X* follow the form

$$X = \frac{U/a}{V/b}$$

where *U* and *V* are independent chi-square random variables with *a* and *b* degrees of freedom, respectively. Then *X* follows an *F*(*a*, *b*) distribution. Recall from Section 5.9 that the random variable $\dfrac{(n-1)s^2}{\sigma^2}$ follows a chi-square distribution with $(n-1)$ degrees of freedom. Therefore, we can rewrite the formula for the *F* random variable as the ratio of two sample standard deviations:

$$X = \left[\frac{\dfrac{(n_1 - 1)s_1^2}{\sigma^2} \Big/ (n_1 - 1)}{\dfrac{(n_2 - 1)s_2^2}{\sigma^2} \Big/ (n_2 - 1)} \right] = \frac{s_1^2}{s_2^2}$$

Here, *X* follows an *F* distribution with $a = n_1 - 1$ and $b = n_2 - 1$.

It should be noted that if $X \sim F(a, b)$, then the reciprocal $1/X$ will also follow an F distribution, but with degrees of freedom (b, a). This relationship is useful when finding cumulative probabilities of the F distribution, as we will see in Section 5.12.3.

The probability density function of the F distribution is shown in Formula 5.59.

Formula 5.59   Probability density function of the F distribution

$$f(x) = \frac{\Gamma\left(\frac{a+b}{2}\right)a^{\left(\frac{a}{2}\right)}b^{\left(\frac{b}{2}\right)}x^{\left(\frac{a}{2}-1\right)}}{\Gamma\left(\frac{a}{2}\right)\Gamma\left(\frac{b}{2}\right)(a+bx)^{\frac{a+b}{2}}}, \qquad x > 0,\ a,b > 0$$

Recall from Section 5.7 that the term Γ is the *gamma function*. The gamma function is an integral, but for any positive integer n, the function simplifies to $\Gamma(n) = (n-1)!$.

This unwieldy probability density function simplifies in a few cases, as shown in Formulas 5.60–5.63.

Formula 5.60 F distribution for $a = 2$

$$\text{For } a = 2, \qquad f(x) = \frac{1}{\left(1 + \frac{2x}{b}\right)^{1+b/2}}, \qquad x > 0$$

Formula 5.61 F distribution for $b = 2$

$$\text{For } b = 2, \qquad f(x) = \frac{\Gamma(a)x^{\left(\frac{a}{2}-1\right)}}{\Gamma^2\left(\frac{a}{2}\right)(1 + x)^a}, \qquad x > 0$$

Formula 5.62 F distribution for $a = b = 2$

$$\text{For } a = b = 2, \qquad f(x) = \frac{1}{(1 + x)^2}, \qquad x > 0$$

Formula 5.63 F distribution for $a = b = 1$

$$\text{For } a = b = 1, \qquad f(x) = \frac{1}{\pi\sqrt{x}(1 + x)}, \qquad x > 0$$

The expected value of the F distribution is infinite for values of b between $0 < b \le 2$. For values of $b > 2$, the expectation is found in Formula 5.64. Note that the mean of the F distribution depends only on the degrees of freedom of V, the chi-square statistic in the denominator of the F statistic.

Formula 5.64 Expected value of F distribution

$$E(X) = \frac{b}{b-2}, \qquad b > 2$$

The variance of F is undefined for $0 < b \le 2$ and is infinite for $2 < b \le 4$. For $b > 4$, the variance can be expressed using Formula 5.65.

Formula 5.65 Variance of F distribution

$$\text{Var}(X) = 2\left(\frac{b}{b-2}\right)^2 \frac{a+b-2}{a(b-4)}, \qquad b > 4$$

The F distribution is related to Student's t distribution. If the random variable X follows Student's t distribution with $(n-1)$ degrees of freedom, then $Y = X^2$ follows an F distribution with $(1, (n-1))$ degrees of freedom.

If the random variable X has a beta distribution with parameters α and β, then

$$Y = \frac{\beta X}{\alpha(1-X)}$$

follows an F distribution with degrees of freedom $(2\alpha, 2\beta)$.

5.12.2 Distribution Shape

The shape of the F distribution is determined by the degrees of freedom a and b. In all cases, F is skewed to the right. Figure 5.53 shows the plots of four F distributions with varying parameters.

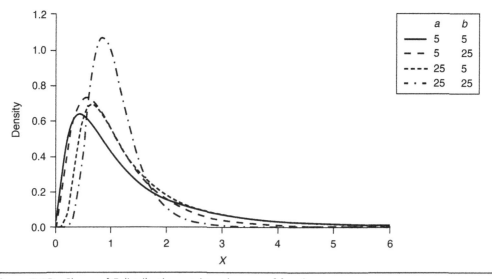

Figure 5.53 Shape of F distribution, various degrees of freedom.

5.12.3 Cumulative *F* Table

The *F* distribution changes shape based on two sets of degrees of freedom. The *F* tables presented in statistics textbooks generally give separate tables often used for right-tail probabilities of 0.05, 0.025, and 0.01, which map to the 95th, 97.5th, and 99th percentiles, respectively. The analyst uses the table that matches the percentile of interest, finds the column and row associated with the numerator and denominator degrees of freedom, respectively, and reads off the value of the *F* statistic. An excerpt of an example 95th percentile table is shown in Table 5.7.

To find the value associated with the 95th percentile of an $F(6,9)$ distribution, we use Table 5.7 to find $f = 3.374$. This value solves the statement $\Pr(F < f) = 0.95$, as shown in Figure 5.54.

Table 5.7   Excerpt from 95th percentile *F* table.

		Degrees of freedom for the numerator								
		1	2	3	4	5	6	7	8	9
Degrees of freedom for the denominator	1	161.448	199.500	215.707	224.583	230.162	233.986	236.768	238.883	240.543
	2	18.513	19.000	19.164	19.247	19.296	19.330	19.353	19.371	19.385
	3	10.128	9.552	9.277	9.117	9.013	8.941	8.887	8.845	8.812
	4	7.709	6.944	6.591	6.388	6.256	6.163	6.094	6.041	5.999
	5	6.608	5.786	5.409	5.192	5.050	4.950	4.876	4.818	4.772
	6	5.987	5.143	4.757	4.534	4.387	4.284	4.207	4.147	4.099
	7	5.591	4.737	4.347	4.120	3.972	3.866	3.787	3.726	3.677
	8	5.318	4.459	4.066	3.838	3.687	3.581	3.500	3.438	3.388
	9	5.117	4.256	3.863	3.633	3.482	3.374	3.293	3.230	3.179
	10	4.965	4.103	3.708	3.478	3.326	3.217	3.135	3.072	3.020

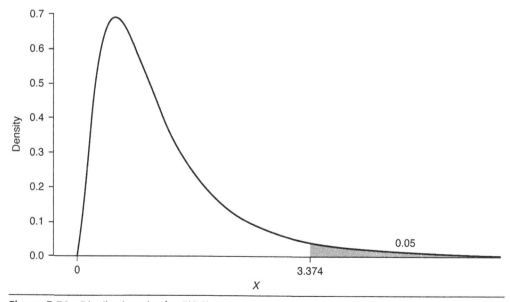

Figure 5.54   Distribution plot for $F(6,9)$.

To find the 0.05, 0.025, and 0.01 left-tail probability values that map to the 5th, 2.5th, and 1st percentiles, respectively, we can use the relationship:

$$F_{0.05}(a,b) = \frac{1}{F_{0.95}(b,a)}$$

To find the value from an $F(20,7)$ distribution associated with the 5th percentile, we use the table to find the value from $F(7,20)$ associated with the 95th percentile. Then we take the reciprocal of this value, as shown in Figure 5.55.

$$F_{0.05}(20,7) = \frac{1}{F_{0.95}(7,20)} = \frac{1}{2.5140} = 0.3978$$

5.12.4 Related Microsoft Excel Functions

There are five Microsoft Excel functions associated with the F distribution. The function $=f.dist()$, shown in Figure 5.56, has arguments for X, numerator degrees of freedom, denominator degrees of freedom, and a cumulative flag. Setting the cumulative flag to 0 returns the value of the F probability distribution function at X, specified by the degrees of freedom. To find the probability of X or less, enter a value of 1 for the cumulative argument.

The function $=f.dist.rt()$, shown in Figure 5.57, returns the probability that X is greater than some value x.

The two Microsoft Excel functions $=f.inv()$ and $=f.inv.rt$, found in Figures 5.58 and 5.59, respectively, return the F values associated with the entered probabilities. For example, using $=f.inv(0.95,4,7)$ returns the F value that maps to the 95th percentile of the $F(4,7)$ distribution. The Microsoft Excel function $=f.inv.rt(0.05,4,7)$ returns the F value associated with the 5th percentile of the $F(4,7)$ distribution.

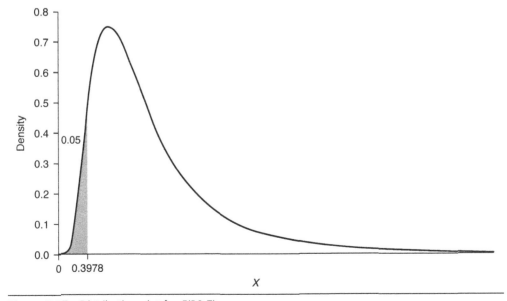

Figure 5.55 Distribution plot for $F(20,7)$.

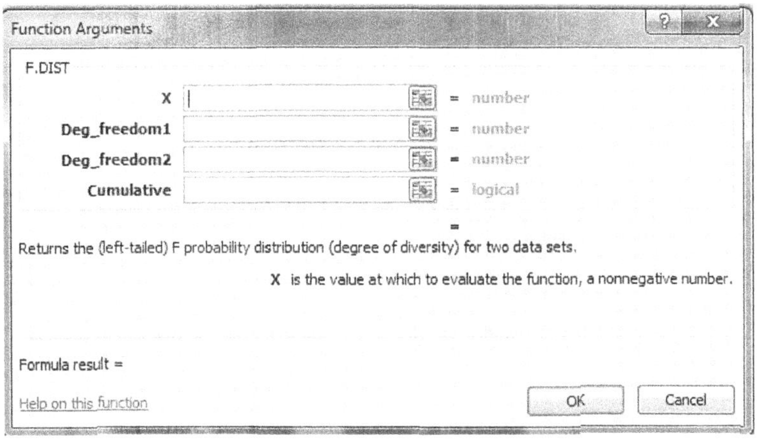

Figure 5.56 Microsoft Excel function =*f.dist()*.

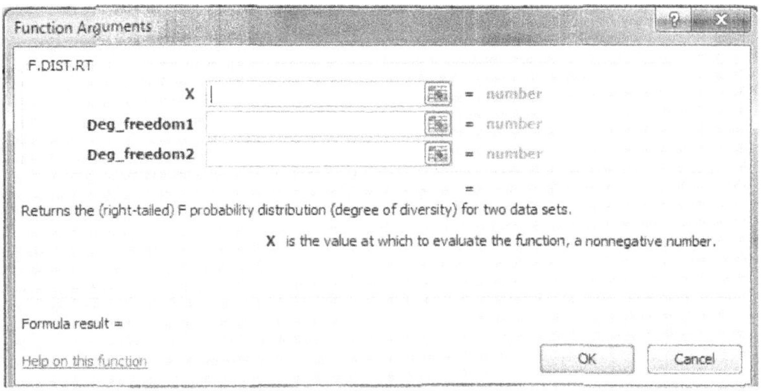

Figure 5.57 Microsoft Excel function =*f.dist.rt()*.

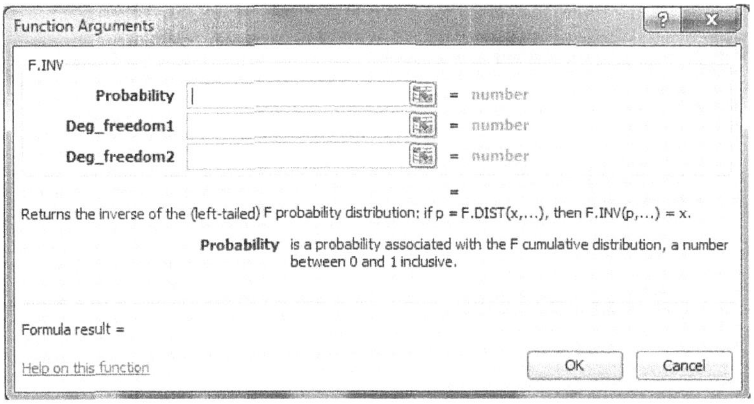

Figure 5.58 Microsoft Excel function =*f.inv()*.

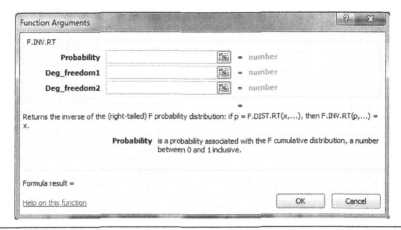

Figure 5.59 Microsoft Excel function =*f.inv.rt()*.

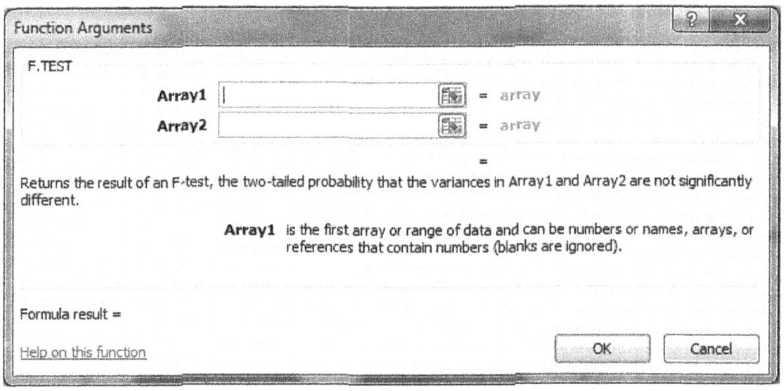

Figure 5.60 Microsoft Excel function =*f.test()*.

Finally, the Microsoft Excel function =*f.test()*, shown in Figure 5.60, takes two arrays of data as arguments and performs an F test for equality of variance. It returns the p value for the hypothesis test:

$$H_0: \frac{\sigma_1^2}{\sigma_2^2} = 1 \ \text{ vs. } \ H_1: \frac{\sigma_1^2}{\sigma_2^2} \neq 1$$

A p value less than the analyst's predefined alpha value will lead the analyst to conclude that the variances are not equal.

5.12.5 Uses and Applications

The F distribution is used in several types of hypothesis tests. For example:

- A quality engineer uses the F distribution to test whether the variability of two production lines is equivalent.

- A Six Sigma Black Belt uses the F distribution to test whether the mean weights of injected molded parts made from four machines are equal.

- A statistician uses the F distribution to perform a lack-of-fit test for a multiple regression model.

- A Six Sigma improvement team uses the F distribution to determine whether a new line design has significantly reduced cycle time variability.

5.13 THE BETA DISTRIBUTION

The beta distribution is quite versatile and is often used to model percent completion since its domain (or allowable X values) is between 0 and 1.

5.13.1 Probability Density Function

The probability density of the beta distribution is shown in Formula 5.66.

Formula 5.66 Probability density of beta distribution

$$f(x) = \frac{(1-x)^{\beta-1}x^{\alpha-1}}{B(\alpha,\beta)}, \qquad 0 \le x \le 1$$

where $B(\alpha, \beta)$ is the *beta function*. The beta function is shown in Formula 5.67.

Formula 5.67 Beta function

$$B(\alpha,\beta) = \frac{\Gamma(\alpha)\Gamma(\beta)}{\Gamma(\alpha+\beta)}$$

Using the definition of the beta function, we can rewrite the density function as Formula 5.68.

Formula 5.68 Probability density of beta distribution, alternate form

$$f(x) = \left[\frac{\Gamma(\alpha+\beta)}{\Gamma(\alpha)\Gamma(\beta)} \right] (1-x)^{\beta-1}x^{\alpha-1}, \qquad 0 \le x \le 1$$

The connection to the negative binomial probability mass function presented in Formula 4.38 can be seen if we evaluate the gamma functions in Formula 5.68, as shown:

$$f(x) = \left[\frac{(\alpha+\beta-1)!}{(\alpha-1)!(\beta-1)!} \right] (1-x)^{\beta-1}x^{\alpha-1}, \qquad 0 \le x \le 1$$

The expected value and variance of the beta distribution are given in Formulas 5.69 and 5.70, respectively.

Formula 5.69 Expected value of beta distribution

$$E(X) = \frac{\alpha}{\alpha+\beta}$$

Formula 5.70   Variance of beta distribution

$$Var(X) = \frac{\alpha\beta}{(\alpha + \beta)^2(\alpha + \beta + 1)}$$

5.13.2 Distribution Shape

The beta distribution is positively skewed if $\alpha < \beta$, symmetric if $\alpha = \beta$, and negatively skewed if $\alpha > \beta$. Shapes of the beta distribution for various values of α and β are shown in Figures 5.61 and 5.62.

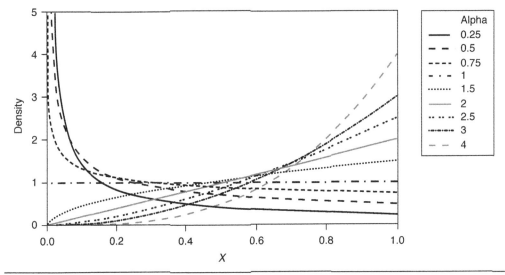

Figure 5.61   Shape of beta distribution: alpha varied, beta = 1.

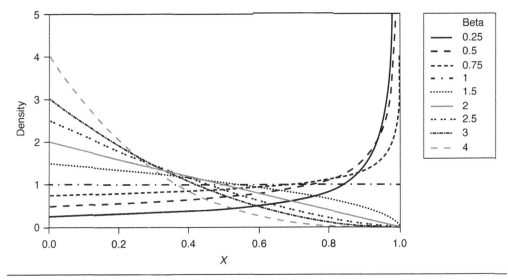

Figure 5.62   Shape of beta distribution: beta varied, alpha = 1.

The beta distribution is related to many other distributions, which makes it quite useful in simulation. If X_1 and X_2 are gamma distributed variables with parameters α and β, the ratio $\dfrac{x_1}{x_1 + x_2}$ follows a beta distribution with parameters α and β.

If $X \sim \text{Beta}(\alpha, \beta)$, then $Y = (1 - X)$ will also follow a beta distribution, but with the values of the parameters switched. For example, $X \sim \text{Beta}(1,4)$, then $Y = (1 - X)$ follows a Beta(4,1).

If the random variable X follows a Poisson distribution with parameter μ, then $Y = 1/X$ follows a beta distribution with $\alpha = 1$ and $\beta = \mu$.

If X follows an F distribution with a and b degrees of freedom, then the random variable Y, in which

$$Y = \frac{\dfrac{aX}{b}}{\left(1 + \dfrac{aX}{b}\right)}$$

follows a beta distribution with $\alpha = a/2$ and $\beta = b/2$.

In addition, a beta distribution with both alpha and beta equal to 1 is equivalent to a uniform $(0, 1)$ distribution.

5.13.3 Related Microsoft Excel Functions

There are two Microsoft Excel functions associated with the beta distribution. The first, shown in Figure 5.63, is =beta.dist(). This function takes five arguments: the value X, parameters alpha and beta, a cumulative flag, and a lower bound, or threshold, A. To find the value of the beta density function for a specified x, enter 0 for the cumulative argument. To find $P(X < x)$, enter 1 in the cumulative argument. If not specified, Microsoft Excel will assume that the lower bound A is zero.

The function =beta.inv(), shown in Figure 5.64, returns the beta random variable X associated with the cumulative probability entered. The arguments A and B

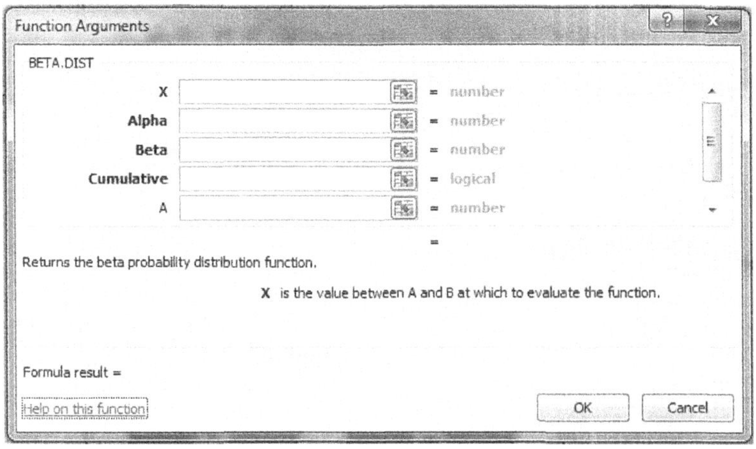

Figure 5.63 Microsoft Excel function =beta.dist().

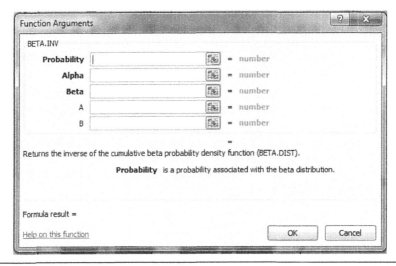

Figure 5.64 Microsoft Excel function =*beta.inv()*.

are optional: *A* allows the user to specify a lower bound on *X*, and *B* allows the user to specify an upper bound. Both of these arguments will default to 0 and 1, respectively, if omitted.

5.13.4 Uses and Applications

The beta distribution can be used to model a proportion. For example:

- A quality engineer uses the beta distribution to model the proportion defective in a lot of product.

- A production engineer uses the beta distribution to track the proportion of total process time used by a certain machine.

- A sports analyst uses the beta distribution to predict a prospective player's batting average for the upcoming season.

5.14 THE LOGNORMAL DISTRIBUTION

The lognormal distribution is useful when modeling random variables that are a product of many other random variables.

5.14.1 Probability Density Function

The lognormal distribution is a bit of a misnomer since it does not describe the distribution of the natural log of the normal. Instead, if $X \sim N(\mu,\sigma^2)$, then e^x will follow a lognormal distribution with parameters μ,σ^2. Therefore, we can say that $X \sim LN(\mu,\sigma^2)$ if and only if $ln\ X \sim N(\mu,\sigma^2)$. The lognormal probability density function is shown in Formula 5.71.

Formula 5.71   Probability density of lognormal distribution

$$f(x) = \frac{1}{x\sqrt{2\pi\sigma^2}}e^{\frac{-(\ln x - \mu)^2}{2\sigma^2}}, \quad x > 0$$

The expected value and variance of the lognormal distribution are shown in Formulas 5.72 and 5.73, respectively.

Formula 5.72   Expected value of lognormal distribution

$$E(X) = e^{\mu + \frac{\sigma^2}{2}}$$

Formula 5.73   Variance of lognormal distribution

$$\text{Var}(X) = e^{2\mu + \sigma^2}(e^{\sigma^2} - 1)$$

5.14.2 Distribution Shape

Figure 5.65 shows the shape of the lognormal distribution for various values of σ. As sigma nears zero, the lognormal distribution has an increasingly higher peak near $e^{-\mu}$.

5.14.3 Related Microsoft Excel Functions

There are two Microsoft Excel functions related to the lognormal distribution. The function =*lognorm.dist*, found in Figure 5.66, gives the value of the probability

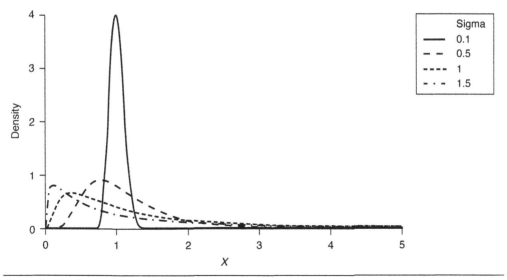

Figure 5.65   Shape of lognormal: various σ, $\mu = 0$.

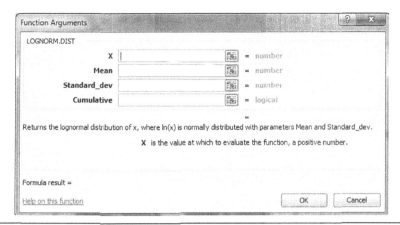

Figure 5.66 Microsoft Excel function =*lognorm.dist()*.

Figure 5.67 Microsoft Excel function =*lognorm.inv()*.

density function for the specified x, μ, and σ when 0 is entered in the cumulative argument. (Note that μ and σ are the mean and standard deviation of the normally distributed variable $ln(X)$, and not the mean and standard deviation of the lognormal distribution.) The function gives $P(X < x)$ when 1 is entered in the cumulative argument.

To find the value of lognormal random variable X associated with a specific cumulative probability, use =*lognorm.inv()*, as shown in Figure 5.67.

5.14.4 Uses and Applications

The lognormal distribution is used when several independent variables are multiplied together. For example:

- A quality engineer uses the lognormal distribution to test whether a multiplicative quality index is significantly greater than a standard value.

- A scientist uses the lognormal distribution to model seismic activity on the Richter scale.

5.15 THE CAUCHY DISTRIBUTION

The Cauchy (pronounced coh'shee) distribution is the result of the ratio of two normal random variables. The distribution is a bit of an oddity since its expected value and variance do not exist.

5.15.1 Probability Density Function

If X_1 and X_2 are independent and follow $N(\mu, \sigma^2)$, the ratio X_1/X_2 follows a Cauchy distribution with location and scale parameters $-\infty < \mu < \infty$ and $\sigma > 0$, respectively. The probability density function is shown in Formula 5.74.

Formula 5.74 Probability density of Cauchy distribution

$$f(x) = \frac{1}{\pi\sigma \left[1 + \left(\dfrac{x - \mu}{\sigma}\right)^2\right]}, \qquad -\infty < x < \infty$$

The cumulative distribution function exists in a closed form, as shown in Formula 5.75.

Formula 5.75 Cumulative distribution of Cauchy distribution

$$F(x) = \frac{1}{\pi} \arctan\left(\frac{x - \mu}{\sigma}\right) + \frac{1}{2}$$

The Cauchy probability density simplifies for a ratio of standard normal variables, as shown in Formula 5.76. The corresponding cumulative distribution function is shown in Formula 5.77.

Formula 5.76 Cauchy probability density function, ratio of standard normal variables

$$f(x) = \frac{1}{\pi[1 + x^2]}, \qquad -\infty < x < \infty$$

Formula 5.77 Cumulative distribution of Cauchy distribution, ratio of standard normal variables

$$F(x) = \frac{1}{\pi} \arctan(x) + \frac{1}{2}$$

We can show that the Cauchy distribution is a special case of Student's t distribution with one degree of freedom. See Formula 5.78, noting that $\Gamma\left(\frac{1}{2}\right) = \sqrt{\pi}$.

Formula 5.78 Student's *t* with *r* = 1 equivalence to Cauchy

$$f(x) = \frac{\Gamma\left(\frac{r+1}{2}\right)}{\sqrt{\pi r}\, \Gamma\left(\frac{r}{2}\right)\left(1 + \frac{x^2}{r}\right)^{\frac{r+1}{2}}} = \frac{\Gamma\left(\frac{1+1}{2}\right)}{\sqrt{\pi r}\, \Gamma\left(\frac{1}{2}\right)\left(1 + \frac{x^2}{1}\right)^{\frac{1+1}{2}}} = \frac{1}{\pi[1 + x^2]}$$

The Cauchy distribution is unusual since its expected value and variance are undefined. This means that if we were to collect samples and calculate an average or sample variance, our estimates would actually become more variable as the sample size increased. However, both the median and the mode of the distribution exist and are equal to μ.

5.15.2 Distribution Shape

The graph of the probability density function is also known as the "Witch of Agnesi" due to a mistranslation of mathematician Maria Agnesi's study of the curve, which was first published in 1748.[8] Figure 5.68 shows the shape of the Cauchy distribution for various values of σ.

5.16 SUMMARY OF CONTINUOUS DISTRIBUTIONS

The table on pages 149–151 provides a summarization of important details on the distributions covered in this chapter.

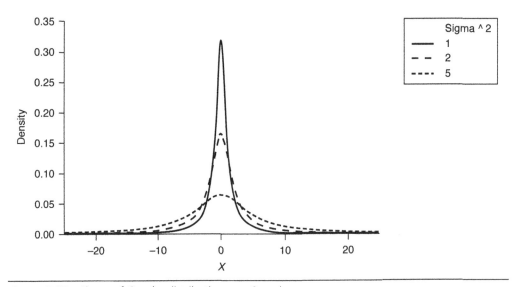

Figure 5.68 Shape of Cauchy distribution: $\mu = 0$, various σ.

---

[8] For an explanation of the curve, its uses, and the mistranslation, see http://mathworld.wolfram.com/WitchofAgnesi.html.

Distribution	Parameters	Expected value and variance	Probability density function	Cumulative distribution function	Special note
Uniform	a, b $b > a$	$E(X) = \dfrac{a+b}{2}$ $\mathrm{Var}(X) = \dfrac{(b-a)^2}{12}$	$f(x) = \dfrac{1}{(b-a)}$, $a \le x \le b \text{ and } b > a$	$F(x) = \begin{cases} 0, & x < a \\ \dfrac{x-a}{(b-a)}, & a \le x \le b \\ 1, & x > b \end{cases}$	
Triangular	$a \le m \le b$	$E(X) = \dfrac{a+b+m}{3}$ $\mathrm{Var}(X) = \dfrac{a^2+b^2+m^2-ab-am-bm}{18}$	$f(x) = \begin{cases} \dfrac{2(x-a)}{(b-a)(m-a)}, & a \le x \le m \\ \dfrac{2(b-x)}{(b-a)(b-m)}, & m < x \le b \\ 0, & \text{otherwise} \end{cases}$	$F(x) = \begin{cases} 0, & x < a \\ \dfrac{(x-a)^2}{(b-a)(m-a)}, & a \le x \le m \\ 1 - \dfrac{(b-x)^2}{(b-a)(b-m)}, & m < x \le b \\ 1, & x > b \end{cases}$	
Normal	μ, σ	$E(X) = \mu$ $\mathrm{Var}(X) = \sigma^2$	$f(x) = \dfrac{1}{\sqrt{2\pi\sigma^2}}e^{-\frac{(x-\mu)^2}{2\sigma^2}}$, $-\infty < x < \infty$	No closed form Convert to standard normal and use Z table	
Standard normal	$\mu = 0$, $\sigma = 1$	$E(X) = 0$ $\mathrm{Var}(X) = 1$	$f(z) = \dfrac{1}{\sqrt{2\pi}}e^{-\frac{z^2}{2}}$, $-\infty < z < \infty$	No closed form Use Z table	$Z = \dfrac{X - \mu}{\sigma}$
Student's t	r, $r > 2$	$E(X) = 0$ $\mathrm{Var}(X) = \dfrac{r}{r-2}$	$f(x) = \dfrac{\Gamma\left(\dfrac{r+1}{2}\right)}{\sqrt{\pi r}\,\Gamma\left(\dfrac{r}{2}\right)}\left(1+\dfrac{x^2}{r}\right)^{-\frac{r+1}{2}}$, $-\infty < x < \infty$	No closed form Use Student's t table	$T = \dfrac{X - \mu}{s}$ $r = (n-1)$
Gamma	$\alpha = 0$, $\beta = 0$	$E(X) = \alpha\beta$ $\mathrm{Var}(X) = \alpha\beta^2$	$f(x) = \dfrac{x^{\alpha-1}e^{-x/\beta}}{\Gamma(\alpha)\beta^\alpha}$, $x > 0$	Closed form exists if α is an integer $F(x) = 1 - e^{-x/\beta}\displaystyle\sum_{k=0}^{\alpha-1}\dfrac{(x/\beta)^k}{k!}$	

Distribution	Parameters	Expected value and variance	Probability density function	Cumulative distribution function	Special note
Chi-square	$r > 0$	$E(X) = r$ $\text{Var}(X) = 2r$	$f(x) = \dfrac{x^{\frac{r}{2}-1}e^{-x/2}}{\Gamma\left(\frac{r}{2}\right)2^{\frac{r}{2}}}, \quad x > 0$	No closed form in general Use chi-square tables	Gamma with $\alpha = r/2$ and $\beta = 2$. If $Z \sim N(0,1)$, Sum $Z^2 \sim \chi^2(r)$ $\dfrac{(n-1)s^2}{\sigma^2} \sim \chi^2(n-1)$
Exponential	$\beta > 0$	$E(X) = \beta$ $\text{Var}(X) = \beta^2$	$f(x) = \dfrac{1}{\beta}e^{-x/\beta}, \quad x > 0$	$F(x) = 1 - e^{-x/\beta}$	Gamma with $\alpha = 1$ Memoryless property
m-Erlang	α positive integer	$E(X) = m\beta$ $\text{Var}(X) = m\beta^2$	$f(x) = \dfrac{x^{\alpha-1}e^{-x/\beta}}{\Gamma(\alpha)\beta^\alpha}, \quad x > 0$	$F(x) = 1 - e^{-x/\beta}\displaystyle\sum_{k=0}^{\alpha-1}\dfrac{(x/\beta)^k}{k!}$	Sum of m independent observations from an exponential (β)
Weibull	$\alpha > 0,$ $\beta > 0$	$E(x) = \beta\Gamma\left(1+\dfrac{1}{\alpha}\right)$ $\text{Var}(x) = \beta^2\left\{\Gamma\left(1+\dfrac{2}{\alpha}\right) - \Gamma^2\left(1+\dfrac{1}{\alpha}\right)\right\}$	$f(x) = \alpha\beta^{-\alpha}x^{\alpha-1}e^{-(x/\beta)^\alpha},$ $x > 0, \alpha > 0, \beta > 0$	$F(x) = 1 - e^{-(x/\beta)^\alpha}, \quad x > 0$	Weibull with $\alpha = 1$ is an exponential
Rayleigh	$\beta > 0$	$E(X) = \sqrt{2\pi}$ $\text{Var}(X) = 2 - 2/\pi$	$f(x) = 2xe^{-(2x/\beta)}, \quad x > 0, \beta > 0$	$F(x) = 1 - e^{-(2x/\beta)}, \quad x > 0$	Weibull with $\alpha = 2$
F	a, b $a, b > 0$	$E(X) = \dfrac{b}{b-2}, \quad b > 2$ $\text{Var}(X) = 2\left(\dfrac{b}{b-2}\right)^2\dfrac{a+b-2}{a(b-4)},$ $b > 4$	$f(x) = \dfrac{\Gamma\left(\frac{a+b}{2}\right)a^{\frac{a}{2}}b^{\frac{b}{2}}x^{\left(\frac{a}{2}-1\right)}}{\Gamma\left(\frac{a}{2}\right)\Gamma\left(\frac{b}{2}\right)(a+bx)^{\frac{a+b}{2}}},$ $x > 0, a, b > 0$	Use F tables	Use for testing equivalence of two variances from a normal distribution Use for ANOVA

Distribution	Parameters	Expected value and variance	Probability density function	Cumulative distribution function	Special note
Beta	α, β	$E(X) = \dfrac{\alpha}{\alpha+\beta}$ $Var(X) = \dfrac{\alpha\beta}{(\alpha+\beta)^2(\alpha+\beta+1)}$	$f(x) = \left[\dfrac{\Gamma(\alpha+\beta)}{\Gamma(\alpha)\Gamma(\beta)}\right](1-x)^{\beta-1}x^{\alpha-1},$ $0 \le x \le 1$	Closed form exists only in special cases of a and b	Reciprocal relationship to Poisson distribution Beta (1,1) is U(0,1)
Lognormal	μ, σ	$E(X) = e^{\mu+\frac{\sigma^2}{2}}$ $Var(X) = e^{2\mu+\sigma^2}(e^{\sigma^2}-1)$	$f(x) = \dfrac{1}{x\sqrt{2\pi\sigma^2}}e^{\frac{-(\ln x-\mu)^2}{2\sigma^2}}, \quad x > 0$	No closed form exists	X is the natural log of a normally distributed variable
Cauchy	μ, σ	Not defined	$f(x) = \dfrac{1}{\pi\sigma\left[1+\left(\dfrac{x-\mu}{\sigma}\right)^2\right]},$ $-\infty < x < \infty$	$F(x) = \dfrac{1}{\pi}\arctan\left(\dfrac{x-\mu}{\sigma}\right)+\dfrac{1}{2}$	X is the ratio of two normally distributed random variables Cauchy equivalent to Student's t distribution with df =1

Appendix A
Distribution Road Map

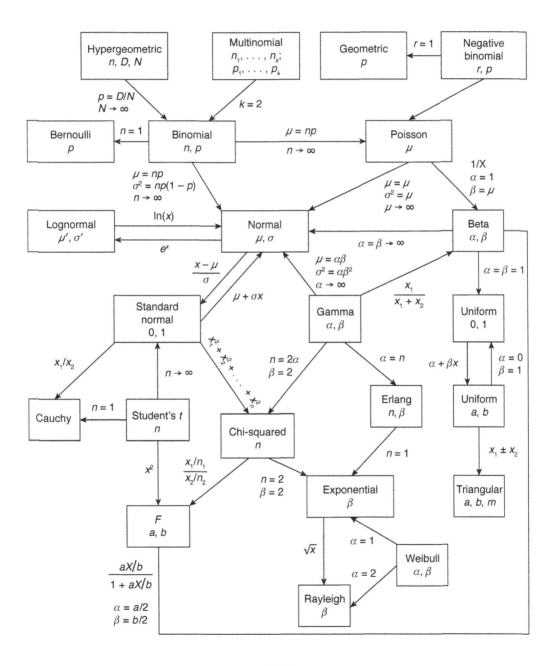

Appendix B
Binomial Table

$$P(X=x)=\binom{n}{x}p^x(1-p)^{n-x}$$

Probability of x occurrences in a sample of size n

n	x	0.05	0.10	0.15	0.20	0.25	0.30	0.35	0.40	0.45	0.50	0.55	0.60	0.65	0.70	0.75	0.80	0.85	0.90	0.95
1	0	0.9500	0.9000	0.8500	0.8000	0.7500	0.7000	0.6500	0.6000	0.5500	0.5000	0.4500	0.4000	0.3500	0.3000	0.2500	0.2000	0.1500	0.1000	0.0500
	1	0.0500	0.1000	0.1500	0.2000	0.2500	0.3000	0.3500	0.4000	0.4500	0.5000	0.5500	0.6000	0.6500	0.7000	0.7500	0.8000	0.8500	0.9000	0.9500
2	0	0.9025	0.8100	0.7225	0.6400	0.5625	0.4900	0.4225	0.3600	0.3025	0.2500	0.2025	0.1600	0.1225	0.0900	0.0625	0.0400	0.0225	0.0100	0.0025
	1	0.0950	0.1800	0.2550	0.3200	0.3750	0.4200	0.4550	0.4800	0.4950	0.5000	0.4950	0.4800	0.4550	0.4200	0.3750	0.3200	0.2550	0.1800	0.0950
	2	0.0025	0.0100	0.0225	0.0400	0.0625	0.0900	0.1225	0.1600	0.2025	0.2500	0.3025	0.3600	0.4225	0.4900	0.5625	0.6400	0.7225	0.8100	0.9025
3	0	0.8574	0.7290	0.6141	0.5120	0.4219	0.3430	0.2746	0.2160	0.1664	0.1250	0.0911	0.0640	0.0429	0.0270	0.0156	0.0080	0.0034	0.0010	0.0001
	1	0.1354	0.2430	0.3251	0.3840	0.4219	0.4410	0.4436	0.4320	0.4084	0.3750	0.3341	0.2880	0.2389	0.1890	0.1406	0.0960	0.0574	0.0270	0.0071
	2	0.0071	0.0270	0.0574	0.0960	0.1406	0.1890	0.2389	0.2880	0.3341	0.3750	0.4084	0.4320	0.4436	0.4410	0.4219	0.3840	0.3251	0.2430	0.1354
	3	0.0001	0.0010	0.0034	0.0080	0.0156	0.0270	0.0429	0.0640	0.0911	0.1250	0.1664	0.2160	0.2746	0.3430	0.4219	0.5120	0.6141	0.7290	0.8574
4	0	0.8145	0.6561	0.5220	0.4096	0.3164	0.2401	0.1785	0.1296	0.0915	0.0625	0.0410	0.0256	0.0150	0.0081	0.0039	0.0016	0.0005	0.0001	0.0000
	1	0.1715	0.2916	0.3685	0.4096	0.4219	0.4116	0.3845	0.3456	0.2995	0.2500	0.2005	0.1536	0.1115	0.0756	0.0469	0.0256	0.0115	0.0036	0.0005
	2	0.0135	0.0486	0.0975	0.1536	0.2109	0.2646	0.3105	0.3456	0.3675	0.3750	0.3675	0.3456	0.3105	0.2646	0.2109	0.1536	0.0975	0.0486	0.0135
	3	0.0005	0.0036	0.0115	0.0256	0.0469	0.0756	0.1115	0.1536	0.2005	0.2500	0.2995	0.3456	0.3845	0.4116	0.4219	0.4096	0.3685	0.2916	0.1715
	4	0.0000	0.0001	0.0005	0.0016	0.0039	0.0081	0.0150	0.0256	0.0410	0.0625	0.0915	0.1296	0.1785	0.2401	0.3164	0.4096	0.5220	0.6561	0.8145
5	0	0.7738	0.5905	0.4437	0.3277	0.2373	0.1681	0.1160	0.0778	0.0503	0.0313	0.0185	0.0102	0.0053	0.0024	0.0010	0.0003	0.0001	0.0000	0.0000
	1	0.2036	0.3281	0.3915	0.4096	0.3955	0.3602	0.3124	0.2592	0.2059	0.1563	0.1128	0.0768	0.0488	0.0284	0.0146	0.0064	0.0022	0.0005	0.0000
	2	0.0214	0.0729	0.1382	0.2048	0.2637	0.3087	0.3364	0.3456	0.3369	0.3125	0.2757	0.2304	0.1811	0.1323	0.0879	0.0512	0.0244	0.0081	0.0011
	3	0.0011	0.0081	0.0244	0.0512	0.0879	0.1323	0.1811	0.2304	0.2757	0.3125	0.3369	0.3456	0.3364	0.3087	0.2637	0.2048	0.1382	0.0729	0.0214
	4	0.0000	0.0005	0.0022	0.0064	0.0146	0.0284	0.0488	0.0768	0.1128	0.1563	0.2059	0.2592	0.3124	0.3602	0.3955	0.4096	0.3915	0.3281	0.2036
	5	0.0000	0.0000	0.0001	0.0003	0.0010	0.0024	0.0053	0.0102	0.0185	0.0313	0.0503	0.0778	0.1160	0.1681	0.2373	0.3277	0.4437	0.5905	0.7738

$$P(X = x) = \binom{n}{x} p^x (1-p)^{n-x}$$

Probability of x occurrences in a sample of size n

n	x	0.05	0.10	0.15	0.20	0.25	0.30	0.35	0.40	0.45	0.50	0.55	0.60	0.65	0.70	0.75	0.80	0.85	0.90	0.95
6	0	0.7351	0.5314	0.3771	0.2621	0.1780	0.1176	0.0754	0.0467	0.0277	0.0156	0.0083	0.0041	0.0018	0.0007	0.0002	0.0001	0.0000	0.0000	0.0000
	1	0.2321	0.3543	0.3993	0.3932	0.3560	0.3025	0.2437	0.1866	0.1359	0.0938	0.0609	0.0369	0.0205	0.0102	0.0044	0.0015	0.0004	0.0001	0.0000
	2	0.0305	0.0984	0.1762	0.2458	0.2966	0.3241	0.3280	0.3110	0.2780	0.2344	0.1861	0.1382	0.0951	0.0595	0.0330	0.0154	0.0055	0.0012	0.0001
	3	0.0021	0.0146	0.0415	0.0819	0.1318	0.1852	0.2355	0.2765	0.3032	0.3125	0.3032	0.2765	0.2355	0.1852	0.1318	0.0819	0.0415	0.0146	0.0021
	4	0.0001	0.0012	0.0055	0.0154	0.0330	0.0595	0.0951	0.1382	0.1861	0.2344	0.2780	0.3110	0.3280	0.3241	0.2966	0.2458	0.1762	0.0984	0.0305
	5	0.0000	0.0001	0.0004	0.0015	0.0044	0.0102	0.0205	0.0369	0.0609	0.0938	0.1359	0.1866	0.2437	0.3025	0.3560	0.3932	0.3993	0.3543	0.2321
	6	0.0000	0.0000	0.0000	0.0001	0.0002	0.0007	0.0018	0.0041	0.0083	0.0156	0.0277	0.0467	0.0754	0.1176	0.1780	0.2621	0.3771	0.5314	0.7351
7	0	0.6983	0.4783	0.3206	0.2097	0.1335	0.0824	0.0490	0.0280	0.0152	0.0078	0.0037	0.0016	0.0006	0.0002	0.0001	0.0000	0.0000	0.0000	0.0000
	1	0.2573	0.3720	0.3960	0.3670	0.3115	0.2471	0.1848	0.1306	0.0872	0.0547	0.0320	0.0172	0.0084	0.0036	0.0013	0.0004	0.0001	0.0000	0.0000
	2	0.0406	0.1240	0.2097	0.2753	0.3115	0.3177	0.2985	0.2613	0.2140	0.1641	0.1172	0.0774	0.0466	0.0250	0.0115	0.0043	0.0012	0.0002	0.0000
	3	0.0036	0.0230	0.0617	0.1147	0.1730	0.2269	0.2679	0.2903	0.2918	0.2734	0.2388	0.1935	0.1442	0.0972	0.0577	0.0287	0.0109	0.0026	0.0002
	4	0.0002	0.0026	0.0109	0.0287	0.0577	0.0972	0.1442	0.1935	0.2388	0.2734	0.2918	0.2903	0.2679	0.2269	0.1730	0.1147	0.0617	0.0230	0.0036
	5	0.0000	0.0002	0.0012	0.0043	0.0115	0.0250	0.0466	0.0774	0.1172	0.1641	0.2140	0.2613	0.2985	0.3177	0.3115	0.2753	0.2097	0.1240	0.0406
	6	0.0000	0.0000	0.0001	0.0004	0.0013	0.0036	0.0084	0.0172	0.0320	0.0547	0.0872	0.1306	0.1848	0.2471	0.3115	0.3670	0.3960	0.3720	0.2573
	7	0.0000	0.0000	0.0000	0.0000	0.0001	0.0002	0.0006	0.0016	0.0037	0.0078	0.0152	0.0280	0.0490	0.0824	0.1335	0.2097	0.3206	0.4783	0.6983
8	0	0.6634	0.4305	0.2725	0.1678	0.1001	0.0576	0.0319	0.0168	0.0084	0.0039	0.0017	0.0007	0.0002	0.0001	0.0000	0.0000	0.0000	0.0000	0.0000
	1	0.2793	0.3826	0.3847	0.3355	0.2670	0.1977	0.1373	0.0896	0.0548	0.0313	0.0164	0.0079	0.0033	0.0012	0.0004	0.0001	0.0000	0.0000	0.0000
	2	0.0515	0.1488	0.2376	0.2936	0.3115	0.2965	0.2587	0.2090	0.1569	0.1094	0.0703	0.0413	0.0217	0.0100	0.0038	0.0011	0.0002	0.0000	0.0000
	3	0.0054	0.0331	0.0839	0.1468	0.2076	0.2541	0.2786	0.2787	0.2568	0.2188	0.1719	0.1239	0.0808	0.0467	0.0231	0.0092	0.0026	0.0004	0.0000
	4	0.0004	0.0046	0.0185	0.0459	0.0865	0.1361	0.1875	0.2322	0.2627	0.2734	0.2627	0.2322	0.1875	0.1361	0.0865	0.0459	0.0185	0.0046	0.0004
	5	0.0000	0.0004	0.0026	0.0092	0.0231	0.0467	0.0808	0.1239	0.1719	0.2188	0.2568	0.2787	0.2786	0.2541	0.2076	0.1468	0.0839	0.0331	0.0054

$$P(X=x)=\binom{n}{x}p^x(1-p)^{n-x}$$

Probability of x occurrences in a sample of size n

n	x	0.05	0.10	0.15	0.20	0.25	0.30	0.35	0.40	0.45	0.50	0.55	0.60	0.65	0.70	0.75	0.80	0.85	0.90	0.95	x	n
	6	0.0000	0.0000	0.0002	0.0011	0.0038	0.0100	0.0217	0.0413	0.0703	0.1094	0.1569	0.2090	0.2587	0.2965	0.3115	0.2936	0.2376	0.1488	0.0515	6	
	7	0.0000	0.0000	0.0000	0.0001	0.0004	0.0012	0.0033	0.0079	0.0164	0.0313	0.0548	0.0896	0.1373	0.1977	0.2670	0.3355	0.3847	0.3826	0.2793	7	
	8	0.0000	0.0000	0.0000	0.0000	0.0000	0.0001	0.0002	0.0007	0.0017	0.0039	0.0084	0.0168	0.0319	0.0576	0.1001	0.1678	0.2725	0.4305	0.6634	8	
9	0	0.6302	0.3874	0.2316	0.1342	0.0751	0.0404	0.0207	0.0101	0.0046	0.0020	0.0008	0.0003	0.0001	0.0000	0.0000	0.0000	0.0000	0.0000	0.0000	0	9
	1	0.2985	0.3874	0.3679	0.3020	0.2253	0.1556	0.1004	0.0605	0.0339	0.0176	0.0083	0.0035	0.0013	0.0004	0.0001	0.0000	0.0000	0.0000	0.0000	1	
	2	0.0629	0.1722	0.2597	0.3020	0.3003	0.2668	0.2162	0.1612	0.1110	0.0703	0.0407	0.0212	0.0098	0.0039	0.0012	0.0003	0.0000	0.0000	0.0000	2	
	3	0.0077	0.0446	0.1069	0.1762	0.2336	0.2668	0.2716	0.2508	0.2119	0.1641	0.1160	0.0743	0.0424	0.0210	0.0087	0.0028	0.0006	0.0001	0.0000	3	
	4	0.0006	0.0074	0.0283	0.0661	0.1168	0.1715	0.2194	0.2508	0.2600	0.2461	0.2128	0.1672	0.1181	0.0735	0.0389	0.0165	0.0050	0.0008	0.0000	4	
	5	0.0000	0.0008	0.0050	0.0165	0.0389	0.0735	0.1181	0.1672	0.2128	0.2461	0.2600	0.2508	0.2194	0.1715	0.1168	0.0661	0.0283	0.0074	0.0006	5	
	6	0.0000	0.0001	0.0006	0.0028	0.0087	0.0210	0.0424	0.0743	0.1160	0.1641	0.2119	0.2508	0.2716	0.2668	0.2336	0.1762	0.1069	0.0446	0.0077	6	
	7	0.0000	0.0000	0.0000	0.0003	0.0012	0.0039	0.0098	0.0212	0.0407	0.0703	0.1110	0.1612	0.2162	0.2668	0.3003	0.3020	0.2597	0.1722	0.0629	7	
	8	0.0000	0.0000	0.0000	0.0000	0.0001	0.0004	0.0013	0.0035	0.0083	0.0176	0.0339	0.0605	0.1004	0.1556	0.2253	0.3020	0.3679	0.3874	0.2985	8	
	9	0.0000	0.0000	0.0000	0.0000	0.0000	0.0000	0.0001	0.0003	0.0008	0.0020	0.0046	0.0101	0.0207	0.0404	0.0751	0.1342	0.2316	0.3874	0.6302	9	
10	0	0.5987	0.3487	0.1969	0.1074	0.0563	0.0282	0.0135	0.0060	0.0025	0.0010	0.0003	0.0001	0.0000	0.0000	0.0000	0.0000	0.0000	0.0000	0.0000	0	10
	1	0.3151	0.3874	0.3474	0.2684	0.1877	0.1211	0.0725	0.0403	0.0207	0.0098	0.0042	0.0016	0.0005	0.0001	0.0000	0.0000	0.0000	0.0000	0.0000	1	
	2	0.0746	0.1937	0.2759	0.3020	0.2816	0.2335	0.1757	0.1209	0.0763	0.0439	0.0229	0.0106	0.0043	0.0014	0.0004	0.0001	0.0000	0.0000	0.0000	2	
	3	0.0105	0.0574	0.1298	0.2013	0.2503	0.2668	0.2522	0.2150	0.1665	0.1172	0.0746	0.0425	0.0212	0.0090	0.0031	0.0008	0.0001	0.0000	0.0000	3	
	4	0.0010	0.0112	0.0401	0.0881	0.1460	0.2001	0.2377	0.2508	0.2384	0.2051	0.1596	0.1115	0.0689	0.0368	0.0162	0.0055	0.0012	0.0001	0.0000	4	
	5	0.0001	0.0015	0.0085	0.0264	0.0584	0.1029	0.1536	0.2007	0.2340	0.2461	0.2340	0.2007	0.1536	0.1029	0.0584	0.0264	0.0085	0.0015	0.0001	5	
	6	0.0000	0.0001	0.0012	0.0055	0.0162	0.0368	0.0689	0.1115	0.1596	0.2051	0.2384	0.2508	0.2377	0.2001	0.1460	0.0881	0.0401	0.0112	0.0010	6	
	7	0.0000	0.0000	0.0001	0.0008	0.0031	0.0090	0.0212	0.0425	0.0746	0.1172	0.1665	0.2150	0.2522	0.2668	0.2503	0.2013	0.1298	0.0574	0.0105	7	
	8	0.0000	0.0000	0.0000	0.0001	0.0004	0.0014	0.0043	0.0106	0.0229	0.0439	0.0763	0.1209	0.1757	0.2335	0.2816	0.3020	0.2759	0.1937	0.0746	8	
	9	0.0000	0.0000	0.0000	0.0000	0.0000	0.0001	0.0005	0.0016	0.0042	0.0098	0.0207	0.0403	0.0725	0.1211	0.1877	0.2684	0.3474	0.3874	0.3151	9	
	10	0.0000	0.0000	0.0000	0.0000	0.0000	0.0000	0.0000	0.0001	0.0003	0.0010	0.0025	0.0060	0.0135	0.0282	0.0563	0.1074	0.1969	0.3487	0.5987	10	

Appendix C
Cumulative Binomial Table

$$P(X \leq x) = \sum_{x=0}^{x} \binom{n}{x} p^x (1-p)^{n-x}$$

Probability of $\leq x$ occurrences in a sample of size n

n	x	0.05	0.10	0.15	0.20	0.25	0.30	0.35	0.40	0.45	0.50	0.55	0.60	0.65	0.70	0.75	0.80	0.85	0.90	0.95	n	x
1	0	0.9500	0.9000	0.8500	0.8000	0.7500	0.7000	0.6500	0.6000	0.5500	0.5000	0.4500	0.4000	0.3500	0.3000	0.2500	0.2000	0.1500	0.1000	0.0500	1	0
	1	1.0000	1.0000	1.0000	1.0000	1.0000	1.0000	1.0000	1.0000	1.0000	1.0000	1.0000	1.0000	1.0000	1.0000	1.0000	1.0000	1.0000	1.0000	1.0000		1
2	0	0.9025	0.8100	0.7225	0.6400	0.5625	0.4900	0.4225	0.3600	0.3025	0.2500	0.2025	0.1600	0.1225	0.0900	0.0625	0.0400	0.0225	0.0100	0.0025	2	0
	1	0.9975	0.9900	0.9775	0.9600	0.9375	0.9100	0.8775	0.8400	0.7975	0.7500	0.6975	0.6400	0.5775	0.5100	0.4375	0.3600	0.2775	0.1900	0.0975		1
	2	1.0000	1.0000	1.0000	1.0000	1.0000	1.0000	1.0000	1.0000	1.0000	1.0000	1.0000	1.0000	1.0000	1.0000	1.0000	1.0000	1.0000	1.0000	1.0000		2
3	0	0.8574	0.7290	0.6141	0.5120	0.4219	0.3430	0.2746	0.2160	0.1664	0.1250	0.0911	0.0640	0.0429	0.0270	0.0156	0.0080	0.0034	0.0010	0.0001	3	0
	1	0.9928	0.9720	0.9393	0.8960	0.8438	0.7840	0.7183	0.6480	0.5748	0.5000	0.4253	0.3520	0.2818	0.2160	0.1563	0.1040	0.0608	0.0280	0.0073		1
	2	0.9999	0.9990	0.9966	0.9920	0.9844	0.9730	0.9571	0.9360	0.9089	0.8750	0.8336	0.7840	0.7254	0.6570	0.5781	0.4880	0.3859	0.2710	0.1426		2
	3	1.0000	1.0000	1.0000	1.0000	1.0000	1.0000	1.0000	1.0000	1.0000	1.0000	1.0000	1.0000	1.0000	1.0000	1.0000	1.0000	1.0000	1.0000	1.0000		3
4	0	0.8145	0.6561	0.5220	0.4096	0.3164	0.2401	0.1785	0.1296	0.0915	0.0625	0.0410	0.0256	0.0150	0.0081	0.0039	0.0016	0.0005	0.0001	0.0000	4	0
	1	0.9860	0.9477	0.8905	0.8192	0.7383	0.6517	0.5630	0.4752	0.3910	0.3125	0.2415	0.1792	0.1265	0.0837	0.0508	0.0272	0.0120	0.0037	0.0005		1
	2	0.9995	0.9963	0.9880	0.9728	0.9492	0.9163	0.8735	0.8208	0.7585	0.6875	0.6090	0.5248	0.4370	0.3483	0.2617	0.1808	0.1095	0.0523	0.0140		2
	3	1.0000	0.9999	0.9995	0.9984	0.9961	0.9919	0.9850	0.9744	0.9590	0.9375	0.9085	0.8704	0.8215	0.7599	0.6836	0.5904	0.4780	0.3439	0.1855		3
	4	1.0000	1.0000	1.0000	1.0000	1.0000	1.0000	1.0000	1.0000	1.0000	1.0000	1.0000	1.0000	1.0000	1.0000	1.0000	1.0000	1.0000	1.0000	1.0000		4
5	0	0.7738	0.5905	0.4437	0.3277	0.2373	0.1681	0.1160	0.0778	0.0503	0.0313	0.0185	0.0102	0.0053	0.0024	0.0010	0.0003	0.0001	0.0000	0.0000	5	0
	1	0.9774	0.9185	0.8352	0.7373	0.6328	0.5282	0.4284	0.3370	0.2562	0.1875	0.1312	0.0870	0.0540	0.0308	0.0156	0.0067	0.0022	0.0005	0.0000		1
	2	0.9988	0.9914	0.9734	0.9421	0.8965	0.8369	0.7648	0.6826	0.5931	0.5000	0.4069	0.3174	0.2352	0.1631	0.1035	0.0579	0.0266	0.0086	0.0012		2
	3	1.0000	0.9995	0.9978	0.9933	0.9844	0.9692	0.9460	0.9130	0.8688	0.8125	0.7438	0.6630	0.5716	0.4718	0.3672	0.2627	0.1648	0.0815	0.0226		3
	4	1.0000	1.0000	0.9999	0.9997	0.9990	0.9976	0.9947	0.9898	0.9815	0.9688	0.9497	0.9222	0.8840	0.8319	0.7627	0.6723	0.5563	0.4095	0.2262		4
	5	1.0000	1.0000	1.0000	1.0000	1.0000	1.0000	1.0000	1.0000	1.0000	1.0000	1.0000	1.0000	1.0000	1.0000	1.0000	1.0000	1.0000	1.0000	1.0000		5
6	0	0.7351	0.5314	0.3771	0.2621	0.1780	0.1176	0.0754	0.0467	0.0277	0.0156	0.0083	0.0041	0.0018	0.0007	0.0002	0.0001	0.0000	0.0000	0.0000	6	0
	1	0.9672	0.8857	0.7765	0.6554	0.5339	0.4202	0.3191	0.2333	0.1636	0.1094	0.0692	0.0410	0.0223	0.0109	0.0046	0.0016	0.0004	0.0001	0.0000		1
	2	0.9978	0.9842	0.9527	0.9011	0.8306	0.7443	0.6471	0.5443	0.4415	0.3438	0.2553	0.1792	0.1174	0.0705	0.0376	0.0170	0.0059	0.0013	0.0001		2
	3	0.9999	0.9987	0.9941	0.9830	0.9624	0.9295	0.8826	0.8208	0.7447	0.6563	0.5585	0.4557	0.3529	0.2557	0.1694	0.0989	0.0473	0.0159	0.0022		3
	4	1.0000	0.9999	0.9996	0.9984	0.9954	0.9891	0.9777	0.9590	0.9308	0.8906	0.8364	0.7667	0.6809	0.5798	0.4661	0.3446	0.2235	0.1143	0.0328		4
	5	1.0000	1.0000	1.0000	0.9999	0.9998	0.9993	0.9982	0.9959	0.9917	0.9844	0.9723	0.9533	0.9246	0.8824	0.8220	0.7379	0.6229	0.4686	0.2649		5
	6	1.0000	1.0000	1.0000	1.0000	1.0000	1.0000	1.0000	1.0000	1.0000	1.0000	1.0000	1.0000	1.0000	1.0000	1.0000	1.0000	1.0000	1.0000	1.0000		6

$$P(X \le x) = \sum_{x=0}^{x} \binom{n}{x} p^x (1-p)^{n-x}$$

Probability of ≤x occurrences in a sample of size n

n	x	0.05	0.10	0.15	0.20	0.25	0.30	0.35	0.40	0.45	0.50	0.55	0.60	0.65	0.70	0.75	0.80	0.85	0.90	0.95
7	0	0.6983	0.4783	0.3206	0.2097	0.1335	0.0824	0.0490	0.0280	0.0152	0.0078	0.0037	0.0016	0.0006	0.0002	0.0001	0.0000	0.0000	0.0000	0.0000
	1	0.9556	0.8503	0.7166	0.5767	0.4449	0.3294	0.2338	0.1586	0.1024	0.0625	0.0357	0.0188	0.0090	0.0038	0.0013	0.0004	0.0001	0.0000	0.0000
	2	0.9962	0.9743	0.9262	0.8520	0.7564	0.6471	0.5323	0.4199	0.3164	0.2266	0.1529	0.0963	0.0556	0.0288	0.0129	0.0047	0.0012	0.0002	0.0000
	3	0.9998	0.9973	0.9879	0.9667	0.9294	0.8740	0.8002	0.7102	0.6083	0.5000	0.3917	0.2898	0.1998	0.1260	0.0706	0.0333	0.0121	0.0027	0.0002
	4	1.0000	0.9998	0.9988	0.9953	0.9871	0.9712	0.9444	0.9037	0.8471	0.7734	0.6836	0.5801	0.4677	0.3529	0.2436	0.1480	0.0738	0.0257	0.0038
	5	1.0000	1.0000	0.9999	0.9996	0.9987	0.9962	0.9910	0.9812	0.9643	0.9375	0.8976	0.8414	0.7662	0.6706	0.5551	0.4233	0.2834	0.1497	0.0444
	6	1.0000	1.0000	1.0000	1.0000	0.9999	0.9998	0.9994	0.9984	0.9963	0.9922	0.9848	0.9720	0.9510	0.9176	0.8665	0.7903	0.6794	0.5217	0.3017
	7	1.0000	1.0000	1.0000	1.0000	1.0000	1.0000	1.0000	1.0000	1.0000	1.0000	1.0000	1.0000	1.0000	1.0000	1.0000	1.0000	1.0000	1.0000	1.0000
8	0	0.6634	0.4305	0.2725	0.1678	0.1001	0.0576	0.0319	0.0168	0.0084	0.0039	0.0017	0.0007	0.0002	0.0001	0.0000	0.0000	0.0000	0.0000	0.0000
	1	0.9428	0.8131	0.6572	0.5033	0.3671	0.2553	0.1691	0.1064	0.0632	0.0352	0.0181	0.0085	0.0036	0.0013	0.0004	0.0001	0.0000	0.0000	0.0000
	2	0.9942	0.9619	0.8948	0.7969	0.6785	0.5518	0.4278	0.3154	0.2201	0.1445	0.0885	0.0498	0.0253	0.0113	0.0042	0.0012	0.0002	0.0000	0.0000
	3	0.9996	0.9950	0.9786	0.9437	0.8862	0.8059	0.7064	0.5941	0.4770	0.3633	0.2604	0.1737	0.1061	0.0580	0.0273	0.0104	0.0029	0.0004	0.0000
	4	1.0000	0.9996	0.9971	0.9896	0.9727	0.9420	0.8939	0.8263	0.7396	0.6367	0.5230	0.4059	0.2936	0.1941	0.1138	0.0563	0.0214	0.0050	0.0004
	5	1.0000	1.0000	0.9998	0.9988	0.9958	0.9887	0.9747	0.9502	0.9115	0.8555	0.7799	0.6846	0.5722	0.4482	0.3215	0.2031	0.1052	0.0381	0.0058
	6	1.0000	1.0000	1.0000	0.9999	0.9996	0.9987	0.9964	0.9915	0.9819	0.9648	0.9368	0.8936	0.8309	0.7447	0.6329	0.4967	0.3428	0.1869	0.0572
	7	1.0000	1.0000	1.0000	1.0000	1.0000	0.9999	0.9998	0.9993	0.9983	0.9961	0.9916	0.9832	0.9681	0.9424	0.8999	0.8322	0.7275	0.5695	0.3366
	8	1.0000	1.0000	1.0000	1.0000	1.0000	1.0000	1.0000	1.0000	1.0000	1.0000	1.0000	1.0000	1.0000	1.0000	1.0000	1.0000	1.0000	1.0000	1.0000
9	0	0.6302	0.3874	0.2316	0.1342	0.0751	0.0404	0.0207	0.0101	0.0046	0.0020	0.0008	0.0003	0.0001	0.0000	0.0000	0.0000	0.0000	0.0000	0.0000
	1	0.9288	0.7748	0.5995	0.4362	0.3003	0.1960	0.1211	0.0705	0.0385	0.0195	0.0091	0.0038	0.0014	0.0004	0.0001	0.0000	0.0000	0.0000	0.0000
	2	0.9916	0.9470	0.8591	0.7382	0.6007	0.4628	0.3373	0.2318	0.1495	0.0898	0.0498	0.0250	0.0112	0.0043	0.0013	0.0003	0.0000	0.0000	0.0000
	3	0.9994	0.9917	0.9661	0.9144	0.8343	0.7297	0.6089	0.4826	0.3614	0.2539	0.1658	0.0994	0.0536	0.0253	0.0100	0.0031	0.0006	0.0001	0.0000
	4	1.0000	0.9991	0.9944	0.9804	0.9511	0.9012	0.8283	0.7334	0.6214	0.5000	0.3786	0.2666	0.1717	0.0988	0.0489	0.0196	0.0056	0.0009	0.0000
	5	1.0000	0.9999	0.9994	0.9969	0.9900	0.9747	0.9464	0.9006	0.8342	0.7461	0.6386	0.5174	0.3911	0.2703	0.1657	0.0856	0.0339	0.0083	0.0006
	6	1.0000	1.0000	1.0000	0.9997	0.9987	0.9957	0.9888	0.9750	0.9502	0.9102	0.8505	0.7682	0.6627	0.5372	0.3993	0.2618	0.1409	0.0530	0.0084
	7	1.0000	1.0000	1.0000	1.0000	0.9999	0.9996	0.9986	0.9962	0.9909	0.9805	0.9615	0.9295	0.8789	0.8040	0.6997	0.5638	0.4005	0.2252	0.0712
	8	1.0000	1.0000	1.0000	1.0000	1.0000	1.0000	0.9999	0.9997	0.9992	0.9980	0.9954	0.9899	0.9793	0.9596	0.9249	0.8658	0.7684	0.6126	0.3698
	9	1.0000	1.0000	1.0000	1.0000	1.0000	1.0000	1.0000	1.0000	1.0000	1.0000	1.0000	1.0000	1.0000	1.0000	1.0000	1.0000	1.0000	1.0000	1.0000

$$P(X \le x) = \sum_{x=0}^{x} \binom{n}{x} p^x (1-p)^{n-x}$$

Probability of ≤ x occurrences in a sample of size n

n	x	0.05	0.10	0.15	0.20	0.25	0.30	0.35	0.40	0.45	0.50	0.55	0.60	0.65	0.70	0.75	0.80	0.85	0.90	0.95
10	0	0.5987	0.3487	0.1969	0.1074	0.0563	0.0282	0.0135	0.0060	0.0025	0.0010	0.0003	0.0001	0.0000	0.0000	0.0000	0.0000	0.0000	0.0000	0.0000
	1	0.9139	0.7361	0.5443	0.3758	0.2440	0.1493	0.0860	0.0464	0.0233	0.0107	0.0045	0.0017	0.0005	0.0001	0.0000	0.0000	0.0000	0.0000	0.0000
	2	0.9885	0.9298	0.8202	0.6778	0.5256	0.3828	0.2616	0.1673	0.0996	0.0547	0.0274	0.0123	0.0048	0.0016	0.0004	0.0001	0.0000	0.0000	0.0000
	3	0.9990	0.9872	0.9500	0.8791	0.7759	0.6496	0.5138	0.3823	0.2660	0.1719	0.1020	0.0548	0.0260	0.0106	0.0035	0.0009	0.0001	0.0000	0.0000
	4	0.9999	0.9984	0.9901	0.9672	0.9219	0.8497	0.7515	0.6331	0.5044	0.3770	0.2616	0.1662	0.0949	0.0473	0.0197	0.0064	0.0014	0.0001	0.0000
	5	1.0000	0.9999	0.9986	0.9936	0.9803	0.9527	0.9051	0.8338	0.7384	0.6230	0.4956	0.3669	0.2485	0.1503	0.0781	0.0328	0.0099	0.0016	0.0001
	6	1.0000	1.0000	0.9999	0.9991	0.9965	0.9894	0.9740	0.9452	0.8980	0.8281	0.7340	0.6177	0.4862	0.3504	0.2241	0.1209	0.0500	0.0128	0.0010
	7	1.0000	1.0000	1.0000	0.9999	0.9996	0.9984	0.9952	0.9877	0.9726	0.9453	0.9004	0.8327	0.7384	0.6172	0.4744	0.3222	0.1798	0.0702	0.0115
	8	1.0000	1.0000	1.0000	1.0000	1.0000	0.9999	0.9995	0.9983	0.9955	0.9893	0.9767	0.9536	0.9140	0.8507	0.7560	0.6242	0.4557	0.2639	0.0861
	9	1.0000	1.0000	1.0000	1.0000	1.0000	1.0000	1.0000	0.9999	0.9997	0.9990	0.9975	0.9940	0.9865	0.9718	0.9437	0.8926	0.8031	0.6513	0.4013
	10	1.0000	1.0000	1.0000	1.0000	1.0000	1.0000	1.0000	1.0000	1.0000	1.0000	1.0000	1.0000	1.0000	1.0000	1.0000	1.0000	1.0000	1.0000	1.0000

Appendix D
Poisson Distribution Table

$$P(X = x) = \frac{e^{-\mu}\mu^x}{x!}$$

μ	0	1	2	3	4	5	6	7	8	9	10	11	12	13	μ
						Probability of x occurrences									
0.05	0.9512	0.0476	0.0012	0.0000	0.0000	0.0000	0.0000	0.0000	0.0000	0.0000	0.0000	0.0000	0.0000	0.0000	0.05
0.10	0.9048	0.0905	0.0045	0.0002	0.0000	0.0000	0.0000	0.0000	0.0000	0.0000	0.0000	0.0000	0.0000	0.0000	0.10
0.15	0.8607	0.1291	0.0097	0.0005	0.0000	0.0000	0.0000	0.0000	0.0000	0.0000	0.0000	0.0000	0.0000	0.0000	0.15
0.20	0.8187	0.1637	0.0164	0.0011	0.0001	0.0000	0.0000	0.0000	0.0000	0.0000	0.0000	0.0000	0.0000	0.0000	0.20
0.25	0.7788	0.1947	0.0243	0.0020	0.0001	0.0000	0.0000	0.0000	0.0000	0.0000	0.0000	0.0000	0.0000	0.0000	0.25
0.30	0.7408	0.2222	0.0333	0.0033	0.0003	0.0000	0.0000	0.0000	0.0000	0.0000	0.0000	0.0000	0.0000	0.0000	0.30
0.35	0.7047	0.2466	0.0432	0.0050	0.0004	0.0000	0.0000	0.0000	0.0000	0.0000	0.0000	0.0000	0.0000	0.0000	0.35
0.40	0.6703	0.2681	0.0536	0.0072	0.0007	0.0001	0.0000	0.0000	0.0000	0.0000	0.0000	0.0000	0.0000	0.0000	0.40
0.45	0.6376	0.2869	0.0646	0.0097	0.0011	0.0001	0.0000	0.0000	0.0000	0.0000	0.0000	0.0000	0.0000	0.0000	0.45
0.50	0.6065	0.3033	0.0758	0.0126	0.0016	0.0002	0.0000	0.0000	0.0000	0.0000	0.0000	0.0000	0.0000	0.0000	0.50
0.55	0.5769	0.3173	0.0873	0.0160	0.0022	0.0002	0.0000	0.0000	0.0000	0.0000	0.0000	0.0000	0.0000	0.0000	0.55
0.60	0.5488	0.3293	0.0988	0.0198	0.0030	0.0004	0.0000	0.0000	0.0000	0.0000	0.0000	0.0000	0.0000	0.0000	0.60
0.65	0.5220	0.3393	0.1103	0.0239	0.0039	0.0005	0.0001	0.0000	0.0000	0.0000	0.0000	0.0000	0.0000	0.0000	0.65
0.70	0.4966	0.3476	0.1217	0.0284	0.0050	0.0007	0.0001	0.0000	0.0000	0.0000	0.0000	0.0000	0.0000	0.0000	0.70
0.75	0.4724	0.3543	0.1329	0.0332	0.0062	0.0009	0.0001	0.0000	0.0000	0.0000	0.0000	0.0000	0.0000	0.0000	0.75
0.80	0.4493	0.3595	0.1438	0.0383	0.0077	0.0012	0.0002	0.0000	0.0000	0.0000	0.0000	0.0000	0.0000	0.0000	0.80
0.85	0.4274	0.3633	0.1544	0.0437	0.0093	0.0016	0.0002	0.0000	0.0000	0.0000	0.0000	0.0000	0.0000	0.0000	0.85
0.90	0.4066	0.3659	0.1647	0.0494	0.0111	0.0020	0.0003	0.0000	0.0000	0.0000	0.0000	0.0000	0.0000	0.0000	0.90
0.95	0.3867	0.3674	0.1745	0.0553	0.0131	0.0025	0.0004	0.0001	0.0000	0.0000	0.0000	0.0000	0.0000	0.0000	0.95
1.00	0.3679	0.3679	0.1839	0.0613	0.0153	0.0031	0.0005	0.0001	0.0000	0.0000	0.0000	0.0000	0.0000	0.0000	1.00
1.10	0.3329	0.3662	0.2014	0.0738	0.0203	0.0045	0.0008	0.0001	0.0000	0.0000	0.0000	0.0000	0.0000	0.0000	1.10
1.20	0.3012	0.3614	0.2169	0.0867	0.0260	0.0062	0.0012	0.0002	0.0000	0.0000	0.0000	0.0000	0.0000	0.0000	1.20
1.30	0.2725	0.3543	0.2303	0.0998	0.0324	0.0084	0.0018	0.0003	0.0001	0.0000	0.0000	0.0000	0.0000	0.0000	1.30
1.40	0.2466	0.3452	0.2417	0.1128	0.0395	0.0111	0.0026	0.0005	0.0001	0.0000	0.0000	0.0000	0.0000	0.0000	1.40
1.50	0.2231	0.3347	0.2510	0.1255	0.0471	0.0141	0.0035	0.0008	0.0001	0.0000	0.0000	0.0000	0.0000	0.0000	1.50
1.60	0.2019	0.3230	0.2584	0.1378	0.0551	0.0176	0.0047	0.0011	0.0002	0.0000	0.0000	0.0000	0.0000	0.0000	1.60
1.70	0.1827	0.3106	0.2640	0.1496	0.0636	0.0216	0.0061	0.0015	0.0003	0.0001	0.0000	0.0000	0.0000	0.0000	1.70
1.80	0.1653	0.2975	0.2678	0.1607	0.0723	0.0260	0.0078	0.0020	0.0005	0.0001	0.0000	0.0000	0.0000	0.0000	1.80
1.90	0.1496	0.2842	0.2700	0.1710	0.0812	0.0309	0.0098	0.0027	0.0006	0.0001	0.0000	0.0000	0.0000	0.0000	1.90
2.00	0.1353	0.2707	0.2707	0.1804	0.0902	0.0361	0.0120	0.0034	0.0009	0.0002	0.0000	0.0000	0.0000	0.0000	2.00
2.10	0.1225	0.2572	0.2700	0.1890	0.0992	0.0417	0.0146	0.0044	0.0011	0.0003	0.0001	0.0000	0.0000	0.0000	2.10
2.20	0.1108	0.2438	0.2681	0.1966	0.1082	0.0476	0.0174	0.0055	0.0015	0.0004	0.0001	0.0000	0.0000	0.0000	2.20
2.30	0.1003	0.2306	0.2652	0.2033	0.1169	0.0538	0.0206	0.0068	0.0019	0.0005	0.0001	0.0000	0.0000	0.0000	2.30
2.40	0.0907	0.2177	0.2613	0.2090	0.1254	0.0602	0.0241	0.0083	0.0025	0.0007	0.0002	0.0000	0.0000	0.0000	2.40
2.50	0.0821	0.2052	0.2565	0.2138	0.1336	0.0668	0.0278	0.0099	0.0031	0.0009	0.0002	0.0000	0.0000	0.0000	2.50
2.60	0.0743	0.1931	0.2510	0.2176	0.1414	0.0735	0.0319	0.0118	0.0038	0.0011	0.0003	0.0001	0.0000	0.0000	2.60
2.70	0.0672	0.1815	0.2450	0.2205	0.1488	0.0804	0.0362	0.0139	0.0047	0.0014	0.0004	0.0001	0.0000	0.0000	2.70
2.80	0.0608	0.1703	0.2384	0.2225	0.1557	0.0872	0.0407	0.0163	0.0057	0.0018	0.0005	0.0001	0.0000	0.0000	2.80
2.90	0.0550	0.1596	0.2314	0.2237	0.1622	0.0940	0.0455	0.0188	0.0068	0.0022	0.0006	0.0002	0.0000	0.0000	2.90

$$P(X = x) = \frac{e^{-\mu}\mu^x}{x!}$$

	Probability of x occurrences												
μ	14	15	16	17	18	19	20	21	22	23	24	25	μ
0.05	0.0000	0.0000	0.0000	0.0000	0.0000	0.0000	0.0000	0.0000	0.0000	0.0000	0.0000	0.0000	0.05
0.10	0.0000	0.0000	0.0000	0.0000	0.0000	0.0000	0.0000	0.0000	0.0000	0.0000	0.0000	0.0000	0.10
0.15	0.0000	0.0000	0.0000	0.0000	0.0000	0.0000	0.0000	0.0000	0.0000	0.0000	0.0000	0.0000	0.15
0.20	0.0000	0.0000	0.0000	0.0000	0.0000	0.0000	0.0000	0.0000	0.0000	0.0000	0.0000	0.0000	0.20
0.25	0.0000	0.0000	0.0000	0.0000	0.0000	0.0000	0.0000	0.0000	0.0000	0.0000	0.0000	0.0000	0.25
0.30	0.0000	0.0000	0.0000	0.0000	0.0000	0.0000	0.0000	0.0000	0.0000	0.0000	0.0000	0.0000	0.30
0.35	0.0000	0.0000	0.0000	0.0000	0.0000	0.0000	0.0000	0.0000	0.0000	0.0000	0.0000	0.0000	0.35
0.40	0.0000	0.0000	0.0000	0.0000	0.0000	0.0000	0.0000	0.0000	0.0000	0.0000	0.0000	0.0000	0.40
0.45	0.0000	0.0000	0.0000	0.0000	0.0000	0.0000	0.0000	0.0000	0.0000	0.0000	0.0000	0.0000	0.45
0.50	0.0000	0.0000	0.0000	0.0000	0.0000	0.0000	0.0000	0.0000	0.0000	0.0000	0.0000	0.0000	0.50
0.55	0.0000	0.0000	0.0000	0.0000	0.0000	0.0000	0.0000	0.0000	0.0000	0.0000	0.0000	0.0000	0.55
0.60	0.0000	0.0000	0.0000	0.0000	0.0000	0.0000	0.0000	0.0000	0.0000	0.0000	0.0000	0.0000	0.60
0.65	0.0000	0.0000	0.0000	0.0000	0.0000	0.0000	0.0000	0.0000	0.0000	0.0000	0.0000	0.0000	0.65
0.70	0.0000	0.0000	0.0000	0.0000	0.0000	0.0000	0.0000	0.0000	0.0000	0.0000	0.0000	0.0000	0.70
0.75	0.0000	0.0000	0.0000	0.0000	0.0000	0.0000	0.0000	0.0000	0.0000	0.0000	0.0000	0.0000	0.75
0.80	0.0000	0.0000	0.0000	0.0000	0.0000	0.0000	0.0000	0.0000	0.0000	0.0000	0.0000	0.0000	0.80
0.85	0.0000	0.0000	0.0000	0.0000	0.0000	0.0000	0.0000	0.0000	0.0000	0.0000	0.0000	0.0000	0.85
0.90	0.0000	0.0000	0.0000	0.0000	0.0000	0.0000	0.0000	0.0000	0.0000	0.0000	0.0000	0.0000	0.90
0.95	0.0000	0.0000	0.0000	0.0000	0.0000	0.0000	0.0000	0.0000	0.0000	0.0000	0.0000	0.0000	0.95
1.00	0.0000	0.0000	0.0000	0.0000	0.0000	0.0000	0.0000	0.0000	0.0000	0.0000	0.0000	0.0000	1.00
1.10	0.0000	0.0000	0.0000	0.0000	0.0000	0.0000	0.0000	0.0000	0.0000	0.0000	0.0000	0.0000	1.10
1.20	0.0000	0.0000	0.0000	0.0000	0.0000	0.0000	0.0000	0.0000	0.0000	0.0000	0.0000	0.0000	1.20
1.30	0.0000	0.0000	0.0000	0.0000	0.0000	0.0000	0.0000	0.0000	0.0000	0.0000	0.0000	0.0000	1.30
1.40	0.0000	0.0000	0.0000	0.0000	0.0000	0.0000	0.0000	0.0000	0.0000	0.0000	0.0000	0.0000	1.40
1.50	0.0000	0.0000	0.0000	0.0000	0.0000	0.0000	0.0000	0.0000	0.0000	0.0000	0.0000	0.0000	1.50
1.60	0.0000	0.0000	0.0000	0.0000	0.0000	0.0000	0.0000	0.0000	0.0000	0.0000	0.0000	0.0000	1.60
1.70	0.0000	0.0000	0.0000	0.0000	0.0000	0.0000	0.0000	0.0000	0.0000	0.0000	0.0000	0.0000	1.70
1.80	0.0000	0.0000	0.0000	0.0000	0.0000	0.0000	0.0000	0.0000	0.0000	0.0000	0.0000	0.0000	1.80
1.90	0.0000	0.0000	0.0000	0.0000	0.0000	0.0000	0.0000	0.0000	0.0000	0.0000	0.0000	0.0000	1.90
2.00	0.0000	0.0000	0.0000	0.0000	0.0000	0.0000	0.0000	0.0000	0.0000	0.0000	0.0000	0.0000	2.00
2.10	0.0000	0.0000	0.0000	0.0000	0.0000	0.0000	0.0000	0.0000	0.0000	0.0000	0.0000	0.0000	2.10
2.20	0.0000	0.0000	0.0000	0.0000	0.0000	0.0000	0.0000	0.0000	0.0000	0.0000	0.0000	0.0000	2.20
2.30	0.0000	0.0000	0.0000	0.0000	0.0000	0.0000	0.0000	0.0000	0.0000	0.0000	0.0000	0.0000	2.30
2.40	0.0000	0.0000	0.0000	0.0000	0.0000	0.0000	0.0000	0.0000	0.0000	0.0000	0.0000	0.0000	2.40
2.50	0.0000	0.0000	0.0000	0.0000	0.0000	0.0000	0.0000	0.0000	0.0000	0.0000	0.0000	0.0000	2.50
2.60	0.0000	0.0000	0.0000	0.0000	0.0000	0.0000	0.0000	0.0000	0.0000	0.0000	0.0000	0.0000	2.60
2.70	0.0000	0.0000	0.0000	0.0000	0.0000	0.0000	0.0000	0.0000	0.0000	0.0000	0.0000	0.0000	2.70
2.80	0.0000	0.0000	0.0000	0.0000	0.0000	0.0000	0.0000	0.0000	0.0000	0.0000	0.0000	0.0000	2.80
2.90	0.0000	0.0000	0.0000	0.0000	0.0000	0.0000	0.0000	0.0000	0.0000	0.0000	0.0000	0.0000	2.90

$$P(X = x) = \frac{e^{-\mu}\mu^x}{x!}$$

	Probability of x occurrences														
μ	0	1	2	3	4	5	6	7	8	9	10	11	12	13	μ
3.00	0.0498	0.1494	0.2240	0.2240	0.1680	0.1008	0.0504	0.0216	0.0081	0.0027	0.0008	0.0002	0.0001	0.0000	3.00
3.10	0.0450	0.1397	0.2165	0.2237	0.1733	0.1075	0.0555	0.0246	0.0095	0.0033	0.0010	0.0003	0.0001	0.0000	3.10
3.20	0.0408	0.1304	0.2087	0.2226	0.1781	0.1140	0.0608	0.0278	0.0111	0.0040	0.0013	0.0004	0.0001	0.0000	3.20
3.30	0.0369	0.1217	0.2008	0.2209	0.1823	0.1203	0.0662	0.0312	0.0129	0.0047	0.0016	0.0005	0.0001	0.0000	3.30
3.40	0.0334	0.1135	0.1929	0.2186	0.1858	0.1264	0.0716	0.0348	0.0148	0.0056	0.0019	0.0006	0.0002	0.0000	3.40
3.50	0.0302	0.1057	0.1850	0.2158	0.1888	0.1322	0.0771	0.0385	0.0169	0.0066	0.0023	0.0007	0.0002	0.0001	3.50
3.60	0.0273	0.0984	0.1771	0.2125	0.1912	0.1377	0.0826	0.0425	0.0191	0.0076	0.0028	0.0009	0.0003	0.0001	3.60
3.70	0.0247	0.0915	0.1692	0.2087	0.1931	0.1429	0.0881	0.0466	0.0215	0.0089	0.0033	0.0011	0.0003	0.0001	3.70
3.80	0.0224	0.0850	0.1615	0.2046	0.1944	0.1477	0.0936	0.0508	0.0241	0.0102	0.0039	0.0013	0.0004	0.0001	3.80
3.90	0.0202	0.0789	0.1539	0.2001	0.1951	0.1522	0.0989	0.0551	0.0269	0.0116	0.0045	0.0016	0.0005	0.0002	3.90
4.00	0.0183	0.0733	0.1465	0.1954	0.1954	0.1563	0.1042	0.0595	0.0298	0.0132	0.0053	0.0019	0.0006	0.0002	4.00
4.10	0.0166	0.0679	0.1393	0.1904	0.1951	0.1600	0.1093	0.0640	0.0328	0.0150	0.0061	0.0023	0.0008	0.0002	4.10
4.20	0.0150	0.0630	0.1323	0.1852	0.1944	0.1633	0.1143	0.0686	0.0360	0.0168	0.0071	0.0027	0.0009	0.0003	4.20
4.30	0.0136	0.0583	0.1254	0.1798	0.1933	0.1662	0.1191	0.0732	0.0393	0.0188	0.0081	0.0032	0.0011	0.0004	4.30
4.40	0.0123	0.0540	0.1188	0.1743	0.1917	0.1687	0.1237	0.0778	0.0428	0.0209	0.0092	0.0037	0.0013	0.0005	4.40
4.50	0.0111	0.0500	0.1125	0.1687	0.1898	0.1708	0.1281	0.0824	0.0463	0.0232	0.0104	0.0043	0.0016	0.0006	4.50
4.60	0.0101	0.0462	0.1063	0.1631	0.1875	0.1725	0.1323	0.0869	0.0500	0.0255	0.0118	0.0049	0.0019	0.0007	4.60
4.70	0.0091	0.0427	0.1005	0.1574	0.1849	0.1738	0.1362	0.0914	0.0537	0.0281	0.0132	0.0056	0.0022	0.0008	4.70
4.80	0.0082	0.0395	0.0948	0.1517	0.1820	0.1747	0.1398	0.0959	0.0575	0.0307	0.0147	0.0064	0.0026	0.0009	4.80
4.90	0.0074	0.0365	0.0894	0.1460	0.1789	0.1753	0.1432	0.1002	0.0614	0.0334	0.0164	0.0073	0.0030	0.0011	4.90
5.00	0.0067	0.0337	0.0842	0.1404	0.1755	0.1755	0.1462	0.1044	0.0653	0.0363	0.0181	0.0082	0.0034	0.0013	5.00
5.10	0.0061	0.0311	0.0793	0.1348	0.1719	0.1753	0.1490	0.1086	0.0692	0.0392	0.0200	0.0093	0.0039	0.0015	5.10
5.20	0.0055	0.0287	0.0746	0.1293	0.1681	0.1748	0.1515	0.1125	0.0731	0.0423	0.0220	0.0104	0.0045	0.0018	5.20
5.30	0.0050	0.0265	0.0701	0.1239	0.1641	0.1740	0.1537	0.1163	0.0771	0.0454	0.0241	0.0116	0.0051	0.0021	5.30
5.40	0.0045	0.0244	0.0659	0.1185	0.1600	0.1728	0.1555	0.1200	0.0810	0.0486	0.0262	0.0129	0.0058	0.0024	5.40
5.50	0.0041	0.0225	0.0618	0.1133	0.1558	0.1714	0.1571	0.1234	0.0849	0.0519	0.0285	0.0143	0.0065	0.0028	5.50
5.60	0.0037	0.0207	0.0580	0.1082	0.1515	0.1697	0.1584	0.1267	0.0887	0.0552	0.0309	0.0157	0.0073	0.0032	5.60
5.70	0.0033	0.0191	0.0544	0.1033	0.1472	0.1678	0.1594	0.1298	0.0925	0.0586	0.0334	0.0173	0.0082	0.0036	5.70
5.80	0.0030	0.0176	0.0509	0.0985	0.1428	0.1656	0.1601	0.1326	0.0962	0.0620	0.0359	0.0190	0.0092	0.0041	5.80
5.90	0.0027	0.0162	0.0477	0.0938	0.1383	0.1632	0.1605	0.1353	0.0998	0.0654	0.0386	0.0207	0.0102	0.0046	5.90
6.00	0.0025	0.0149	0.0446	0.0892	0.1339	0.1606	0.1606	0.1377	0.1033	0.0688	0.0413	0.0225	0.0113	0.0052	6.00
6.10	0.0022	0.0137	0.0417	0.0848	0.1294	0.1579	0.1605	0.1399	0.1066	0.0723	0.0441	0.0244	0.0124	0.0058	6.10
6.20	0.0020	0.0126	0.0390	0.0806	0.1249	0.1549	0.1601	0.1418	0.1099	0.0757	0.0469	0.0265	0.0137	0.0065	6.20
6.30	0.0018	0.0116	0.0364	0.0765	0.1205	0.1519	0.1595	0.1435	0.1130	0.0791	0.0498	0.0285	0.0150	0.0073	6.30
6.40	0.0017	0.0106	0.0340	0.0726	0.1162	0.1487	0.1586	0.1450	0.1160	0.0825	0.0528	0.0307	0.0164	0.0081	6.40
6.50	0.0015	0.0098	0.0318	0.0688	0.1118	0.1454	0.1575	0.1462	0.1188	0.0858	0.0558	0.0330	0.0179	0.0089	6.50
6.60	0.0014	0.0090	0.0296	0.0652	0.1076	0.1420	0.1562	0.1472	0.1215	0.0891	0.0588	0.0353	0.0194	0.0099	6.60
6.70	0.0012	0.0082	0.0276	0.0617	0.1034	0.1385	0.1546	0.1480	0.1240	0.0923	0.0618	0.0377	0.0210	0.0108	6.70
6.80	0.0011	0.0076	0.0258	0.0584	0.0992	0.1349	0.1529	0.1486	0.1263	0.0954	0.0649	0.0401	0.0227	0.0119	6.80

$$P(X = x) = \frac{e^{-\mu}\mu^x}{x!}$$

					Probability of x occurrences								
μ	14	15	16	17	18	19	20	21	22	23	24	25	μ
3.00	0.0000	0.0000	0.0000	0.0000	0.0000	0.0000	0.0000	0.0000	0.0000	0.0000	0.0000	0.0000	3.00
3.10	0.0000	0.0000	0.0000	0.0000	0.0000	0.0000	0.0000	0.0000	0.0000	0.0000	0.0000	0.0000	3.10
3.20	0.0000	0.0000	0.0000	0.0000	0.0000	0.0000	0.0000	0.0000	0.0000	0.0000	0.0000	0.0000	3.20
3.30	0.0000	0.0000	0.0000	0.0000	0.0000	0.0000	0.0000	0.0000	0.0000	0.0000	0.0000	0.0000	3.30
3.40	0.0000	0.0000	0.0000	0.0000	0.0000	0.0000	0.0000	0.0000	0.0000	0.0000	0.0000	0.0000	3.40
3.50	0.0000	0.0000	0.0000	0.0000	0.0000	0.0000	0.0000	0.0000	0.0000	0.0000	0.0000	0.0000	3.50
3.60	0.0000	0.0000	0.0000	0.0000	0.0000	0.0000	0.0000	0.0000	0.0000	0.0000	0.0000	0.0000	3.60
3.70	0.0000	0.0000	0.0000	0.0000	0.0000	0.0000	0.0000	0.0000	0.0000	0.0000	0.0000	0.0000	3.70
3.80	0.0000	0.0000	0.0000	0.0000	0.0000	0.0000	0.0000	0.0000	0.0000	0.0000	0.0000	0.0000	3.80
3.90	0.0000	0.0000	0.0000	0.0000	0.0000	0.0000	0.0000	0.0000	0.0000	0.0000	0.0000	0.0000	3.90
4.00	0.0001	0.0000	0.0000	0.0000	0.0000	0.0000	0.0000	0.0000	0.0000	0.0000	0.0000	0.0000	4.00
4.10	0.0001	0.0000	0.0000	0.0000	0.0000	0.0000	0.0000	0.0000	0.0000	0.0000	0.0000	0.0000	4.10
4.20	0.0001	0.0000	0.0000	0.0000	0.0000	0.0000	0.0000	0.0000	0.0000	0.0000	0.0000	0.0000	4.20
4.30	0.0001	0.0000	0.0000	0.0000	0.0000	0.0000	0.0000	0.0000	0.0000	0.0000	0.0000	0.0000	4.30
4.40	0.0001	0.0000	0.0000	0.0000	0.0000	0.0000	0.0000	0.0000	0.0000	0.0000	0.0000	0.0000	4.40
4.50	0.0002	0.0001	0.0000	0.0000	0.0000	0.0000	0.0000	0.0000	0.0000	0.0000	0.0000	0.0000	4.50
4.60	0.0002	0.0001	0.0000	0.0000	0.0000	0.0000	0.0000	0.0000	0.0000	0.0000	0.0000	0.0000	4.60
4.70	0.0003	0.0001	0.0000	0.0000	0.0000	0.0000	0.0000	0.0000	0.0000	0.0000	0.0000	0.0000	4.70
4.80	0.0003	0.0001	0.0000	0.0000	0.0000	0.0000	0.0000	0.0000	0.0000	0.0000	0.0000	0.0000	4.80
4.90	0.0004	0.0001	0.0000	0.0000	0.0000	0.0000	0.0000	0.0000	0.0000	0.0000	0.0000	0.0000	4.90
5.00	0.0005	0.0002	0.0000	0.0000	0.0000	0.0000	0.0000	0.0000	0.0000	0.0000	0.0000	0.0000	5.00
5.10	0.0006	0.0002	0.0001	0.0000	0.0000	0.0000	0.0000	0.0000	0.0000	0.0000	0.0000	0.0000	5.10
5.20	0.0007	0.0002	0.0001	0.0000	0.0000	0.0000	0.0000	0.0000	0.0000	0.0000	0.0000	0.0000	5.20
5.30	0.0008	0.0003	0.0001	0.0000	0.0000	0.0000	0.0000	0.0000	0.0000	0.0000	0.0000	0.0000	5.30
5.40	0.0009	0.0003	0.0001	0.0000	0.0000	0.0000	0.0000	0.0000	0.0000	0.0000	0.0000	0.0000	5.40
5.50	0.0011	0.0004	0.0001	0.0000	0.0000	0.0000	0.0000	0.0000	0.0000	0.0000	0.0000	0.0000	5.50
5.60	0.0013	0.0005	0.0002	0.0001	0.0000	0.0000	0.0000	0.0000	0.0000	0.0000	0.0000	0.0000	5.60
5.70	0.0015	0.0006	0.0002	0.0001	0.0000	0.0000	0.0000	0.0000	0.0000	0.0000	0.0000	0.0000	5.70
5.80	0.0017	0.0007	0.0002	0.0001	0.0000	0.0000	0.0000	0.0000	0.0000	0.0000	0.0000	0.0000	5.80
5.90	0.0019	0.0008	0.0003	0.0001	0.0000	0.0000	0.0000	0.0000	0.0000	0.0000	0.0000	0.0000	5.90
6.00	0.0022	0.0009	0.0003	0.0001	0.0000	0.0000	0.0000	0.0000	0.0000	0.0000	0.0000	0.0000	6.00
6.10	0.0025	0.0010	0.0004	0.0001	0.0000	0.0000	0.0000	0.0000	0.0000	0.0000	0.0000	0.0000	6.10
6.20	0.0029	0.0012	0.0005	0.0002	0.0001	0.0000	0.0000	0.0000	0.0000	0.0000	0.0000	0.0000	6.20
6.30	0.0033	0.0014	0.0005	0.0002	0.0001	0.0000	0.0000	0.0000	0.0000	0.0000	0.0000	0.0000	6.30
6.40	0.0037	0.0016	0.0006	0.0002	0.0001	0.0000	0.0000	0.0000	0.0000	0.0000	0.0000	0.0000	6.40
6.50	0.0041	0.0018	0.0007	0.0003	0.0001	0.0000	0.0000	0.0000	0.0000	0.0000	0.0000	0.0000	6.50
6.60	0.0046	0.0020	0.0008	0.0003	0.0001	0.0000	0.0000	0.0000	0.0000	0.0000	0.0000	0.0000	6.60
6.70	0.0052	0.0023	0.0010	0.0004	0.0001	0.0001	0.0000	0.0000	0.0000	0.0000	0.0000	0.0000	6.70
6.80	0.0058	0.0026	0.0011	0.0004	0.0002	0.0001	0.0000	0.0000	0.0000	0.0000	0.0000	0.0000	6.80

$$P(X = x) = \frac{e^{-\mu}\mu^x}{x!}$$

μ	0	1	2	3	4	5	6	7	8	9	10	11	12	13	μ
						Probability of x occurrences									
6.90	0.0010	0.0070	0.0240	0.0552	0.0952	0.1314	0.1511	0.1489	0.1284	0.0985	0.0679	0.0426	0.0245	0.0130	6.90
7.00	0.0009	0.0064	0.0223	0.0521	0.0912	0.1277	0.1490	0.1490	0.1304	0.1014	0.0710	0.0452	0.0263	0.0142	7.00
7.10	0.0008	0.0059	0.0208	0.0492	0.0874	0.1241	0.1468	0.1489	0.1321	0.1042	0.0740	0.0478	0.0283	0.0154	7.10
7.20	0.0007	0.0054	0.0194	0.0464	0.0836	0.1204	0.1445	0.1486	0.1337	0.1070	0.0770	0.0504	0.0303	0.0168	7.20
7.30	0.0007	0.0049	0.0180	0.0438	0.0799	0.1167	0.1420	0.1481	0.1351	0.1096	0.0800	0.0531	0.0323	0.0181	7.30
7.40	0.0006	0.0045	0.0167	0.0413	0.0764	0.1130	0.1394	0.1474	0.1363	0.1121	0.0829	0.0558	0.0344	0.0196	7.40
7.50	0.0006	0.0041	0.0156	0.0389	0.0729	0.1094	0.1367	0.1465	0.1373	0.1144	0.0858	0.0585	0.0366	0.0211	7.50
7.60	0.0005	0.0038	0.0145	0.0366	0.0696	0.1057	0.1339	0.1454	0.1381	0.1167	0.0887	0.0613	0.0388	0.0227	7.60
7.70	0.0005	0.0035	0.0134	0.0345	0.0663	0.1021	0.1311	0.1442	0.1388	0.1187	0.0914	0.0640	0.0411	0.0243	7.70
7.80	0.0004	0.0032	0.0125	0.0324	0.0632	0.0986	0.1282	0.1428	0.1392	0.1207	0.0941	0.0667	0.0434	0.0260	7.80
7.90	0.0004	0.0029	0.0116	0.0305	0.0602	0.0951	0.1252	0.1413	0.1395	0.1224	0.0967	0.0695	0.0457	0.0278	7.90
8.00	0.0003	0.0027	0.0107	0.0286	0.0573	0.0916	0.1221	0.1396	0.1396	0.1241	0.0993	0.0722	0.0481	0.0296	8.00
8.10	0.0003	0.0025	0.0100	0.0269	0.0544	0.0882	0.1191	0.1378	0.1395	0.1256	0.1017	0.0749	0.0505	0.0315	8.10
8.20	0.0003	0.0023	0.0092	0.0252	0.0517	0.0849	0.1160	0.1358	0.1392	0.1269	0.1040	0.0776	0.0530	0.0334	8.20
8.30	0.0002	0.0021	0.0086	0.0237	0.0491	0.0816	0.1128	0.1338	0.1388	0.1280	0.1063	0.0802	0.0555	0.0354	8.30
8.40	0.0002	0.0019	0.0079	0.0222	0.0466	0.0784	0.1097	0.1317	0.1382	0.1290	0.1084	0.0828	0.0579	0.0374	8.40
8.50	0.0002	0.0017	0.0074	0.0208	0.0443	0.0752	0.1066	0.1294	0.1375	0.1299	0.1104	0.0853	0.0604	0.0395	8.50
8.60	0.0002	0.0016	0.0068	0.0195	0.0420	0.0722	0.1034	0.1271	0.1366	0.1306	0.1123	0.0878	0.0629	0.0416	8.60
8.70	0.0002	0.0014	0.0063	0.0183	0.0398	0.0692	0.1003	0.1247	0.1356	0.1311	0.1140	0.0902	0.0654	0.0438	8.70
8.80	0.0002	0.0013	0.0058	0.0171	0.0377	0.0663	0.0972	0.1222	0.1344	0.1315	0.1157	0.0925	0.0679	0.0459	8.80
8.90	0.0001	0.0012	0.0054	0.0160	0.0357	0.0635	0.0941	0.1197	0.1332	0.1317	0.1172	0.0948	0.0703	0.0481	8.90
9.00	0.0001	0.0011	0.0050	0.0150	0.0337	0.0607	0.0911	0.1171	0.1318	0.1318	0.1186	0.0970	0.0728	0.0504	9.00
9.10	0.0001	0.0010	0.0046	0.0140	0.0319	0.0581	0.0881	0.1145	0.1302	0.1317	0.1198	0.0991	0.0752	0.0526	9.10
9.20	0.0001	0.0009	0.0043	0.0131	0.0302	0.0555	0.0851	0.1118	0.1286	0.1315	0.1210	0.1012	0.0776	0.0549	9.20
9.30	0.0001	0.0009	0.0040	0.0123	0.0285	0.0530	0.0822	0.1091	0.1269	0.1311	0.1219	0.1031	0.0799	0.0572	9.30
9.40	0.0001	0.0008	0.0037	0.0115	0.0269	0.0506	0.0793	0.1064	0.1251	0.1306	0.1228	0.1049	0.0822	0.0594	9.40
9.50	0.0001	0.0007	0.0034	0.0107	0.0254	0.0483	0.0764	0.1037	0.1232	0.1300	0.1235	0.1067	0.0844	0.0617	9.50
9.60	0.0001	0.0007	0.0031	0.0100	0.0240	0.0460	0.0736	0.1010	0.1212	0.1293	0.1241	0.1083	0.0866	0.0640	9.60
9.70	0.0001	0.0006	0.0029	0.0093	0.0226	0.0439	0.0709	0.0982	0.1191	0.1284	0.1245	0.1098	0.0888	0.0662	9.70
9.80	0.0001	0.0005	0.0027	0.0087	0.0213	0.0418	0.0682	0.0955	0.1170	0.1274	0.1249	0.1112	0.0908	0.0685	9.80
9.90	0.0001	0.0005	0.0025	0.0081	0.0201	0.0398	0.0656	0.0928	0.1148	0.1263	0.1250	0.1125	0.0928	0.0707	9.90
10.00	0.0000	0.0005	0.0023	0.0076	0.0189	0.0378	0.0631	0.0901	0.1126	0.1251	0.1251	0.1137	0.0948	0.0729	10.00

$$P(X = x) = \frac{e^{-\mu}\mu^x}{x!}$$

	Probability of x occurrences											
μ	14	15	16	17	18	19	20	21	22	23	24	25	μ
6.90	0.0064	0.0029	0.0013	0.0005	0.0002	0.0001	0.0000	0.0000	0.0000	0.0000	0.0000	0.0000	6.90
7.00	0.0071	0.0033	0.0014	0.0006	0.0002	0.0001	0.0000	0.0000	0.0000	0.0000	0.0000	0.0000	7.00
7.10	0.0078	0.0037	0.0016	0.0007	0.0003	0.0001	0.0000	0.0000	0.0000	0.0000	0.0000	0.0000	7.10
7.20	0.0086	0.0041	0.0019	0.0008	0.0003	0.0001	0.0000	0.0000	0.0000	0.0000	0.0000	0.0000	7.20
7.30	0.0095	0.0046	0.0021	0.0009	0.0004	0.0001	0.0001	0.0000	0.0000	0.0000	0.0000	0.0000	7.30
7.40	0.0104	0.0051	0.0024	0.0010	0.0004	0.0002	0.0001	0.0000	0.0000	0.0000	0.0000	0.0000	7.40
7.50	0.0113	0.0057	0.0026	0.0012	0.0005	0.0002	0.0001	0.0000	0.0000	0.0000	0.0000	0.0000	7.50
7.60	0.0123	0.0062	0.0030	0.0013	0.0006	0.0002	0.0001	0.0000	0.0000	0.0000	0.0000	0.0000	7.60
7.70	0.0134	0.0069	0.0033	0.0015	0.0006	0.0003	0.0001	0.0000	0.0000	0.0000	0.0000	0.0000	7.70
7.80	0.0145	0.0075	0.0037	0.0017	0.0007	0.0003	0.0001	0.0000	0.0000	0.0000	0.0000	0.0000	7.80
7.90	0.0157	0.0083	0.0041	0.0019	0.0008	0.0003	0.0001	0.0001	0.0000	0.0000	0.0000	0.0000	7.90
8.00	0.0169	0.0090	0.0045	0.0021	0.0009	0.0004	0.0002	0.0001	0.0000	0.0000	0.0000	0.0000	8.00
8.10	0.0182	0.0098	0.0050	0.0024	0.0011	0.0005	0.0002	0.0001	0.0000	0.0000	0.0000	0.0000	8.10
8.20	0.0196	0.0107	0.0055	0.0026	0.0012	0.0005	0.0002	0.0001	0.0000	0.0000	0.0000	0.0000	8.20
8.30	0.0210	0.0116	0.0060	0.0029	0.0014	0.0006	0.0002	0.0001	0.0000	0.0000	0.0000	0.0000	8.30
8.40	0.0225	0.0126	0.0066	0.0033	0.0015	0.0007	0.0003	0.0001	0.0000	0.0000	0.0000	0.0000	8.40
8.50	0.0240	0.0136	0.0072	0.0036	0.0017	0.0008	0.0003	0.0001	0.0001	0.0000	0.0000	0.0000	8.50
8.60	0.0256	0.0147	0.0079	0.0040	0.0019	0.0009	0.0004	0.0002	0.0001	0.0000	0.0000	0.0000	8.60
8.70	0.0272	0.0158	0.0086	0.0044	0.0021	0.0010	0.0004	0.0002	0.0001	0.0000	0.0000	0.0000	8.70
8.80	0.0289	0.0169	0.0093	0.0048	0.0024	0.0011	0.0005	0.0002	0.0001	0.0000	0.0000	0.0000	8.80
8.90	0.0306	0.0182	0.0101	0.0053	0.0026	0.0012	0.0005	0.0002	0.0001	0.0000	0.0000	0.0000	8.90
9.00	0.0324	0.0194	0.0109	0.0058	0.0029	0.0014	0.0006	0.0003	0.0001	0.0000	0.0000	0.0000	9.00
9.10	0.0342	0.0208	0.0118	0.0063	0.0032	0.0015	0.0007	0.0003	0.0001	0.0000	0.0000	0.0000	9.10
9.20	0.0361	0.0221	0.0127	0.0069	0.0035	0.0017	0.0008	0.0003	0.0001	0.0001	0.0000	0.0000	9.20
9.30	0.0380	0.0235	0.0137	0.0075	0.0039	0.0019	0.0009	0.0004	0.0002	0.0001	0.0000	0.0000	9.30
9.40	0.0399	0.0250	0.0147	0.0081	0.0042	0.0021	0.0010	0.0004	0.0002	0.0001	0.0000	0.0000	9.40
9.50	0.0419	0.0265	0.0157	0.0088	0.0046	0.0023	0.0011	0.0005	0.0002	0.0001	0.0000	0.0000	9.50
9.60	0.0439	0.0281	0.0168	0.0095	0.0051	0.0026	0.0012	0.0006	0.0002	0.0001	0.0000	0.0000	9.60
9.70	0.0459	0.0297	0.0180	0.0103	0.0055	0.0028	0.0014	0.0006	0.0003	0.0001	0.0000	0.0000	9.70
9.80	0.0479	0.0313	0.0192	0.0111	0.0060	0.0031	0.0015	0.0007	0.0003	0.0001	0.0001	0.0000	9.80
9.90	0.0500	0.0330	0.0204	0.0119	0.0065	0.0034	0.0017	0.0008	0.0004	0.0002	0.0001	0.0000	9.90
10.00	0.0521	0.0347	0.0217	0.0128	0.0071	0.0037	0.0019	0.0009	0.0004	0.0002	0.0001	0.0000	10.00

Appendix E
Cumulative Poisson Table

$$P(X \le x) = \sum_{x=0}^{x} \frac{e^{-\mu}\mu^x}{x!}$$

μ	0	1	2	3	4	5	6	7	8	9	10	11	12	13	μ
					Probability of less than or equal to x occurrences										
0.05	0.9512	0.9988	1.0000	1.0000	1.0000	1.0000	1.0000	1.0000	1.0000	1.0000	1.0000	1.0000	1.0000	1.0000	0.05
0.10	0.9048	0.9953	0.9998	1.0000	1.0000	1.0000	1.0000	1.0000	1.0000	1.0000	1.0000	1.0000	1.0000	1.0000	0.10
0.15	0.8607	0.9898	0.9995	1.0000	1.0000	1.0000	1.0000	1.0000	1.0000	1.0000	1.0000	1.0000	1.0000	1.0000	0.15
0.20	0.8187	0.9825	0.9989	0.9999	1.0000	1.0000	1.0000	1.0000	1.0000	1.0000	1.0000	1.0000	1.0000	1.0000	0.20
0.25	0.7788	0.9735	0.9978	0.9999	1.0000	1.0000	1.0000	1.0000	1.0000	1.0000	1.0000	1.0000	1.0000	1.0000	0.25
0.30	0.7408	0.9631	0.9964	0.9997	1.0000	1.0000	1.0000	1.0000	1.0000	1.0000	1.0000	1.0000	1.0000	1.0000	0.30
0.35	0.7047	0.9513	0.9945	0.9995	1.0000	1.0000	1.0000	1.0000	1.0000	1.0000	1.0000	1.0000	1.0000	1.0000	0.35
0.40	0.6703	0.9384	0.9921	0.9992	0.9999	1.0000	1.0000	1.0000	1.0000	1.0000	1.0000	1.0000	1.0000	1.0000	0.40
0.45	0.6376	0.9246	0.9891	0.9988	0.9999	1.0000	1.0000	1.0000	1.0000	1.0000	1.0000	1.0000	1.0000	1.0000	0.45
0.50	0.6065	0.9098	0.9856	0.9982	0.9998	1.0000	1.0000	1.0000	1.0000	1.0000	1.0000	1.0000	1.0000	1.0000	0.50
0.55	0.5769	0.8943	0.9815	0.9975	0.9997	1.0000	1.0000	1.0000	1.0000	1.0000	1.0000	1.0000	1.0000	1.0000	0.55
0.60	0.5488	0.8781	0.9769	0.9966	0.9996	1.0000	1.0000	1.0000	1.0000	1.0000	1.0000	1.0000	1.0000	1.0000	0.60
0.65	0.5220	0.8614	0.9717	0.9956	0.9994	0.9999	1.0000	1.0000	1.0000	1.0000	1.0000	1.0000	1.0000	1.0000	0.65
0.70	0.4966	0.8442	0.9659	0.9942	0.9992	0.9999	1.0000	1.0000	1.0000	1.0000	1.0000	1.0000	1.0000	1.0000	0.70
0.75	0.4724	0.8266	0.9595	0.9927	0.9989	0.9999	1.0000	1.0000	1.0000	1.0000	1.0000	1.0000	1.0000	1.0000	0.75
0.80	0.4493	0.8088	0.9526	0.9909	0.9986	0.9998	1.0000	1.0000	1.0000	1.0000	1.0000	1.0000	1.0000	1.0000	0.80
0.85	0.4274	0.7907	0.9451	0.9889	0.9982	0.9997	1.0000	1.0000	1.0000	1.0000	1.0000	1.0000	1.0000	1.0000	0.85
0.90	0.4066	0.7725	0.9371	0.9865	0.9977	0.9997	1.0000	1.0000	1.0000	1.0000	1.0000	1.0000	1.0000	1.0000	0.90
0.95	0.3867	0.7541	0.9287	0.9839	0.9971	0.9995	0.9999	1.0000	1.0000	1.0000	1.0000	1.0000	1.0000	1.0000	0.95
1.00	0.3679	0.7358	0.9197	0.9810	0.9963	0.9994	0.9999	1.0000	1.0000	1.0000	1.0000	1.0000	1.0000	1.0000	1.00
1.10	0.3329	0.6990	0.9004	0.9743	0.9946	0.9990	0.9999	1.0000	1.0000	1.0000	1.0000	1.0000	1.0000	1.0000	1.10
1.20	0.3012	0.6626	0.8795	0.9662	0.9923	0.9985	0.9997	1.0000	1.0000	1.0000	1.0000	1.0000	1.0000	1.0000	1.20
1.30	0.2725	0.6268	0.8571	0.9569	0.9893	0.9978	0.9996	0.9999	1.0000	1.0000	1.0000	1.0000	1.0000	1.0000	1.30
1.40	0.2466	0.5918	0.8335	0.9463	0.9857	0.9968	0.9994	0.9999	1.0000	1.0000	1.0000	1.0000	1.0000	1.0000	1.40
1.50	0.2231	0.5578	0.8088	0.9344	0.9814	0.9955	0.9991	0.9998	1.0000	1.0000	1.0000	1.0000	1.0000	1.0000	1.50
1.60	0.2019	0.5249	0.7834	0.9212	0.9763	0.9940	0.9987	0.9997	1.0000	1.0000	1.0000	1.0000	1.0000	1.0000	1.60
1.70	0.1827	0.4932	0.7572	0.9068	0.9704	0.9920	0.9981	0.9996	0.9999	1.0000	1.0000	1.0000	1.0000	1.0000	1.70
1.80	0.1653	0.4628	0.7306	0.8913	0.9636	0.9896	0.9974	0.9994	0.9999	1.0000	1.0000	1.0000	1.0000	1.0000	1.80
1.90	0.1496	0.4337	0.7037	0.8747	0.9559	0.9868	0.9966	0.9992	0.9998	1.0000	1.0000	1.0000	1.0000	1.0000	1.90
2.00	0.1353	0.4060	0.6767	0.8571	0.9473	0.9834	0.9955	0.9989	0.9998	1.0000	1.0000	1.0000	1.0000	1.0000	2.00
2.10	0.1225	0.3796	0.6496	0.8386	0.9379	0.9796	0.9941	0.9985	0.9997	0.9999	1.0000	1.0000	1.0000	1.0000	2.10
2.20	0.1108	0.3546	0.6227	0.8194	0.9275	0.9751	0.9925	0.9980	0.9995	0.9999	1.0000	1.0000	1.0000	1.0000	2.20
2.30	0.1003	0.3309	0.5960	0.7993	0.9162	0.9700	0.9906	0.9974	0.9994	0.9999	1.0000	1.0000	1.0000	1.0000	2.30
2.40	0.0907	0.3084	0.5697	0.7787	0.9041	0.9643	0.9884	0.9967	0.9991	0.9998	1.0000	1.0000	1.0000	1.0000	2.40
2.50	0.0821	0.2873	0.5438	0.7576	0.8912	0.9580	0.9858	0.9958	0.9989	0.9997	0.9999	1.0000	1.0000	1.0000	2.50
2.60	0.0743	0.2674	0.5184	0.7360	0.8774	0.9510	0.9828	0.9947	0.9985	0.9996	0.9999	1.0000	1.0000	1.0000	2.60
2.70	0.0672	0.2487	0.4936	0.7141	0.8629	0.9433	0.9794	0.9934	0.9981	0.9995	0.9999	1.0000	1.0000	1.0000	2.70
2.80	0.0608	0.2311	0.4695	0.6919	0.8477	0.9349	0.9756	0.9919	0.9976	0.9993	0.9998	1.0000	1.0000	1.0000	2.80
2.90	0.0550	0.2146	0.4460	0.6696	0.8318	0.9258	0.9713	0.9901	0.9969	0.9991	0.9998	0.9999	1.0000	1.0000	2.90

$$P(X \le x) = \sum_{x=0}^{x} \frac{e^{-\mu}\mu^x}{x!}$$

	Probability of less than or equal to x occurrences											
μ	14	15	16	17	18	19	20	21	22	23	24	25	μ
0.05	1.0000	1.0000	1.0000	1.0000	1.0000	1.0000	1.0000	1.0000	1.0000	1.0000	1.0000	1.0000	0.05
0.10	1.0000	1.0000	1.0000	1.0000	1.0000	1.0000	1.0000	1.0000	1.0000	1.0000	1.0000	1.0000	0.10
0.15	1.0000	1.0000	1.0000	1.0000	1.0000	1.0000	1.0000	1.0000	1.0000	1.0000	1.0000	1.0000	0.15
0.20	1.0000	1.0000	1.0000	1.0000	1.0000	1.0000	1.0000	1.0000	1.0000	1.0000	1.0000	1.0000	0.20
0.25	1.0000	1.0000	1.0000	1.0000	1.0000	1.0000	1.0000	1.0000	1.0000	1.0000	1.0000	1.0000	0.25
0.30	1.0000	1.0000	1.0000	1.0000	1.0000	1.0000	1.0000	1.0000	1.0000	1.0000	1.0000	1.0000	0.30
0.35	1.0000	1.0000	1.0000	1.0000	1.0000	1.0000	1.0000	1.0000	1.0000	1.0000	1.0000	1.0000	0.35
0.40	1.0000	1.0000	1.0000	1.0000	1.0000	1.0000	1.0000	1.0000	1.0000	1.0000	1.0000	1.0000	0.40
0.45	1.0000	1.0000	1.0000	1.0000	1.0000	1.0000	1.0000	1.0000	1.0000	1.0000	1.0000	1.0000	0.45
0.50	1.0000	1.0000	1.0000	1.0000	1.0000	1.0000	1.0000	1.0000	1.0000	1.0000	1.0000	1.0000	0.50
0.55	1.0000	1.0000	1.0000	1.0000	1.0000	1.0000	1.0000	1.0000	1.0000	1.0000	1.0000	1.0000	0.55
0.60	1.0000	1.0000	1.0000	1.0000	1.0000	1.0000	1.0000	1.0000	1.0000	1.0000	1.0000	1.0000	0.60
0.65	1.0000	1.0000	1.0000	1.0000	1.0000	1.0000	1.0000	1.0000	1.0000	1.0000	1.0000	1.0000	0.65
0.70	1.0000	1.0000	1.0000	1.0000	1.0000	1.0000	1.0000	1.0000	1.0000	1.0000	1.0000	1.0000	0.70
0.75	1.0000	1.0000	1.0000	1.0000	1.0000	1.0000	1.0000	1.0000	1.0000	1.0000	1.0000	1.0000	0.75
0.80	1.0000	1.0000	1.0000	1.0000	1.0000	1.0000	1.0000	1.0000	1.0000	1.0000	1.0000	1.0000	0.80
0.85	1.0000	1.0000	1.0000	1.0000	1.0000	1.0000	1.0000	1.0000	1.0000	1.0000	1.0000	1.0000	0.85
0.90	1.0000	1.0000	1.0000	1.0000	1.0000	1.0000	1.0000	1.0000	1.0000	1.0000	1.0000	1.0000	0.90
0.95	1.0000	1.0000	1.0000	1.0000	1.0000	1.0000	1.0000	1.0000	1.0000	1.0000	1.0000	1.0000	0.95
1.00	1.0000	1.0000	1.0000	1.0000	1.0000	1.0000	1.0000	1.0000	1.0000	1.0000	1.0000	1.0000	1.00
1.10	1.0000	1.0000	1.0000	1.0000	1.0000	1.0000	1.0000	1.0000	1.0000	1.0000	1.0000	1.0000	1.10
1.20	1.0000	1.0000	1.0000	1.0000	1.0000	1.0000	1.0000	1.0000	1.0000	1.0000	1.0000	1.0000	1.20
1.30	1.0000	1.0000	1.0000	1.0000	1.0000	1.0000	1.0000	1.0000	1.0000	1.0000	1.0000	1.0000	1.30
1.40	1.0000	1.0000	1.0000	1.0000	1.0000	1.0000	1.0000	1.0000	1.0000	1.0000	1.0000	1.0000	1.40
1.50	1.0000	1.0000	1.0000	1.0000	1.0000	1.0000	1.0000	1.0000	1.0000	1.0000	1.0000	1.0000	1.50
1.60	1.0000	1.0000	1.0000	1.0000	1.0000	1.0000	1.0000	1.0000	1.0000	1.0000	1.0000	1.0000	1.60
1.70	1.0000	1.0000	1.0000	1.0000	1.0000	1.0000	1.0000	1.0000	1.0000	1.0000	1.0000	1.0000	1.70
1.80	1.0000	1.0000	1.0000	1.0000	1.0000	1.0000	1.0000	1.0000	1.0000	1.0000	1.0000	1.0000	1.80
1.90	1.0000	1.0000	1.0000	1.0000	1.0000	1.0000	1.0000	1.0000	1.0000	1.0000	1.0000	1.0000	1.90
2.00	1.0000	1.0000	1.0000	1.0000	1.0000	1.0000	1.0000	1.0000	1.0000	1.0000	1.0000	1.0000	2.00
2.10	1.0000	1.0000	1.0000	1.0000	1.0000	1.0000	1.0000	1.0000	1.0000	1.0000	1.0000	1.0000	2.10
2.20	1.0000	1.0000	1.0000	1.0000	1.0000	1.0000	1.0000	1.0000	1.0000	1.0000	1.0000	1.0000	2.20
2.30	1.0000	1.0000	1.0000	1.0000	1.0000	1.0000	1.0000	1.0000	1.0000	1.0000	1.0000	1.0000	2.30
2.40	1.0000	1.0000	1.0000	1.0000	1.0000	1.0000	1.0000	1.0000	1.0000	1.0000	1.0000	1.0000	2.40
2.50	1.0000	1.0000	1.0000	1.0000	1.0000	1.0000	1.0000	1.0000	1.0000	1.0000	1.0000	1.0000	2.50
2.60	1.0000	1.0000	1.0000	1.0000	1.0000	1.0000	1.0000	1.0000	1.0000	1.0000	1.0000	1.0000	2.60
2.70	1.0000	1.0000	1.0000	1.0000	1.0000	1.0000	1.0000	1.0000	1.0000	1.0000	1.0000	1.0000	2.70
2.80	1.0000	1.0000	1.0000	1.0000	1.0000	1.0000	1.0000	1.0000	1.0000	1.0000	1.0000	1.0000	2.80
2.90	1.0000	1.0000	1.0000	1.0000	1.0000	1.0000	1.0000	1.0000	1.0000	1.0000	1.0000	1.0000	2.90

$$P(X \leq x) = \sum_{x=0}^{x} \frac{e^{-\mu}\mu^x}{x!}$$

μ						Probability of less than or equal to x occurrences									μ
	0	1	2	3	4	5	6	7	8	9	10	11	12	13	
3.00	0.0498	0.1991	0.4232	0.6472	0.8153	0.9161	0.9665	0.9881	0.9962	0.9989	0.9997	0.9999	1.0000	1.0000	3.00
3.10	0.0450	0.1847	0.4012	0.6248	0.7982	0.9057	0.9612	0.9858	0.9953	0.9986	0.9996	0.9999	1.0000	1.0000	3.10
3.20	0.0408	0.1712	0.3799	0.6025	0.7806	0.8946	0.9554	0.9832	0.9943	0.9982	0.9995	0.9999	1.0000	1.0000	3.20
3.30	0.0369	0.1586	0.3594	0.5803	0.7626	0.8829	0.9490	0.9802	0.9931	0.9978	0.9994	0.9998	1.0000	1.0000	3.30
3.40	0.0334	0.1468	0.3397	0.5584	0.7442	0.8705	0.9421	0.9769	0.9917	0.9973	0.9992	0.9998	0.9999	1.0000	3.40
3.50	0.0302	0.1359	0.3208	0.5366	0.7254	0.8576	0.9347	0.9733	0.9901	0.9967	0.9990	0.9997	0.9999	1.0000	3.50
3.60	0.0273	0.1257	0.3027	0.5152	0.7064	0.8441	0.9267	0.9692	0.9883	0.9960	0.9987	0.9996	0.9999	1.0000	3.60
3.70	0.0247	0.1162	0.2854	0.4942	0.6872	0.8301	0.9182	0.9648	0.9863	0.9952	0.9984	0.9995	0.9999	1.0000	3.70
3.80	0.0224	0.1074	0.2689	0.4735	0.6678	0.8156	0.9091	0.9599	0.9840	0.9942	0.9981	0.9994	0.9998	1.0000	3.80
3.90	0.0202	0.0992	0.2531	0.4532	0.6484	0.8006	0.8995	0.9546	0.9815	0.9931	0.9977	0.9993	0.9998	0.9999	3.90
4.00	0.0183	0.0916	0.2381	0.4335	0.6288	0.7851	0.8893	0.9489	0.9786	0.9919	0.9972	0.9991	0.9997	0.9999	4.00
4.10	0.0166	0.0845	0.2238	0.4142	0.6093	0.7693	0.8786	0.9427	0.9755	0.9905	0.9966	0.9989	0.9997	0.9999	4.10
4.20	0.0150	0.0780	0.2102	0.3954	0.5898	0.7531	0.8675	0.9361	0.9721	0.9889	0.9959	0.9986	0.9996	0.9999	4.20
4.30	0.0136	0.0719	0.1974	0.3772	0.5704	0.7367	0.8558	0.9290	0.9683	0.9871	0.9952	0.9983	0.9995	0.9998	4.30
4.40	0.0123	0.0663	0.1851	0.3594	0.5512	0.7199	0.8436	0.9214	0.9642	0.9851	0.9943	0.9980	0.9993	0.9998	4.40
4.50	0.0111	0.0611	0.1736	0.3423	0.5321	0.7029	0.8311	0.9134	0.9597	0.9829	0.9933	0.9976	0.9992	0.9997	4.50
4.60	0.0101	0.0563	0.1626	0.3257	0.5132	0.6858	0.8180	0.9049	0.9549	0.9805	0.9922	0.9971	0.9990	0.9997	4.60
4.70	0.0091	0.0518	0.1523	0.3097	0.4946	0.6684	0.8046	0.8960	0.9497	0.9778	0.9910	0.9966	0.9988	0.9996	4.70
4.80	0.0082	0.0477	0.1425	0.2942	0.4763	0.6510	0.7908	0.8867	0.9442	0.9749	0.9896	0.9960	0.9986	0.9995	4.80
4.90	0.0074	0.0439	0.1333	0.2793	0.4582	0.6335	0.7767	0.8769	0.9382	0.9717	0.9880	0.9953	0.9983	0.9994	4.90
5.00	0.0067	0.0404	0.1247	0.2650	0.4405	0.6160	0.7622	0.8666	0.9319	0.9682	0.9863	0.9945	0.9980	0.9993	5.00
5.10	0.0061	0.0372	0.1165	0.2513	0.4231	0.5984	0.7474	0.8560	0.9252	0.9644	0.9844	0.9937	0.9976	0.9992	5.10
5.20	0.0055	0.0342	0.1088	0.2381	0.4061	0.5809	0.7324	0.8449	0.9181	0.9603	0.9823	0.9927	0.9972	0.9990	5.20
5.30	0.0050	0.0314	0.1016	0.2254	0.3895	0.5635	0.7171	0.8335	0.9106	0.9559	0.9800	0.9916	0.9967	0.9988	5.30
5.40	0.0045	0.0289	0.0948	0.2133	0.3733	0.5461	0.7017	0.8217	0.9027	0.9512	0.9775	0.9904	0.9962	0.9986	5.40
5.50	0.0041	0.0266	0.0884	0.2017	0.3575	0.5289	0.6860	0.8095	0.8944	0.9462	0.9747	0.9890	0.9955	0.9983	5.50
5.60	0.0037	0.0244	0.0824	0.1906	0.3422	0.5119	0.6703	0.7970	0.8857	0.9409	0.9718	0.9875	0.9949	0.9980	5.60
5.70	0.0033	0.0224	0.0768	0.1800	0.3272	0.4950	0.6544	0.7841	0.8766	0.9352	0.9686	0.9859	0.9941	0.9977	5.70
5.80	0.0030	0.0206	0.0715	0.1700	0.3127	0.4783	0.6384	0.7710	0.8672	0.9292	0.9651	0.9841	0.9932	0.9973	5.80
5.90	0.0027	0.0189	0.0666	0.1604	0.2987	0.4619	0.6224	0.7576	0.8574	0.9228	0.9614	0.9821	0.9922	0.9969	5.90
6.00	0.0025	0.0174	0.0620	0.1512	0.2851	0.4457	0.6063	0.7440	0.8472	0.9161	0.9574	0.9799	0.9912	0.9964	6.00
6.10	0.0022	0.0159	0.0577	0.1425	0.2719	0.4298	0.5902	0.7301	0.8367	0.9090	0.9531	0.9776	0.9900	0.9958	6.10
6.20	0.0020	0.0146	0.0536	0.1342	0.2592	0.4141	0.5742	0.7160	0.8259	0.9016	0.9486	0.9750	0.9887	0.9952	6.20
6.30	0.0018	0.0134	0.0498	0.1264	0.2469	0.3988	0.5582	0.7017	0.8148	0.8939	0.9437	0.9723	0.9873	0.9945	6.30
6.40	0.0017	0.0123	0.0463	0.1189	0.2351	0.3837	0.5423	0.6873	0.8033	0.8858	0.9386	0.9693	0.9857	0.9937	6.40
6.50	0.0015	0.0113	0.0430	0.1118	0.2237	0.3690	0.5265	0.6728	0.7916	0.8774	0.9332	0.9661	0.9840	0.9929	6.50
6.60	0.0014	0.0103	0.0400	0.1052	0.2127	0.3547	0.5108	0.6581	0.7796	0.8686	0.9274	0.9627	0.9821	0.9920	6.60
6.70	0.0012	0.0095	0.0371	0.0988	0.2022	0.3406	0.4953	0.6433	0.7673	0.8596	0.9214	0.9591	0.9801	0.9909	6.70
6.80	0.0011	0.0087	0.0344	0.0928	0.1920	0.3270	0.4799	0.6285	0.7548	0.8502	0.9151	0.9552	0.9779	0.9898	6.80
6.90	0.0010	0.0080	0.0320	0.0871	0.1823	0.3137	0.4647	0.6136	0.7420	0.8405	0.9084	0.9510	0.9755	0.9885	6.90

$$P(X \le x) = \sum_{x=0}^{x} \frac{e^{-\mu}\mu^x}{x!}$$

	Probability of less than or equal to x occurrences											
μ	14	15	16	17	18	19	20	21	22	23	24	25	μ
3.00	1.0000	1.0000	1.0000	1.0000	1.0000	1.0000	1.0000	1.0000	1.0000	1.0000	1.0000	1.0000	3.00
3.10	1.0000	1.0000	1.0000	1.0000	1.0000	1.0000	1.0000	1.0000	1.0000	1.0000	1.0000	1.0000	3.10
3.20	1.0000	1.0000	1.0000	1.0000	1.0000	1.0000	1.0000	1.0000	1.0000	1.0000	1.0000	1.0000	3.20
3.30	1.0000	1.0000	1.0000	1.0000	1.0000	1.0000	1.0000	1.0000	1.0000	1.0000	1.0000	1.0000	3.30
3.40	1.0000	1.0000	1.0000	1.0000	1.0000	1.0000	1.0000	1.0000	1.0000	1.0000	1.0000	1.0000	3.40
3.50	1.0000	1.0000	1.0000	1.0000	1.0000	1.0000	1.0000	1.0000	1.0000	1.0000	1.0000	1.0000	3.50
3.60	1.0000	1.0000	1.0000	1.0000	1.0000	1.0000	1.0000	1.0000	1.0000	1.0000	1.0000	1.0000	3.60
3.70	1.0000	1.0000	1.0000	1.0000	1.0000	1.0000	1.0000	1.0000	1.0000	1.0000	1.0000	1.0000	3.70
3.80	1.0000	1.0000	1.0000	1.0000	1.0000	1.0000	1.0000	1.0000	1.0000	1.0000	1.0000	1.0000	3.80
3.90	1.0000	1.0000	1.0000	1.0000	1.0000	1.0000	1.0000	1.0000	1.0000	1.0000	1.0000	1.0000	3.90
4.00	1.0000	1.0000	1.0000	1.0000	1.0000	1.0000	1.0000	1.0000	1.0000	1.0000	1.0000	1.0000	4.00
4.10	1.0000	1.0000	1.0000	1.0000	1.0000	1.0000	1.0000	1.0000	1.0000	1.0000	1.0000	1.0000	4.10
4.20	1.0000	1.0000	1.0000	1.0000	1.0000	1.0000	1.0000	1.0000	1.0000	1.0000	1.0000	1.0000	4.20
4.30	1.0000	1.0000	1.0000	1.0000	1.0000	1.0000	1.0000	1.0000	1.0000	1.0000	1.0000	1.0000	4.30
4.40	0.9999	1.0000	1.0000	1.0000	1.0000	1.0000	1.0000	1.0000	1.0000	1.0000	1.0000	1.0000	4.40
4.50	0.9999	1.0000	1.0000	1.0000	1.0000	1.0000	1.0000	1.0000	1.0000	1.0000	1.0000	1.0000	4.50
4.60	0.9999	1.0000	1.0000	1.0000	1.0000	1.0000	1.0000	1.0000	1.0000	1.0000	1.0000	1.0000	4.60
4.70	0.9999	1.0000	1.0000	1.0000	1.0000	1.0000	1.0000	1.0000	1.0000	1.0000	1.0000	1.0000	4.70
4.80	0.9999	1.0000	1.0000	1.0000	1.0000	1.0000	1.0000	1.0000	1.0000	1.0000	1.0000	1.0000	4.80
4.90	0.9998	0.9999	1.0000	1.0000	1.0000	1.0000	1.0000	1.0000	1.0000	1.0000	1.0000	1.0000	4.90
5.00	0.9998	0.9999	1.0000	1.0000	1.0000	1.0000	1.0000	1.0000	1.0000	1.0000	1.0000	1.0000	5.00
5.10	0.9997	0.9999	1.0000	1.0000	1.0000	1.0000	1.0000	1.0000	1.0000	1.0000	1.0000	1.0000	5.10
5.20	0.9997	0.9999	1.0000	1.0000	1.0000	1.0000	1.0000	1.0000	1.0000	1.0000	1.0000	1.0000	5.20
5.30	0.9996	0.9999	1.0000	1.0000	1.0000	1.0000	1.0000	1.0000	1.0000	1.0000	1.0000	1.0000	5.30
5.40	0.9995	0.9998	0.9999	1.0000	1.0000	1.0000	1.0000	1.0000	1.0000	1.0000	1.0000	1.0000	5.40
5.50	0.9994	0.9998	0.9999	1.0000	1.0000	1.0000	1.0000	1.0000	1.0000	1.0000	1.0000	1.0000	5.50
5.60	0.9993	0.9998	0.9999	1.0000	1.0000	1.0000	1.0000	1.0000	1.0000	1.0000	1.0000	1.0000	5.60
5.70	0.9991	0.9997	0.9999	1.0000	1.0000	1.0000	1.0000	1.0000	1.0000	1.0000	1.0000	1.0000	5.70
5.80	0.9990	0.9996	0.9999	1.0000	1.0000	1.0000	1.0000	1.0000	1.0000	1.0000	1.0000	1.0000	5.80
5.90	0.9988	0.9996	0.9999	1.0000	1.0000	1.0000	1.0000	1.0000	1.0000	1.0000	1.0000	1.0000	5.90
6.00	0.9986	0.9995	0.9998	0.9999	1.0000	1.0000	1.0000	1.0000	1.0000	1.0000	1.0000	1.0000	6.00
6.10	0.9984	0.9994	0.9998	0.9999	1.0000	1.0000	1.0000	1.0000	1.0000	1.0000	1.0000	1.0000	6.10
6.20	0.9981	0.9993	0.9997	0.9999	1.0000	1.0000	1.0000	1.0000	1.0000	1.0000	1.0000	1.0000	6.20
6.30	0.9978	0.9992	0.9997	0.9999	1.0000	1.0000	1.0000	1.0000	1.0000	1.0000	1.0000	1.0000	6.30
6.40	0.9974	0.9990	0.9996	0.9999	1.0000	1.0000	1.0000	1.0000	1.0000	1.0000	1.0000	1.0000	6.40
6.50	0.9970	0.9988	0.9996	0.9998	0.9999	1.0000	1.0000	1.0000	1.0000	1.0000	1.0000	1.0000	6.50
6.60	0.9966	0.9986	0.9995	0.9998	0.9999	1.0000	1.0000	1.0000	1.0000	1.0000	1.0000	1.0000	6.60
6.70	0.9961	0.9984	0.9994	0.9998	0.9999	1.0000	1.0000	1.0000	1.0000	1.0000	1.0000	1.0000	6.70
6.80	0.9956	0.9982	0.9993	0.9997	0.9999	1.0000	1.0000	1.0000	1.0000	1.0000	1.0000	1.0000	6.80
6.90	0.9950	0.9979	0.9992	0.9997	0.9999	1.0000	1.0000	1.0000	1.0000	1.0000	1.0000	1.0000	6.90

$$P(X \le x) = \sum_{x=0}^{x} \frac{e^{-\mu}\mu^x}{x!}$$

	Probability of less than or equal to x occurrences													
μ	0	1	2	3	4	5	6	7	8	9	10	11	12	13	μ
7.00	0.0009	0.0073	0.0296	0.0818	0.1730	0.3007	0.4497	0.5987	0.7291	0.8305	0.9015	0.9467	0.9730	0.9872	7.00
7.10	0.0008	0.0067	0.0275	0.0767	0.1641	0.2881	0.4349	0.5838	0.7160	0.8202	0.8942	0.9420	0.9703	0.9857	7.10
7.20	0.0007	0.0061	0.0255	0.0719	0.1555	0.2759	0.4204	0.5689	0.7027	0.8096	0.8867	0.9371	0.9673	0.9841	7.20
7.30	0.0007	0.0056	0.0236	0.0674	0.1473	0.2640	0.4060	0.5541	0.6892	0.7988	0.8788	0.9319	0.9642	0.9824	7.30
7.40	0.0006	0.0051	0.0219	0.0632	0.1395	0.2526	0.3920	0.5393	0.6757	0.7877	0.8707	0.9265	0.9609	0.9805	7.40
7.50	0.0006	0.0047	0.0203	0.0591	0.1321	0.2414	0.3782	0.5246	0.6620	0.7764	0.8622	0.9208	0.9573	0.9784	7.50
7.60	0.0005	0.0043	0.0188	0.0554	0.1249	0.2307	0.3646	0.5100	0.6482	0.7649	0.8535	0.9148	0.9536	0.9762	7.60
7.70	0.0005	0.0039	0.0174	0.0518	0.1181	0.2203	0.3514	0.4956	0.6343	0.7531	0.8445	0.9085	0.9496	0.9739	7.70
7.80	0.0004	0.0036	0.0161	0.0485	0.1117	0.2103	0.3384	0.4812	0.6204	0.7411	0.8352	0.9020	0.9454	0.9714	7.80
7.90	0.0004	0.0033	0.0149	0.0453	0.1055	0.2006	0.3257	0.4670	0.6065	0.7290	0.8257	0.8952	0.9409	0.9687	7.90
8.00	0.0003	0.0030	0.0138	0.0424	0.0996	0.1912	0.3134	0.4530	0.5925	0.7166	0.8159	0.8881	0.9362	0.9658	8.00
8.10	0.0003	0.0028	0.0127	0.0396	0.0940	0.1822	0.3013	0.4391	0.5786	0.7041	0.8058	0.8807	0.9313	0.9628	8.10
8.20	0.0003	0.0025	0.0118	0.0370	0.0887	0.1736	0.2896	0.4254	0.5647	0.6915	0.7955	0.8731	0.9261	0.9595	8.20
8.30	0.0002	0.0023	0.0109	0.0346	0.0837	0.1653	0.2781	0.4119	0.5507	0.6788	0.7850	0.8652	0.9207	0.9561	8.30
8.40	0.0002	0.0021	0.0100	0.0323	0.0789	0.1573	0.2670	0.3987	0.5369	0.6659	0.7743	0.8571	0.9150	0.9524	8.40
8.50	0.0002	0.0019	0.0093	0.0301	0.0744	0.1496	0.2562	0.3856	0.5231	0.6530	0.7634	0.8487	0.9091	0.9486	8.50
8.60	0.0002	0.0018	0.0086	0.0281	0.0701	0.1422	0.2457	0.3728	0.5094	0.6400	0.7522	0.8400	0.9029	0.9445	8.60
8.70	0.0002	0.0016	0.0079	0.0262	0.0660	0.1352	0.2355	0.3602	0.4958	0.6269	0.7409	0.8311	0.8965	0.9403	8.70
8.80	0.0002	0.0015	0.0073	0.0244	0.0621	0.1284	0.2256	0.3478	0.4823	0.6137	0.7294	0.8220	0.8898	0.9358	8.80
8.90	0.0001	0.0014	0.0068	0.0228	0.0584	0.1219	0.2160	0.3357	0.4689	0.6006	0.7178	0.8126	0.8829	0.9311	8.90
9.00	0.0001	0.0012	0.0062	0.0212	0.0550	0.1157	0.2068	0.3239	0.4557	0.5874	0.7060	0.8030	0.8758	0.9261	9.00
9.10	0.0001	0.0011	0.0058	0.0198	0.0517	0.1098	0.1978	0.3123	0.4426	0.5742	0.6941	0.7932	0.8684	0.9210	9.10
9.20	0.0001	0.0010	0.0053	0.0184	0.0486	0.1041	0.1892	0.3010	0.4296	0.5611	0.6820	0.7832	0.8607	0.9156	9.20
9.30	0.0001	0.0009	0.0049	0.0172	0.0456	0.0986	0.1808	0.2900	0.4168	0.5479	0.6699	0.7730	0.8529	0.9100	9.30
9.40	0.0001	0.0009	0.0045	0.0160	0.0429	0.0935	0.1727	0.2792	0.4042	0.5349	0.6576	0.7626	0.8448	0.9042	9.40
9.50	0.0001	0.0008	0.0042	0.0149	0.0403	0.0885	0.1649	0.2687	0.3918	0.5218	0.6453	0.7520	0.8364	0.8981	9.50
9.60	0.0001	0.0007	0.0038	0.0138	0.0378	0.0838	0.1574	0.2584	0.3796	0.5089	0.6329	0.7412	0.8279	0.8919	9.60
9.70	0.0001	0.0007	0.0035	0.0129	0.0355	0.0793	0.1502	0.2485	0.3676	0.4960	0.6205	0.7303	0.8191	0.8853	9.70
9.80	0.0001	0.0006	0.0033	0.0120	0.0333	0.0750	0.1433	0.2388	0.3558	0.4832	0.6080	0.7193	0.8101	0.8786	9.80
9.90	0.0001	0.0005	0.0030	0.0111	0.0312	0.0710	0.1366	0.2294	0.3442	0.4705	0.5955	0.7081	0.8009	0.8716	9.90
10.00	0.0000	0.0005	0.0028	0.0103	0.0293	0.0671	0.1301	0.2202	0.3328	0.4579	0.5830	0.6968	0.7916	0.8645	10.00

$$P(X \le x) = \sum_{x = 0}^{x} \frac{e^{-\mu}\mu^{x}}{x!}$$

μ	Probability of less than or equal to x occurrences												μ
	14	15	16	17	18	19	20	21	22	23	24	25	
7.00	0.9943	0.9976	0.9990	0.9996	0.9999	1.0000	1.0000	1.0000	1.0000	1.0000	1.0000	1.0000	7.00
7.10	0.9935	0.9972	0.9989	0.9996	0.9998	0.9999	1.0000	1.0000	1.0000	1.0000	1.0000	1.0000	7.10
7.20	0.9927	0.9969	0.9987	0.9995	0.9998	0.9999	1.0000	1.0000	1.0000	1.0000	1.0000	1.0000	7.20
7.30	0.9918	0.9964	0.9985	0.9994	0.9998	0.9999	1.0000	1.0000	1.0000	1.0000	1.0000	1.0000	7.30
7.40	0.9908	0.9959	0.9983	0.9993	0.9997	0.9999	1.0000	1.0000	1.0000	1.0000	1.0000	1.0000	7.40
7.50	0.9897	0.9954	0.9980	0.9992	0.9997	0.9999	1.0000	1.0000	1.0000	1.0000	1.0000	1.0000	7.50
7.60	0.9886	0.9948	0.9978	0.9991	0.9996	0.9999	1.0000	1.0000	1.0000	1.0000	1.0000	1.0000	7.60
7.70	0.9873	0.9941	0.9974	0.9989	0.9996	0.9998	0.9999	1.0000	1.0000	1.0000	1.0000	1.0000	7.70
7.80	0.9859	0.9934	0.9971	0.9988	0.9995	0.9998	0.9999	1.0000	1.0000	1.0000	1.0000	1.0000	7.80
7.90	0.9844	0.9926	0.9967	0.9986	0.9994	0.9998	0.9999	1.0000	1.0000	1.0000	1.0000	1.0000	7.90
8.00	0.9827	0.9918	0.9963	0.9984	0.9993	0.9997	0.9999	1.0000	1.0000	1.0000	1.0000	1.0000	8.00
8.10	0.9810	0.9908	0.9958	0.9982	0.9992	0.9997	0.9999	1.0000	1.0000	1.0000	1.0000	1.0000	8.10
8.20	0.9791	0.9898	0.9953	0.9979	0.9991	0.9997	0.9999	1.0000	1.0000	1.0000	1.0000	1.0000	8.20
8.30	0.9771	0.9887	0.9947	0.9977	0.9990	0.9996	0.9998	0.9999	1.0000	1.0000	1.0000	1.0000	8.30
8.40	0.9749	0.9875	0.9941	0.9973	0.9989	0.9995	0.9998	0.9999	1.0000	1.0000	1.0000	1.0000	8.40
8.50	0.9726	0.9862	0.9934	0.9970	0.9987	0.9995	0.9998	0.9999	1.0000	1.0000	1.0000	1.0000	8.50
8.60	0.9701	0.9848	0.9926	0.9966	0.9985	0.9994	0.9998	0.9999	1.0000	1.0000	1.0000	1.0000	8.60
8.70	0.9675	0.9832	0.9918	0.9962	0.9983	0.9993	0.9997	0.9999	1.0000	1.0000	1.0000	1.0000	8.70
8.80	0.9647	0.9816	0.9909	0.9957	0.9981	0.9992	0.9997	0.9999	1.0000	1.0000	1.0000	1.0000	8.80
8.90	0.9617	0.9798	0.9899	0.9952	0.9978	0.9991	0.9996	0.9998	0.9999	1.0000	1.0000	1.0000	8.90
9.00	0.9585	0.9780	0.9889	0.9947	0.9976	0.9989	0.9996	0.9998	0.9999	1.0000	1.0000	1.0000	9.00
9.10	0.9552	0.9760	0.9878	0.9941	0.9973	0.9988	0.9995	0.9998	0.9999	1.0000	1.0000	1.0000	9.10
9.20	0.9517	0.9738	0.9865	0.9934	0.9969	0.9986	0.9994	0.9998	0.9999	1.0000	1.0000	1.0000	9.20
9.30	0.9480	0.9715	0.9852	0.9927	0.9966	0.9985	0.9993	0.9997	0.9999	1.0000	1.0000	1.0000	9.30
9.40	0.9441	0.9691	0.9838	0.9919	0.9962	0.9983	0.9992	0.9997	0.9999	1.0000	1.0000	1.0000	9.40
9.50	0.9400	0.9665	0.9823	0.9911	0.9957	0.9980	0.9991	0.9996	0.9999	0.9999	1.0000	1.0000	9.50
9.60	0.9357	0.9638	0.9806	0.9902	0.9952	0.9978	0.9990	0.9996	0.9998	0.9999	1.0000	1.0000	9.60
9.70	0.9312	0.9609	0.9789	0.9892	0.9947	0.9975	0.9989	0.9995	0.9998	0.9999	1.0000	1.0000	9.70
9.80	0.9265	0.9579	0.9770	0.9881	0.9941	0.9972	0.9987	0.9995	0.9998	0.9999	1.0000	1.0000	9.80
9.90	0.9216	0.9546	0.9751	0.9870	0.9935	0.9969	0.9986	0.9994	0.9997	0.9999	1.0000	1.0000	9.90
10.00	0.9165	0.9513	0.9730	0.9857	0.9928	0.9965	0.9984	0.9993	0.9997	0.9999	1.0000	1.0000	10.00

Appendix F
Control Chart Table Values

n	A_2	A_3	B_3	B_4	d_2	D_3	D_4	n
2	1.881	2.659	0.000	3.266	3.686	0.000	3.267	2
3	1.023	1.954	0.000	2.568	4.358	0.000	2.574	3
4	0.729	1.628	0.000	2.266	4.698	0.000	2.282	4
5	0.577	1.427	0.000	2.089	4.918	0.000	2.114	5
6	0.483	1.287	0.030	1.970	5.078	0.000	2.004	6
7	0.419	1.182	0.118	1.882	5.204	0.076	1.924	7
8	0.373	1.099	0.185	1.815	5.306	0.136	1.864	8
9	0.337	1.032	0.239	1.761	5.393	0.184	1.816	9
10	0.308	0.975	0.284	1.716	5.469	0.223	1.777	10
11	0.285	0.927	0.322	1.678	5.535	0.256	1.744	11
12	0.266	0.886	0.354	1.646	5.594	0.283	1.717	12
13	0.249	0.850	0.381	1.619	5.647	0.307	1.693	13
14	0.235	0.817	0.407	1.593	5.696	0.328	1.672	14
15	0.223	0.789	0.428	1.572	5.741	0.347	1.653	15
16	0.212	0.763	0.448	1.552	5.782	0.363	1.637	16
17	0.203	0.739	0.466	1.534	5.820	0.378	1.622	17
18	0.194	0.718	0.482	1.518	5.856	0.391	1.609	18
19	0.187	0.698	0.496	1.504	5.890	0.403	1.597	19
20	0.180	0.680	0.510	1.490	5.921	0.415	1.585	20
21	0.173	0.663	0.523	1.477	5.960	0.423	1.577	21
22	0.167	0.647	0.535	1.465	5.979	0.434	1.566	22
23	0.162	0.633	0.545	1.455	6.006	0.443	1.557	23
24	0.157	0.619	0.555	1.445	6.031	0.452	1.548	24
25	0.153	0.606	0.564	1.436	6.056	0.459	1.541	25

Appendix G
Cumulative Standard Normal Table

Z	0.00	0.01	0.02	0.03	0.04	0.05	0.06	0.07	0.08	0.09	Z
0.0	0.5000	0.5040	0.5080	0.5120	0.5160	0.5199	0.5239	0.5279	0.5319	0.5359	0.0
0.1	0.5398	0.5438	0.5478	0.5517	0.5557	0.5596	0.5636	0.5675	0.5714	0.5753	0.1
0.2	0.5793	0.5832	0.5871	0.5910	0.5948	0.5987	0.6026	0.6064	0.6103	0.6141	0.2
0.3	0.6179	0.6217	0.6255	0.6293	0.6331	0.6368	0.6406	0.6443	0.6480	0.6517	0.3
0.4	0.6554	0.6591	0.6628	0.6664	0.6700	0.6736	0.6772	0.6808	0.6844	0.6879	0.4
0.5	0.6915	0.6950	0.6985	0.7019	0.7054	0.7088	0.7123	0.7157	0.7190	0.7224	0.5
0.6	0.7257	0.7291	0.7324	0.7357	0.7389	0.7422	0.7454	0.7486	0.7517	0.7549	0.6
0.7	0.7580	0.7611	0.7642	0.7673	0.7704	0.7734	0.7764	0.7794	0.7823	0.7852	0.7
0.8	0.7881	0.7910	0.7939	0.7967	0.7995	0.8023	0.8051	0.8078	0.8106	0.8133	0.8
0.9	0.8159	0.8186	0.8212	0.8238	0.8264	0.8289	0.8315	0.8340	0.8365	0.8389	0.9
1.0	0.8413	0.8438	0.8461	0.8485	0.8508	0.8531	0.8554	0.8577	0.8599	0.8621	1.0
1.1	0.8643	0.8665	0.8686	0.8708	0.8729	0.8749	0.8770	0.8790	0.8810	0.8830	1.1
1.2	0.8849	0.8869	0.8888	0.8907	0.8925	0.8944	0.8962	0.8980	0.8997	0.9015	1.2
1.3	0.9032	0.9049	0.9066	0.9082	0.9099	0.9115	0.9131	0.9147	0.9162	0.9177	1.3
1.4	0.9192	0.9207	0.9222	0.9236	0.9251	0.9265	0.9279	0.9292	0.9306	0.9319	1.4
1.5	0.9332	0.9345	0.9357	0.9370	0.9382	0.9394	0.9406	0.9418	0.9429	0.9441	1.5
1.6	0.9452	0.9463	0.9474	0.9484	0.9495	0.9505	0.9515	0.9525	0.9535	0.9545	1.6
1.7	0.9554	0.9564	0.9573	0.9582	0.9591	0.9599	0.9608	0.9616	0.9625	0.9633	1.7
1.8	0.9641	0.9649	0.9656	0.9664	0.9671	0.9678	0.9686	0.9693	0.9699	0.9706	1.8
1.9	0.9713	0.9719	0.9726	0.9732	0.9738	0.9744	0.9750	0.9756	0.9761	0.9767	1.9
2.0	0.9772	0.9778	0.9783	0.9788	0.9793	0.9798	0.9803	0.9808	0.9812	0.9817	2.0
2.1	0.9821	0.9826	0.9830	0.9834	0.9838	0.9842	0.9846	0.9850	0.9854	0.9857	2.1
2.2	0.9861	0.9864	0.9868	0.9871	0.9875	0.9878	0.9881	0.9884	0.9887	0.9890	2.2
2.3	0.9893	0.9896	0.9898	0.9901	0.9904	0.9906	0.9909	0.9911	0.9913	0.9916	2.3
2.4	0.9918	0.9920	0.9922	0.9925	0.9927	0.9929	0.9931	0.9932	0.9934	0.9936	2.4
2.5	0.9938	0.9940	0.9941	0.9943	0.9945	0.9946	0.9948	0.9949	0.9951	0.9952	2.5
2.6	0.9953	0.9955	0.9956	0.9957	0.9959	0.9960	0.9961	0.9962	0.9963	0.9964	2.6
2.7	0.9965	0.9966	0.9967	0.9968	0.9969	0.9970	0.9971	0.9972	0.9973	0.9974	2.7
2.8	0.9974	0.9975	0.9976	0.9977	0.9977	0.9978	0.9979	0.9979	0.9980	0.9981	2.8
2.9	0.9981	0.9982	0.9982	0.9983	0.9984	0.9984	0.9985	0.9985	0.9986	0.9986	2.9
3.0	0.9987	0.9987	0.9987	0.9988	0.9988	0.9989	0.9989	0.9989	0.9990	0.9990	3.0
3.1	0.9990	0.9991	0.9991	0.9991	0.9992	0.9992	0.9992	0.9992	0.9993	0.9993	3.1
3.2	0.9993	0.9993	0.9994	0.9994	0.9994	0.9994	0.9994	0.9995	0.9995	0.9995	3.2
3.3	0.9995	0.9995	0.9995	0.9996	0.9996	0.9996	0.9996	0.9996	0.9996	0.9997	3.3
3.4	0.9997	0.9997	0.9997	0.9997	0.9997	0.9997	0.9997	0.9997	0.9997	0.9998	3.4

Appendix H
Student's *t* Table

	Area in upper tail					
	0.005	0.01	0.025	0.05	0.10	
Degrees of freedom	Area in two tails					Degrees of freedom
	0.01	0.02	0.05	0.10	0.20	
1	63.657	31.821	12.706	6.314	3.078	1
2	9.925	6.965	4.303	2.920	1.886	2
3	5.841	4.541	3.182	2.353	1.638	3
4	4.604	3.747	2.776	2.132	1.533	4
5	4.032	3.365	2.571	2.015	1.476	5
6	3.707	3.143	2.447	1.943	1.440	6
7	3.499	2.998	2.365	1.895	1.415	7
8	3.355	2.896	2.306	1.860	1.397	8
9	3.250	2.821	2.262	1.833	1.383	9
10	3.169	2.764	2.228	1.812	1.372	10
11	3.106	2.718	2.201	1.796	1.363	11
12	3.055	2.681	2.179	1.782	1.356	12
13	3.012	2.650	2.160	1.771	1.350	13
14	2.977	2.624	2.145	1.761	1.345	14
15	2.947	2.602	2.131	1.753	1.341	15
16	2.921	2.583	2.120	1.746	1.337	16
17	2.898	2.567	2.110	1.740	1.333	17
18	2.878	2.552	2.101	1.734	1.330	18
19	2.861	2.539	2.093	1.729	1.328	19
20	2.845	2.528	2.086	1.725	1.325	20
21	2.831	2.518	2.080	1.721	1.323	21
22	2.819	2.508	2.074	1.717	1.321	22
23	2.807	2.500	2.069	1.714	1.319	23
24	2.797	2.492	2.064	1.711	1.318	24
25	2.787	2.485	2.060	1.708	1.316	25
26	2.779	2.479	2.056	1.706	1.315	26
27	2.771	2.473	2.052	1.703	1.314	27

Degrees of freedom	Area in upper tail					Degrees of freedom
	0.005	0.01	0.025	0.05	0.10	
	Area in two tails					
	0.01	0.02	0.05	0.10	0.20	
28	2.763	2.467	2.048	1.701	1.313	28
29	2.756	2.462	2.045	1.699	1.311	29
30	2.750	2.457	2.042	1.697	1.310	30
31	2.744	2.453	2.040	1.696	1.309	31
32	2.738	2.449	2.037	1.694	1.309	32
33	2.733	2.445	2.035	1.692	1.308	33
34	2.728	2.441	2.032	1.691	1.307	34
35	2.724	2.438	2.030	1.690	1.306	35
36	2.719	2.434	2.028	1.688	1.306	36
37	2.715	2.431	2.026	1.687	1.305	37
38	2.712	2.429	2.024	1.686	1.304	38
39	2.708	2.426	2.023	1.685	1.304	39
40	2.704	2.423	2.021	1.684	1.303	40
45	2.690	2.412	2.014	1.679	1.301	45
50	2.678	2.403	2.009	1.676	1.299	50
55	2.668	2.396	2.004	1.673	1.297	55
60	2.660	2.390	2.000	1.671	1.296	60
65	2.654	2.385	1.997	1.669	1.295	65
70	2.648	2.381	1.994	1.667	1.294	70
75	2.643	2.377	1.992	1.665	1.293	75
80	2.639	2.374	1.990	1.664	1.292	80
85	2.635	2.371	1.988	1.663	1.292	85
90	2.632	2.368	1.987	1.662	1.291	90
100	2.626	2.364	1.984	1.660	1.290	100
200	2.601	2.345	1.972	1.653	1.286	200
300	2.592	2.339	1.968	1.650	1.284	300
400	2.588	2.336	1.966	1.649	1.284	400
500	2.586	2.334	1.965	1.648	1.283	500
1000	2.581	2.330	1.962	1.646	1.282	1000
2000	2.578	2.328	1.961	1.646	1.282	2000
∞	2.576	2.326	1.960	1.645	1.282	∞

Appendix I
Chi-square Table

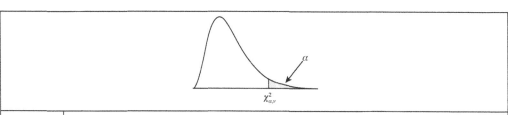

Degrees of freedom	Upper tail probability									
	0.995	0.990	0.975	0.950	0.900	0.100	0.050	0.025	0.010	0.005
1	3.93E-05	0.0002	0.001	0.004	0.016	2.706	3.841	5.024	6.635	7.879
2	0.010	0.020	0.051	0.103	0.211	4.605	5.991	7.378	9.210	10.597
3	0.072	0.115	0.216	0.352	0.584	6.251	7.815	9.348	11.345	12.838
4	0.207	0.297	0.484	0.711	1.064	7.779	9.488	11.143	13.277	14.860
5	0.412	0.554	0.831	1.145	1.610	9.236	11.070	12.833	15.086	16.750
6	0.676	0.872	1.237	1.635	2.204	10.645	12.592	14.449	16.812	18.548
7	0.989	1.239	1.690	2.167	2.833	12.017	14.067	16.013	18.475	20.278
8	1.344	1.646	2.180	2.733	3.490	13.362	15.507	17.535	20.090	21.955
9	1.735	2.088	2.700	3.325	4.168	14.684	16.919	19.023	21.666	23.589
10	2.156	2.558	3.247	3.940	4.865	15.987	18.307	20.483	23.209	25.188
11	2.603	3.053	3.816	4.575	5.578	17.275	19.675	21.920	24.725	26.757
12	3.074	3.571	4.404	5.226	6.304	18.549	21.026	23.337	26.217	28.300
13	3.565	4.107	5.009	5.892	7.042	19.812	22.362	24.736	27.688	29.819
14	4.075	4.660	5.629	6.571	7.790	21.064	23.685	26.119	29.141	31.319
15	4.601	5.229	6.262	7.261	8.547	22.307	24.996	27.488	30.578	32.801
16	5.142	5.812	6.908	7.962	9.312	23.542	26.296	28.845	32.000	34.267
17	5.697	6.408	7.564	8.672	10.085	24.769	27.587	30.191	33.409	35.718
18	6.265	7.015	8.231	9.390	10.865	25.989	28.869	31.526	34.805	37.156
19	6.844	7.633	8.907	10.117	11.651	27.204	30.144	32.852	36.191	38.582
20	7.434	8.260	9.591	10.851	12.443	28.412	31.410	34.170	37.566	39.997
21	8.034	8.897	10.283	11.591	13.240	29.615	32.671	35.479	38.932	41.401
22	8.643	9.542	10.982	12.338	14.041	30.813	33.924	36.781	40.289	42.796
23	9.260	10.196	11.689	13.091	14.848	32.007	35.172	38.076	41.638	44.181
24	9.886	10.856	12.401	13.848	15.659	33.196	36.415	39.364	42.980	45.559
25	10.520	11.524	13.120	14.611	16.473	34.382	37.652	40.646	44.314	46.928

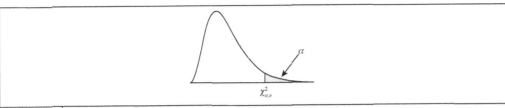

$$\chi^2_{\alpha,\nu}$$

Degrees of freedom	Upper tail probability									
	0.995	0.990	0.975	0.950	0.900	0.100	0.050	0.025	0.010	0.005
26	11.160	12.198	13.844	15.379	17.292	35.563	38.885	41.923	45.642	48.290
27	11.808	12.879	14.573	16.151	18.114	36.741	40.113	43.195	46.963	49.645
28	12.461	13.565	15.308	16.928	18.939	37.916	41.337	44.461	48.278	50.993
29	13.121	14.256	16.047	17.708	19.768	39.087	42.557	45.722	49.588	52.336
30	13.787	14.953	16.791	18.493	20.599	40.256	43.773	46.979	50.892	53.672
40	20.707	22.164	24.433	26.509	29.051	51.805	55.758	59.342	63.691	66.766
50	27.991	29.707	32.357	34.764	37.689	63.167	67.505	71.420	76.154	79.490
60	35.534	37.485	40.482	43.188	46.459	74.397	79.082	83.298	88.379	91.952
70	43.275	45.442	48.758	51.739	55.329	85.527	90.531	95.023	100.425	104.215
80	51.172	53.540	57.153	60.391	64.278	96.578	101.879	106.629	112.329	116.321
90	59.196	61.754	65.647	69.126	73.291	107.565	113.145	118.136	124.116	128.299
100	67.328	70.065	74.222	77.929	82.358	118.498	124.342	129.561	135.807	140.169

Appendix J
Cumulative *F* Table

F(0.99) Distribution Table

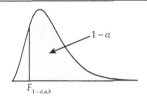

	Degrees of freedom for the numerator																	
	(a)																	
(b)	1	2	3	4	5	6	7	8	9	10	11	12	13	14	15	16	17	(b)
1	0.00	0.01	0.03	0.05	0.06	0.07	0.08	0.09	0.09	0.10	0.10	0.11	0.11	0.11	0.12	0.12	0.12	1
2	0.00	0.01	0.03	0.06	0.08	0.09	0.10	0.12	0.12	0.13	0.14	0.14	0.15	0.15	0.16	0.16	0.16	2
3	0.00	0.01	0.03	0.06	0.08	0.10	0.12	0.13	0.14	0.15	0.16	0.17	0.17	0.18	0.18	0.19	0.19	3
4	0.00	0.01	0.03	0.06	0.09	0.11	0.13	0.14	0.16	0.17	0.18	0.18	0.19	0.20	0.20	0.21	0.21	4
5	0.00	0.01	0.04	0.06	0.09	0.11	0.13	0.15	0.17	0.18	0.19	0.20	0.21	0.21	0.22	0.23	0.23	5
6	0.00	0.01	0.04	0.07	0.09	0.12	0.14	0.16	0.17	0.19	0.20	0.21	0.22	0.22	0.23	0.24	0.24	6
7	0.00	0.01	0.04	0.07	0.10	0.12	0.14	0.16	0.18	0.19	0.20	0.22	0.23	0.23	0.24	0.25	0.25	7
8	0.00	0.01	0.04	0.07	0.10	0.12	0.15	0.17	0.18	0.20	0.21	0.22	0.23	0.24	0.25	0.26	0.26	8
9	0.00	0.01	0.04	0.07	0.10	0.13	0.15	0.17	0.19	0.20	0.22	0.23	0.24	0.25	0.26	0.26	0.27	9
10	0.00	0.01	0.04	0.07	0.10	0.13	0.15	0.17	0.19	0.21	0.22	0.23	0.24	0.25	0.26	0.27	0.28	10
11	0.00	0.01	0.04	0.07	0.10	0.13	0.15	0.17	0.19	0.21	0.22	0.24	0.25	0.26	0.27	0.28	0.28	11
12	0.00	0.01	0.04	0.07	0.10	0.13	0.15	0.18	0.20	0.21	0.23	0.24	0.25	0.26	0.27	0.28	0.29	12
13	0.00	0.01	0.04	0.07	0.10	0.13	0.16	0.18	0.20	0.22	0.23	0.24	0.26	0.27	0.28	0.29	0.29	13
14	0.00	0.01	0.04	0.07	0.10	0.13	0.16	0.18	0.20	0.22	0.23	0.25	0.26	0.27	0.28	0.29	0.30	14
15	0.00	0.01	0.04	0.07	0.10	0.13	0.16	0.18	0.20	0.22	0.24	0.25	0.26	0.27	0.28	0.29	0.30	15
16	0.00	0.01	0.04	0.07	0.10	0.13	0.16	0.18	0.20	0.22	0.24	0.25	0.26	0.28	0.29	0.30	0.31	16
17	0.00	0.01	0.04	0.07	0.10	0.13	0.16	0.18	0.20	0.22	0.24	0.25	0.27	0.28	0.29	0.30	0.31	17
18	0.00	0.01	0.04	0.07	0.10	0.13	0.16	0.18	0.21	0.22	0.24	0.26	0.27	0.28	0.29	0.30	0.31	18
19	0.00	0.01	0.04	0.07	0.10	0.13	0.16	0.19	0.21	0.23	0.24	0.26	0.27	0.28	0.29	0.30	0.31	19
20	0.00	0.01	0.04	0.07	0.10	0.14	0.16	0.19	0.21	0.23	0.24	0.26	0.27	0.29	0.30	0.31	0.32	20
21	0.00	0.01	0.04	0.07	0.10	0.14	0.16	0.19	0.21	0.23	0.25	0.26	0.27	0.29	0.30	0.31	0.32	21
22	0.00	0.01	0.04	0.07	0.11	0.14	0.16	0.19	0.21	0.23	0.25	0.26	0.28	0.29	0.30	0.31	0.32	22
23	0.00	0.01	0.04	0.07	0.11	0.14	0.16	0.19	0.21	0.23	0.25	0.26	0.28	0.29	0.30	0.31	0.32	23
24	0.00	0.01	0.04	0.07	0.11	0.14	0.16	0.19	0.21	0.23	0.25	0.26	0.28	0.29	0.30	0.31	0.32	24
25	0.00	0.01	0.04	0.07	0.11	0.14	0.17	0.19	0.21	0.23	0.25	0.27	0.28	0.29	0.31	0.32	0.33	25
26	0.00	0.01	0.04	0.07	0.11	0.14	0.17	0.19	0.21	0.23	0.25	0.27	0.28	0.29	0.31	0.32	0.33	26
27	0.00	0.01	0.04	0.07	0.11	0.14	0.17	0.19	0.21	0.23	0.25	0.27	0.28	0.30	0.31	0.32	0.33	27
28	0.00	0.01	0.04	0.07	0.11	0.14	0.17	0.19	0.21	0.23	0.25	0.27	0.28	0.30	0.31	0.32	0.33	28
29	0.00	0.01	0.04	0.07	0.11	0.14	0.17	0.19	0.21	0.23	0.25	0.27	0.28	0.30	0.31	0.32	0.33	29
30	0.00	0.01	0.04	0.07	0.11	0.14	0.17	0.19	0.22	0.24	0.25	0.27	0.29	0.30	0.31	0.32	0.33	30
40	0.00	0.01	0.04	0.07	0.11	0.14	0.17	0.20	0.22	0.24	0.26	0.28	0.29	0.31	0.32	0.33	0.34	40
60	0.00	0.01	0.04	0.07	0.11	0.14	0.17	0.20	0.22	0.24	0.26	0.28	0.30	0.31	0.33	0.34	0.35	60
100	0.00	0.01	0.04	0.07	0.11	0.14	0.17	0.20	0.23	0.25	0.27	0.29	0.31	0.32	0.34	0.35	0.36	100
∞	0.00	0.01	0.04	0.07	0.11	0.15	0.18	0.21	0.23	0.26	0.28	0.30	0.32	0.33	0.35	0.36	0.38	∞

Degrees of freedom for the denominator

F(0.99) Distribution Table

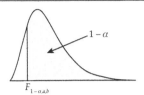

	Degrees of freedom for the numerator																	
	(a)																	
(b)	18	19	20	21	22	23	24	25	26	27	28	29	30	40	60	100	∞	(b)
1	0.12	0.12	0.12	0.12	0.13	0.13	0.13	0.13	0.13	0.13	0.13	0.13	0.13	0.14	0.14	0.15	0.15	1
2	0.17	0.17	0.17	0.17	0.17	0.18	0.18	0.18	0.18	0.18	0.18	0.18	0.19	0.19	0.20	0.21	0.22	2
3	0.20	0.20	0.20	0.21	0.21	0.21	0.21	0.21	0.22	0.22	0.22	0.22	0.22	0.23	0.24	0.25	0.26	3
4	0.22	0.22	0.23	0.23	0.23	0.23	0.24	0.24	0.24	0.24	0.25	0.25	0.25	0.26	0.27	0.28	0.30	4
5	0.24	0.24	0.24	0.25	0.25	0.25	0.26	0.26	0.26	0.26	0.27	0.27	0.27	0.28	0.30	0.31	0.33	5
6	0.25	0.25	0.26	0.26	0.27	0.27	0.27	0.28	0.28	0.28	0.28	0.29	0.29	0.30	0.32	0.33	0.36	6
7	0.26	0.27	0.27	0.27	0.28	0.28	0.29	0.29	0.29	0.30	0.30	0.30	0.30	0.32	0.34	0.35	0.38	7
8	0.27	0.28	0.28	0.29	0.29	0.29	0.30	0.30	0.30	0.31	0.31	0.31	0.32	0.33	0.35	0.37	0.40	8
9	0.28	0.28	0.29	0.29	0.30	0.30	0.31	0.31	0.31	0.32	0.32	0.32	0.33	0.35	0.37	0.39	0.42	9
10	0.29	0.29	0.30	0.30	0.31	0.31	0.32	0.32	0.32	0.33	0.33	0.33	0.34	0.36	0.38	0.40	0.43	10
11	0.29	0.30	0.30	0.31	0.31	0.32	0.32	0.33	0.33	0.33	0.34	0.34	0.34	0.37	0.39	0.41	0.44	11
12	0.30	0.30	0.31	0.32	0.32	0.33	0.33	0.33	0.34	0.34	0.35	0.35	0.35	0.38	0.40	0.42	0.46	12
13	0.30	0.31	0.31	0.32	0.33	0.33	0.34	0.34	0.34	0.35	0.35	0.36	0.36	0.38	0.41	0.43	0.47	13
14	0.31	0.31	0.32	0.33	0.33	0.34	0.34	0.35	0.35	0.35	0.36	0.36	0.36	0.39	0.42	0.44	0.48	14
15	0.31	0.32	0.32	0.33	0.34	0.34	0.35	0.35	0.36	0.36	0.36	0.37	0.37	0.40	0.43	0.45	0.49	15
16	0.31	0.32	0.33	0.33	0.34	0.35	0.35	0.36	0.36	0.36	0.37	0.37	0.38	0.40	0.43	0.46	0.50	16
17	0.32	0.32	0.33	0.34	0.34	0.35	0.35	0.36	0.36	0.37	0.37	0.38	0.38	0.41	0.44	0.46	0.51	17
18	0.32	0.33	0.33	0.34	0.35	0.35	0.36	0.36	0.37	0.37	0.38	0.38	0.38	0.41	0.44	0.47	0.52	18
19	0.32	0.33	0.34	0.34	0.35	0.36	0.36	0.37	0.37	0.38	0.38	0.38	0.39	0.42	0.45	0.48	0.52	19
20	0.32	0.33	0.34	0.35	0.35	0.36	0.37	0.37	0.38	0.38	0.38	0.39	0.39	0.42	0.45	0.48	0.53	20
21	0.33	0.34	0.34	0.35	0.36	0.36	0.37	0.37	0.38	0.38	0.39	0.39	0.40	0.43	0.46	0.49	0.54	21
22	0.33	0.34	0.35	0.35	0.36	0.37	0.37	0.38	0.38	0.39	0.39	0.40	0.40	0.43	0.46	0.49	0.55	22
23	0.33	0.34	0.35	0.35	0.36	0.37	0.37	0.38	0.38	0.39	0.39	0.40	0.40	0.43	0.47	0.50	0.55	23
24	0.33	0.34	0.35	0.36	0.36	0.37	0.38	0.38	0.39	0.39	0.40	0.40	0.41	0.44	0.47	0.50	0.56	24
25	0.34	0.34	0.35	0.36	0.37	0.37	0.38	0.38	0.39	0.39	0.40	0.40	0.41	0.44	0.48	0.51	0.56	25
26	0.34	0.35	0.35	0.36	0.37	0.37	0.38	0.39	0.39	0.40	0.40	0.41	0.41	0.44	0.48	0.51	0.57	26
27	0.34	0.35	0.36	0.36	0.37	0.38	0.38	0.39	0.39	0.40	0.40	0.41	0.41	0.45	0.48	0.52	0.57	27
28	0.34	0.35	0.36	0.36	0.37	0.38	0.38	0.39	0.40	0.40	0.41	0.41	0.41	0.45	0.49	0.52	0.58	28
29	0.34	0.35	0.36	0.37	0.37	0.38	0.39	0.39	0.40	0.40	0.41	0.41	0.42	0.45	0.49	0.52	0.58	29
30	0.34	0.35	0.36	0.37	0.37	0.38	0.39	0.39	0.40	0.40	0.41	0.41	0.42	0.45	0.49	0.53	0.59	30
40	0.35	0.36	0.37	0.38	0.39	0.39	0.40	0.41	0.41	0.42	0.42	0.43	0.43	0.47	0.52	0.56	0.63	40
60	0.36	0.37	0.38	0.39	0.40	0.41	0.42	0.42	0.43	0.44	0.44	0.45	0.45	0.50	0.54	0.59	0.68	60
100	0.37	0.38	0.39	0.40	0.41	0.42	0.43	0.44	0.44	0.45	0.46	0.46	0.47	0.52	0.57	0.63	0.74	100
∞	0.39	0.40	0.41	0.42	0.43	0.44	0.45	0.46	0.47	0.48	0.48	0.49	0.50	0.55	0.62	0.70	1.00	∞

Degrees of freedom for the denominator

$F(0.975)$ Distribution Table

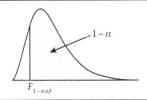

		Degrees of freedom for the numerator																
							(a)											
(b)	1	2	3	4	5	6	7	8	9	10	11	12	13	14	15	16	17	(b)
1	0.00	0.03	0.06	0.08	0.10	0.11	0.12	0.13	0.14	0.14	0.15	0.15	0.16	0.16	0.16	0.16	0.17	1
2	0.00	0.03	0.06	0.09	0.12	0.14	0.15	0.17	0.17	0.18	0.19	0.20	0.20	0.21	0.21	0.21	0.22	2
3	0.00	0.03	0.06	0.10	0.13	0.15	0.17	0.18	0.20	0.21	0.22	0.22	0.23	0.24	0.24	0.25	0.25	3
4	0.00	0.03	0.07	0.10	0.14	0.16	0.18	0.20	0.21	0.22	0.23	0.24	0.25	0.26	0.26	0.27	0.27	4
5	0.00	0.03	0.07	0.11	0.14	0.17	0.19	0.21	0.22	0.24	0.25	0.26	0.27	0.27	0.28	0.29	0.29	5
6	0.00	0.03	0.07	0.11	0.14	0.17	0.20	0.21	0.23	0.25	0.26	0.27	0.28	0.29	0.29	0.30	0.31	6
7	0.00	0.03	0.07	0.11	0.15	0.18	0.20	0.22	0.24	0.25	0.27	0.28	0.29	0.30	0.30	0.31	0.32	7
8	0.00	0.03	0.07	0.11	0.15	0.18	0.20	0.23	0.24	0.26	0.27	0.28	0.30	0.30	0.31	0.32	0.33	8
9	0.00	0.03	0.07	0.11	0.15	0.18	0.21	0.23	0.25	0.26	0.28	0.29	0.30	0.31	0.32	0.33	0.34	9
10	0.00	0.03	0.07	0.11	0.15	0.18	0.21	0.23	0.25	0.27	0.28	0.30	0.31	0.32	0.33	0.33	0.34	10
11	0.00	0.03	0.07	0.11	0.15	0.18	0.21	0.24	0.26	0.27	0.29	0.30	0.31	0.32	0.33	0.34	0.35	11
12	0.00	0.03	0.07	0.11	0.15	0.19	0.21	0.24	0.26	0.28	0.29	0.31	0.32	0.33	0.34	0.35	0.35	12
13	0.00	0.03	0.07	0.11	0.15	0.19	0.22	0.24	0.26	0.28	0.29	0.31	0.32	0.33	0.34	0.35	0.36	13
14	0.00	0.03	0.07	0.12	0.15	0.19	0.22	0.24	0.26	0.28	0.30	0.31	0.32	0.34	0.35	0.35	0.36	14
15	0.00	0.03	0.07	0.12	0.16	0.19	0.22	0.24	0.27	0.28	0.30	0.31	0.33	0.34	0.35	0.36	0.37	15
16	0.00	0.03	0.07	0.12	0.16	0.19	0.22	0.25	0.27	0.29	0.30	0.32	0.33	0.34	0.35	0.36	0.37	16
17	0.00	0.03	0.07	0.12	0.16	0.19	0.22	0.25	0.27	0.29	0.30	0.32	0.33	0.34	0.36	0.37	0.37	17
18	0.00	0.03	0.07	0.12	0.16	0.19	0.22	0.25	0.27	0.29	0.31	0.32	0.34	0.35	0.36	0.37	0.38	18
19	0.00	0.03	0.07	0.12	0.16	0.19	0.22	0.25	0.27	0.29	0.31	0.32	0.34	0.35	0.36	0.37	0.38	19
20	0.00	0.03	0.07	0.12	0.16	0.19	0.22	0.25	0.27	0.29	0.31	0.33	0.34	0.35	0.36	0.37	0.38	20
21	0.00	0.03	0.07	0.12	0.16	0.19	0.22	0.25	0.27	0.29	0.31	0.33	0.34	0.35	0.36	0.38	0.38	21
22	0.00	0.03	0.07	0.12	0.16	0.19	0.23	0.25	0.27	0.30	0.31	0.33	0.34	0.36	0.37	0.38	0.39	22
23	0.00	0.03	0.07	0.12	0.16	0.19	0.23	0.25	0.28	0.30	0.31	0.33	0.34	0.36	0.37	0.38	0.39	23
24	0.00	0.03	0.07	0.12	0.16	0.20	0.23	0.25	0.28	0.30	0.32	0.33	0.35	0.36	0.37	0.38	0.39	24
25	0.00	0.03	0.07	0.12	0.16	0.20	0.23	0.25	0.28	0.30	0.32	0.33	0.35	0.36	0.37	0.38	0.39	25
26	0.00	0.03	0.07	0.12	0.16	0.20	0.23	0.25	0.28	0.30	0.32	0.33	0.35	0.36	0.37	0.38	0.39	26
27	0.00	0.03	0.07	0.12	0.16	0.20	0.23	0.26	0.28	0.30	0.32	0.33	0.35	0.36	0.37	0.39	0.40	27
28	0.00	0.03	0.07	0.12	0.16	0.20	0.23	0.26	0.28	0.30	0.32	0.34	0.35	0.36	0.38	0.39	0.40	28
29	0.00	0.03	0.07	0.12	0.16	0.20	0.23	0.26	0.28	0.30	0.32	0.34	0.35	0.36	0.38	0.39	0.40	29
30	0.00	0.03	0.07	0.12	0.16	0.20	0.23	0.26	0.28	0.30	0.32	0.34	0.35	0.37	0.38	0.39	0.40	30
40	0.00	0.03	0.07	0.12	0.16	0.20	0.23	0.26	0.29	0.31	0.33	0.34	0.36	0.37	0.39	0.40	0.41	40
60	0.00	0.03	0.07	0.12	0.16	0.20	0.24	0.26	0.29	0.31	0.33	0.35	0.37	0.38	0.40	0.41	0.42	60
100	0.00	0.03	0.07	0.12	0.16	0.20	0.24	0.27	0.29	0.32	0.34	0.36	0.37	0.39	0.40	0.42	0.43	100
∞	0.00	0.03	0.07	0.12	0.17	0.21	0.24	0.27	0.30	0.32	0.35	0.37	0.39	0.40	0.42	0.43	0.44	∞

Degrees of freedom for the denominator

F(0.975) Distribution Table

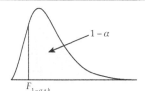

$$1-\alpha$$

$$F_{1-\alpha,a,b}$$

	Degrees of freedom for the numerator (a)																	
(b)	18	19	20	21	22	23	24	25	26	27	28	29	30	40	60	100	∞	(b)
1	0.17	0.17	0.17	0.17	0.17	0.17	0.17	0.18	0.18	0.18	0.18	0.18	0.18	0.18	0.19	0.19	0.20	1
2	0.22	0.22	0.22	0.23	0.23	0.23	0.23	0.23	0.23	0.24	0.24	0.24	0.24	0.25	0.25	0.26	0.27	2
3	0.25	0.26	0.26	0.26	0.26	0.27	0.27	0.27	0.27	0.27	0.28	0.28	0.28	0.29	0.30	0.31	0.32	3
4	0.28	0.28	0.28	0.29	0.29	0.29	0.30	0.30	0.30	0.30	0.30	0.31	0.31	0.32	0.33	0.34	0.36	4
5	0.30	0.30	0.30	0.31	0.31	0.31	0.32	0.32	0.32	0.32	0.33	0.33	0.33	0.34	0.36	0.37	0.39	5
6	0.31	0.32	0.32	0.32	0.33	0.33	0.33	0.34	0.34	0.34	0.34	0.35	0.35	0.36	0.38	0.39	0.42	6
7	0.32	0.33	0.33	0.34	0.34	0.34	0.35	0.35	0.35	0.36	0.36	0.36	0.36	0.38	0.40	0.41	0.44	7
8	0.33	0.34	0.34	0.35	0.35	0.36	0.36	0.36	0.37	0.37	0.37	0.37	0.38	0.40	0.41	0.43	0.46	8
9	0.34	0.35	0.35	0.36	0.36	0.37	0.37	0.37	0.38	0.38	0.38	0.39	0.39	0.41	0.43	0.45	0.47	9
10	0.35	0.35	0.36	0.37	0.37	0.37	0.38	0.38	0.39	0.39	0.39	0.40	0.40	0.42	0.44	0.46	0.49	10
11	0.36	0.36	0.37	0.37	0.38	0.38	0.39	0.39	0.39	0.40	0.40	0.40	0.41	0.43	0.45	0.47	0.50	11
12	0.36	0.37	0.37	0.38	0.38	0.39	0.39	0.40	0.40	0.41	0.41	0.41	0.41	0.44	0.46	0.48	0.51	12
13	0.37	0.37	0.38	0.38	0.39	0.40	0.40	0.40	0.41	0.41	0.42	0.42	0.42	0.44	0.47	0.49	0.53	13
14	0.37	0.38	0.38	0.39	0.40	0.40	0.41	0.41	0.41	0.42	0.42	0.42	0.43	0.45	0.48	0.50	0.54	14
15	0.37	0.38	0.39	0.39	0.40	0.41	0.41	0.41	0.42	0.42	0.43	0.43	0.43	0.46	0.49	0.51	0.55	15
16	0.38	0.39	0.39	0.40	0.40	0.41	0.41	0.42	0.42	0.43	0.43	0.44	0.44	0.46	0.49	0.52	0.55	16
17	0.38	0.39	0.40	0.40	0.41	0.41	0.42	0.42	0.43	0.43	0.44	0.44	0.44	0.47	0.50	0.52	0.56	17
18	0.39	0.39	0.40	0.41	0.41	0.42	0.42	0.43	0.43	0.44	0.44	0.44	0.45	0.47	0.50	0.53	0.57	18
19	0.39	0.40	0.40	0.41	0.42	0.42	0.43	0.43	0.44	0.44	0.44	0.45	0.45	0.48	0.51	0.54	0.58	19
20	0.39	0.40	0.41	0.41	0.42	0.42	0.43	0.43	0.44	0.44	0.45	0.45	0.46	0.48	0.51	0.54	0.59	20
21	0.39	0.40	0.41	0.42	0.42	0.43	0.43	0.44	0.44	0.45	0.45	0.46	0.46	0.49	0.52	0.55	0.59	21
22	0.40	0.40	0.41	0.42	0.42	0.43	0.44	0.44	0.45	0.45	0.45	0.46	0.46	0.49	0.52	0.55	0.60	22
23	0.40	0.41	0.41	0.42	0.43	0.43	0.44	0.44	0.45	0.45	0.46	0.46	0.47	0.49	0.53	0.56	0.60	23
24	0.40	0.41	0.42	0.42	0.43	0.43	0.44	0.45	0.45	0.46	0.46	0.46	0.47	0.50	0.53	0.56	0.61	24
25	0.40	0.41	0.42	0.42	0.43	0.44	0.44	0.45	0.45	0.46	0.46	0.47	0.47	0.50	0.54	0.56	0.62	25
26	0.40	0.41	0.42	0.43	0.43	0.44	0.45	0.45	0.46	0.46	0.47	0.47	0.47	0.50	0.54	0.57	0.62	26
27	0.40	0.41	0.42	0.43	0.44	0.44	0.45	0.45	0.46	0.46	0.47	0.47	0.48	0.51	0.54	0.57	0.63	27
28	0.41	0.41	0.42	0.43	0.44	0.44	0.45	0.45	0.46	0.46	0.47	0.47	0.48	0.51	0.55	0.58	0.63	28
29	0.41	0.42	0.42	0.43	0.44	0.44	0.45	0.46	0.46	0.47	0.47	0.48	0.48	0.51	0.55	0.58	0.63	29
30	0.41	0.42	0.43	0.43	0.44	0.45	0.45	0.46	0.46	0.47	0.47	0.48	0.48	0.51	0.55	0.58	0.64	30
40	0.42	0.43	0.44	0.45	0.45	0.46	0.47	0.47	0.48	0.48	0.49	0.49	0.50	0.53	0.57	0.61	0.67	40
60	0.43	0.44	0.45	0.46	0.47	0.47	0.48	0.49	0.49	0.50	0.51	0.51	0.52	0.55	0.60	0.64	0.72	60
100	0.44	0.45	0.46	0.47	0.48	0.49	0.49	0.50	0.51	0.51	0.52	0.53	0.53	0.57	0.63	0.67	0.77	100
∞	0.46	0.47	0.48	0.49	0.50	0.51	0.52	0.52	0.53	0.54	0.55	0.55	0.56	0.61	0.67	0.74	1.00	∞

Degrees of freedom for the denominator

F(0.95) Distribution Table

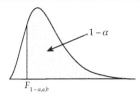

	Degrees of freedom for the numerator																	
	(a)																	
(b)	1	2	3	4	5	6	7	8	9	10	11	12	13	14	15	16	17	(b)
1	0.01	0.05	0.10	0.13	0.15	0.17	0.18	0.19	0.20	0.20	0.21	0.21	0.21	0.22	0.22	0.22	0.22	1
2	0.01	0.05	0.10	0.14	0.17	0.19	0.21	0.22	0.23	0.24	0.25	0.26	0.26	0.27	0.27	0.28	0.28	2
3	0.00	0.05	0.11	0.15	0.18	0.21	0.23	0.25	0.26	0.27	0.28	0.29	0.29	0.30	0.30	0.31	0.31	3
4	0.00	0.05	0.11	0.16	0.19	0.22	0.24	0.26	0.28	0.29	0.30	0.31	0.31	0.32	0.33	0.33	0.34	4
5	0.00	0.05	0.11	0.16	0.19	0.23	0.25	0.27	0.29	0.30	0.31	0.32	0.33	0.34	0.34	0.35	0.36	5
6	0.00	0.05	0.11	0.16	0.20	0.23	0.26	0.28	0.30	0.31	0.32	0.33	0.34	0.35	0.36	0.36	0.37	6
7	0.00	0.05	0.11	0.16	0.21	0.24	0.26	0.29	0.30	0.32	0.33	0.34	0.35	0.36	0.37	0.38	0.38	7
8	0.00	0.05	0.11	0.17	0.21	0.24	0.27	0.29	0.31	0.33	0.34	0.35	0.36	0.37	0.38	0.39	0.39	8
9	0.00	0.05	0.11	0.17	0.21	0.24	0.27	0.30	0.31	0.33	0.35	0.36	0.37	0.38	0.39	0.39	0.40	9
10	0.00	0.05	0.11	0.17	0.21	0.25	0.27	0.30	0.32	0.34	0.35	0.36	0.37	0.38	0.39	0.40	0.41	10
11	0.00	0.05	0.11	0.17	0.21	0.25	0.28	0.30	0.32	0.34	0.35	0.37	0.38	0.39	0.40	0.41	0.41	11
12	0.00	0.05	0.11	0.17	0.21	0.25	0.28	0.30	0.33	0.34	0.36	0.37	0.38	0.39	0.40	0.41	0.42	12
13	0.00	0.05	0.11	0.17	0.21	0.25	0.28	0.31	0.33	0.35	0.36	0.38	0.39	0.40	0.41	0.42	0.42	13
14	0.00	0.05	0.11	0.17	0.22	0.25	0.28	0.31	0.33	0.35	0.37	0.38	0.39	0.40	0.41	0.42	0.43	14
15	0.00	0.05	0.11	0.17	0.22	0.25	0.28	0.31	0.33	0.35	0.37	0.38	0.39	0.41	0.42	0.43	0.43	15
16	0.00	0.05	0.12	0.17	0.22	0.25	0.29	0.31	0.33	0.35	0.37	0.38	0.40	0.41	0.42	0.43	0.44	16
17	0.00	0.05	0.12	0.17	0.22	0.26	0.29	0.31	0.34	0.36	0.37	0.39	0.40	0.41	0.42	0.43	0.44	17
18	0.00	0.05	0.12	0.17	0.22	0.26	0.29	0.32	0.34	0.36	0.37	0.39	0.40	0.41	0.42	0.43	0.44	18
19	0.00	0.05	0.12	0.17	0.22	0.26	0.29	0.32	0.34	0.36	0.38	0.39	0.40	0.42	0.43	0.44	0.45	19
20	0.00	0.05	0.12	0.17	0.22	0.26	0.29	0.32	0.34	0.36	0.38	0.39	0.41	0.42	0.43	0.44	0.45	20
21	0.00	0.05	0.12	0.17	0.22	0.26	0.29	0.32	0.34	0.36	0.38	0.39	0.41	0.42	0.43	0.44	0.45	21
22	0.00	0.05	0.12	0.17	0.22	0.26	0.29	0.32	0.34	0.36	0.38	0.40	0.41	0.42	0.43	0.44	0.45	22
23	0.00	0.05	0.12	0.17	0.22	0.26	0.29	0.32	0.34	0.36	0.38	0.40	0.41	0.42	0.44	0.45	0.45	23
24	0.00	0.05	0.12	0.17	0.22	0.26	0.29	0.32	0.34	0.37	0.38	0.40	0.41	0.43	0.44	0.45	0.46	24
25	0.00	0.05	0.12	0.17	0.22	0.26	0.29	0.32	0.35	0.37	0.38	0.40	0.41	0.43	0.44	0.45	0.46	25
26	0.00	0.05	0.12	0.17	0.22	0.26	0.29	0.32	0.35	0.37	0.39	0.40	0.42	0.43	0.44	0.45	0.46	26
27	0.00	0.05	0.12	0.17	0.22	0.26	0.29	0.32	0.35	0.37	0.39	0.40	0.42	0.43	0.44	0.45	0.46	27
28	0.00	0.05	0.12	0.17	0.22	0.26	0.30	0.32	0.35	0.37	0.39	0.40	0.42	0.43	0.44	0.45	0.46	28
29	0.00	0.05	0.12	0.17	0.22	0.26	0.30	0.32	0.35	0.37	0.39	0.40	0.42	0.43	0.44	0.45	0.46	29
30	0.00	0.05	0.12	0.17	0.22	0.26	0.30	0.32	0.35	0.37	0.39	0.41	0.42	0.43	0.45	0.46	0.47	30
40	0.00	0.05	0.12	0.17	0.22	0.26	0.30	0.33	0.35	0.38	0.40	0.41	0.43	0.44	0.45	0.46	0.48	40
60	0.00	0.05	0.12	0.18	0.23	0.27	0.30	0.33	0.36	0.38	0.40	0.42	0.44	0.45	0.46	0.47	0.49	60
100	0.00	0.05	0.12	0.18	0.23	0.27	0.31	0.34	0.36	0.39	0.41	0.43	0.44	0.46	0.47	0.48	0.49	100
∞	0.00	0.05	0.12	0.18	0.23	0.27	0.31	0.34	0.37	0.39	0.42	0.44	0.45	0.47	0.48	0.50	0.51	∞

Degrees of freedom for the denominator

F(0.95) Distribution Table

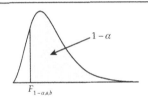

	Degrees of freedom for the numerator																	
	(a)																	
(b)	18	19	20	21	22	23	24	25	26	27	28	29	30	40	60	100	∞	(b)
1	0.23	0.23	0.23	0.23	0.23	0.23	0.23	0.24	0.24	0.24	0.24	0.24	0.24	0.24	0.25	0.25	0.26	1
2	0.28	0.28	0.29	0.29	0.29	0.29	0.29	0.30	0.30	0.30	0.30	0.30	0.30	0.31	0.32	0.32	0.33	2
3	0.32	0.32	0.32	0.33	0.33	0.33	0.33	0.33	0.34	0.34	0.34	0.34	0.34	0.35	0.36	0.37	0.38	3
4	0.34	0.35	0.35	0.35	0.36	0.36	0.36	0.36	0.36	0.37	0.37	0.37	0.37	0.38	0.40	0.41	0.42	4
5	0.36	0.36	0.37	0.37	0.38	0.38	0.38	0.38	0.39	0.39	0.39	0.39	0.39	0.41	0.42	0.43	0.45	5
6	0.38	0.38	0.38	0.39	0.39	0.40	0.40	0.40	0.40	0.41	0.41	0.41	0.41	0.43	0.44	0.46	0.48	6
7	0.39	0.39	0.40	0.40	0.41	0.41	0.41	0.42	0.42	0.42	0.42	0.43	0.43	0.44	0.46	0.48	0.50	7
8	0.40	0.40	0.41	0.41	0.42	0.42	0.42	0.43	0.43	0.43	0.44	0.44	0.44	0.46	0.48	0.49	0.52	8
9	0.41	0.41	0.42	0.42	0.43	0.43	0.43	0.44	0.44	0.44	0.45	0.45	0.45	0.47	0.49	0.51	0.53	9
10	0.41	0.42	0.43	0.43	0.44	0.44	0.44	0.45	0.45	0.45	0.46	0.46	0.46	0.48	0.50	0.52	0.55	10
11	0.42	0.43	0.43	0.44	0.44	0.45	0.45	0.45	0.46	0.46	0.46	0.47	0.47	0.49	0.51	0.53	0.56	11
12	0.43	0.43	0.44	0.44	0.45	0.45	0.46	0.46	0.47	0.47	0.47	0.48	0.48	0.50	0.52	0.54	0.57	12
13	0.43	0.44	0.44	0.45	0.46	0.46	0.46	0.47	0.47	0.48	0.48	0.48	0.48	0.51	0.53	0.55	0.58	13
14	0.44	0.44	0.45	0.46	0.46	0.47	0.47	0.47	0.48	0.48	0.48	0.49	0.49	0.51	0.54	0.56	0.59	14
15	0.44	0.45	0.45	0.46	0.46	0.47	0.47	0.48	0.48	0.49	0.49	0.49	0.50	0.52	0.54	0.57	0.60	15
16	0.44	0.45	0.46	0.46	0.47	0.47	0.48	0.48	0.49	0.49	0.49	0.50	0.50	0.53	0.55	0.57	0.61	16
17	0.45	0.46	0.46	0.47	0.47	0.48	0.48	0.49	0.49	0.50	0.50	0.50	0.51	0.53	0.56	0.58	0.62	17
18	0.45	0.46	0.46	0.47	0.48	0.48	0.49	0.49	0.50	0.50	0.50	0.51	0.51	0.54	0.56	0.59	0.62	18
19	0.45	0.46	0.47	0.47	0.48	0.49	0.49	0.49	0.50	0.50	0.51	0.51	0.51	0.54	0.57	0.59	0.63	19
20	0.46	0.46	0.47	0.48	0.48	0.49	0.49	0.50	0.50	0.51	0.51	0.51	0.52	0.54	0.57	0.60	0.64	20
21	0.46	0.47	0.47	0.48	0.49	0.49	0.50	0.50	0.51	0.51	0.51	0.52	0.52	0.55	0.58	0.60	0.64	21
22	0.46	0.47	0.48	0.48	0.49	0.49	0.50	0.50	0.51	0.51	0.52	0.52	0.52	0.55	0.58	0.61	0.65	22
23	0.46	0.47	0.48	0.48	0.49	0.50	0.50	0.51	0.51	0.52	0.52	0.52	0.53	0.55	0.58	0.61	0.65	23
24	0.47	0.47	0.48	0.49	0.49	0.50	0.50	0.51	0.51	0.52	0.52	0.53	0.53	0.56	0.59	0.61	0.66	24
25	0.47	0.47	0.48	0.49	0.50	0.50	0.51	0.51	0.52	0.52	0.52	0.53	0.53	0.56	0.59	0.62	0.66	25
26	0.47	0.48	0.48	0.49	0.50	0.50	0.51	0.51	0.52	0.52	0.53	0.53	0.53	0.56	0.59	0.62	0.67	26
27	0.47	0.48	0.49	0.49	0.50	0.50	0.51	0.52	0.52	0.52	0.53	0.53	0.54	0.57	0.60	0.63	0.67	27
28	0.47	0.48	0.49	0.49	0.50	0.51	0.51	0.52	0.52	0.53	0.53	0.54	0.54	0.57	0.60	0.63	0.68	28
29	0.47	0.48	0.49	0.50	0.50	0.51	0.51	0.52	0.52	0.53	0.53	0.54	0.54	0.57	0.60	0.63	0.68	29
30	0.47	0.48	0.49	0.50	0.50	0.51	0.52	0.52	0.53	0.53	0.54	0.54	0.54	0.57	0.61	0.64	0.69	30
40	0.48	0.49	0.50	0.51	0.52	0.52	0.53	0.53	0.54	0.54	0.55	0.55	0.56	0.59	0.63	0.66	0.72	40
60	0.50	0.51	0.51	0.52	0.53	0.54	0.54	0.55	0.55	0.56	0.57	0.57	0.57	0.61	0.65	0.69	0.76	60
100	0.51	0.52	0.52	0.53	0.54	0.55	0.56	0.56	0.57	0.57	0.58	0.58	0.59	0.63	0.68	0.72	0.80	100
∞	0.52	0.53	0.54	0.55	0.56	0.57	0.58	0.58	0.59	0.60	0.60	0.61	0.62	0.66	0.72	0.78	1.00	∞

Degrees of freedom for the denominator

F(0.90) Distribution Table

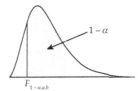

$F_{1-\alpha,a,b}$

| (b) | — Degrees of freedom for the numerator (a) | | | | | | | | | | | | | | | | | (b) |

(b)	1	2	3	4	5	6	7	8	9	10	11	12	13	14	15	16	17	(b)
1	0.03	0.12	0.18	0.22	0.25	0.26	0.28	0.29	0.30	0.30	0.31	0.31	0.32	0.32	0.33	0.33	0.33	1
2	0.02	0.11	0.18	0.23	0.26	0.29	0.31	0.32	0.33	0.34	0.35	0.36	0.36	0.37	0.37	0.37	0.38	2
3	0.02	0.11	0.19	0.24	0.28	0.30	0.33	0.34	0.36	0.37	0.38	0.38	0.39	0.40	0.40	0.41	0.41	3
4	0.02	0.11	0.19	0.24	0.28	0.31	0.34	0.36	0.37	0.38	0.39	0.40	0.41	0.42	0.42	0.43	0.43	4
5	0.02	0.11	0.19	0.25	0.29	0.32	0.35	0.37	0.38	0.40	0.41	0.42	0.43	0.43	0.44	0.45	0.45	5
6	0.02	0.11	0.19	0.25	0.29	0.33	0.35	0.37	0.39	0.41	0.42	0.43	0.44	0.45	0.45	0.46	0.46	6
7	0.02	0.11	0.19	0.25	0.30	0.33	0.36	0.38	0.40	0.41	0.43	0.44	0.45	0.46	0.46	0.47	0.48	7
8	0.02	0.11	0.19	0.25	0.30	0.34	0.36	0.39	0.40	0.42	0.43	0.45	0.46	0.46	0.47	0.48	0.49	8
9	0.02	0.11	0.19	0.25	0.30	0.34	0.37	0.39	0.41	0.43	0.44	0.45	0.46	0.47	0.48	0.49	0.49	9
10	0.02	0.11	0.19	0.26	0.30	0.34	0.37	0.39	0.41	0.43	0.44	0.46	0.47	0.48	0.49	0.49	0.50	10
11	0.02	0.11	0.19	0.26	0.30	0.34	0.37	0.40	0.42	0.43	0.45	0.46	0.47	0.48	0.49	0.50	0.51	11
12	0.02	0.11	0.19	0.26	0.31	0.34	0.37	0.40	0.42	0.44	0.45	0.47	0.48	0.49	0.50	0.50	0.51	12
13	0.02	0.11	0.19	0.26	0.31	0.35	0.38	0.40	0.42	0.44	0.46	0.47	0.48	0.49	0.50	0.51	0.52	13
14	0.02	0.11	0.19	0.26	0.31	0.35	0.38	0.40	0.43	0.44	0.46	0.47	0.48	0.49	0.50	0.51	0.52	14
15	0.02	0.11	0.19	0.26	0.31	0.35	0.38	0.41	0.43	0.45	0.46	0.48	0.49	0.50	0.51	0.52	0.52	15
16	0.02	0.11	0.19	0.26	0.31	0.35	0.38	0.41	0.43	0.45	0.46	0.48	0.49	0.50	0.51	0.52	0.53	16
17	0.02	0.11	0.19	0.26	0.31	0.35	0.38	0.41	0.43	0.45	0.47	0.48	0.49	0.50	0.51	0.52	0.53	17
18	0.02	0.11	0.19	0.26	0.31	0.35	0.38	0.41	0.43	0.45	0.47	0.48	0.49	0.51	0.52	0.52	0.53	18
19	0.02	0.11	0.19	0.26	0.31	0.35	0.38	0.41	0.43	0.45	0.47	0.48	0.50	0.51	0.52	0.53	0.53	19
20	0.02	0.11	0.19	0.26	0.31	0.35	0.39	0.41	0.44	0.45	0.47	0.49	0.50	0.51	0.52	0.53	0.54	20
21	0.02	0.11	0.19	0.26	0.31	0.35	0.39	0.41	0.44	0.46	0.47	0.49	0.50	0.51	0.52	0.53	0.54	21
22	0.02	0.11	0.19	0.26	0.31	0.35	0.39	0.41	0.44	0.46	0.47	0.49	0.50	0.51	0.52	0.53	0.54	22
23	0.02	0.11	0.19	0.26	0.31	0.35	0.39	0.42	0.44	0.46	0.48	0.49	0.50	0.51	0.53	0.53	0.54	23
24	0.02	0.11	0.19	0.26	0.31	0.35	0.39	0.42	0.44	0.46	0.48	0.49	0.50	0.52	0.53	0.54	0.54	24
25	0.02	0.11	0.19	0.26	0.31	0.36	0.39	0.42	0.44	0.46	0.48	0.49	0.51	0.52	0.53	0.54	0.55	25
26	0.02	0.11	0.19	0.26	0.31	0.36	0.39	0.42	0.44	0.46	0.48	0.49	0.51	0.52	0.53	0.54	0.55	26
27	0.02	0.11	0.19	0.26	0.31	0.36	0.39	0.42	0.44	0.46	0.48	0.49	0.51	0.52	0.53	0.54	0.55	27
28	0.02	0.11	0.19	0.26	0.31	0.36	0.39	0.42	0.44	0.46	0.48	0.50	0.51	0.52	0.53	0.54	0.55	28
29	0.02	0.11	0.19	0.26	0.31	0.36	0.39	0.42	0.44	0.46	0.48	0.50	0.51	0.52	0.53	0.54	0.55	29
30	0.02	0.11	0.19	0.26	0.32	0.36	0.39	0.42	0.44	0.46	0.48	0.50	0.51	0.52	0.53	0.54	0.55	30
40	0.02	0.11	0.19	0.26	0.32	0.36	0.39	0.42	0.45	0.47	0.49	0.50	0.52	0.53	0.54	0.55	0.56	40
60	0.02	0.11	0.19	0.26	0.32	0.36	0.40	0.43	0.45	0.47	0.49	0.51	0.53	0.54	0.55	0.56	0.57	60
100	0.02	0.11	0.19	0.26	0.32	0.36	0.40	0.43	0.46	0.48	0.50	0.52	0.53	0.55	0.56	0.57	0.58	100
∞	0.02	0.11	0.19	0.27	0.32	0.37	0.40	0.44	0.46	0.49	0.51	0.53	0.54	0.56	0.57	0.58	0.59	∞

Degrees of freedom for the denominator

F(0.90) Distribution Table

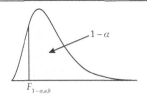

(b)							Degrees of freedom for the numerator (a)											(b)
	18	19	20	21	22	23	24	25	26	27	28	29	30	40	60	100	∞	
1	0.33	0.33	0.34	0.34	0.34	0.34	0.34	0.34	0.34	0.34	0.35	0.35	0.35	0.35	0.36	0.36	0.37	1
2	0.38	0.38	0.39	0.39	0.39	0.39	0.39	0.40	0.40	0.40	0.40	0.40	0.40	0.41	0.42	0.42	0.43	2
3	0.41	0.42	0.42	0.42	0.43	0.43	0.43	0.43	0.43	0.44	0.44	0.44	0.44	0.45	0.46	0.47	0.48	3
4	0.44	0.44	0.44	0.45	0.45	0.45	0.46	0.46	0.46	0.46	0.46	0.47	0.47	0.48	0.49	0.50	0.51	4
5	0.46	0.46	0.46	0.47	0.47	0.47	0.48	0.48	0.48	0.48	0.48	0.49	0.49	0.50	0.51	0.52	0.54	5
6	0.47	0.47	0.48	0.48	0.49	0.49	0.49	0.49	0.50	0.50	0.50	0.50	0.50	0.52	0.53	0.55	0.56	6
7	0.48	0.49	0.49	0.49	0.50	0.50	0.50	0.51	0.51	0.51	0.51	0.52	0.52	0.53	0.55	0.56	0.58	7
8	0.49	0.50	0.50	0.50	0.51	0.51	0.52	0.52	0.52	0.52	0.53	0.53	0.53	0.55	0.56	0.58	0.60	8
9	0.50	0.50	0.51	0.51	0.52	0.52	0.52	0.53	0.53	0.53	0.54	0.54	0.54	0.56	0.58	0.59	0.61	9
10	0.51	0.51	0.52	0.52	0.53	0.53	0.53	0.54	0.54	0.54	0.54	0.55	0.55	0.57	0.59	0.60	0.63	10
11	0.51	0.52	0.52	0.53	0.53	0.54	0.54	0.54	0.55	0.55	0.55	0.55	0.56	0.58	0.60	0.61	0.64	11
12	0.52	0.52	0.53	0.53	0.54	0.54	0.55	0.55	0.55	0.56	0.56	0.56	0.56	0.58	0.60	0.62	0.65	12
13	0.52	0.53	0.53	0.54	0.54	0.55	0.55	0.56	0.56	0.56	0.56	0.57	0.57	0.59	0.61	0.63	0.66	13
14	0.53	0.53	0.54	0.54	0.55	0.55	0.56	0.56	0.56	0.57	0.57	0.57	0.58	0.60	0.62	0.64	0.66	14
15	0.53	0.54	0.54	0.55	0.55	0.56	0.56	0.56	0.57	0.57	0.57	0.58	0.58	0.60	0.62	0.64	0.67	15
16	0.53	0.54	0.55	0.55	0.56	0.56	0.56	0.57	0.57	0.58	0.58	0.58	0.59	0.61	0.63	0.65	0.68	16
17	0.54	0.54	0.55	0.55	0.56	0.56	0.57	0.57	0.58	0.58	0.58	0.59	0.59	0.61	0.63	0.65	0.69	17
18	0.54	0.55	0.55	0.56	0.56	0.57	0.57	0.58	0.58	0.58	0.59	0.59	0.59	0.62	0.64	0.66	0.69	18
19	0.54	0.55	0.55	0.56	0.57	0.57	0.58	0.58	0.58	0.59	0.59	0.59	0.60	0.62	0.64	0.66	0.70	19
20	0.54	0.55	0.56	0.56	0.57	0.57	0.58	0.58	0.59	0.59	0.59	0.60	0.60	0.62	0.65	0.67	0.70	20
21	0.55	0.55	0.56	0.57	0.57	0.58	0.58	0.58	0.59	0.59	0.60	0.60	0.60	0.63	0.65	0.67	0.71	21
22	0.55	0.56	0.56	0.57	0.57	0.58	0.58	0.59	0.59	0.60	0.60	0.60	0.61	0.63	0.66	0.68	0.71	22
23	0.55	0.56	0.56	0.57	0.58	0.58	0.59	0.59	0.59	0.60	0.60	0.60	0.61	0.63	0.66	0.68	0.72	23
24	0.55	0.56	0.57	0.57	0.58	0.58	0.59	0.59	0.60	0.60	0.60	0.61	0.61	0.64	0.66	0.68	0.72	24
25	0.55	0.56	0.57	0.57	0.58	0.58	0.59	0.59	0.60	0.60	0.61	0.61	0.61	0.64	0.66	0.69	0.73	25
26	0.56	0.56	0.57	0.58	0.58	0.59	0.59	0.60	0.60	0.60	0.61	0.61	0.62	0.64	0.67	0.69	0.73	26
27	0.56	0.56	0.57	0.58	0.58	0.59	0.59	0.60	0.60	0.61	0.61	0.61	0.62	0.64	0.67	0.69	0.73	27
28	0.56	0.57	0.57	0.58	0.58	0.59	0.59	0.60	0.60	0.61	0.61	0.62	0.62	0.64	0.67	0.70	0.74	28
29	0.56	0.57	0.57	0.58	0.59	0.59	0.60	0.60	0.61	0.61	0.61	0.62	0.62	0.65	0.68	0.70	0.74	29
30	0.56	0.57	0.58	0.58	0.59	0.59	0.60	0.60	0.61	0.61	0.62	0.62	0.62	0.65	0.68	0.70	0.75	30
40	0.57	0.58	0.59	0.59	0.60	0.60	0.61	0.61	0.62	0.62	0.63	0.63	0.64	0.66	0.70	0.72	0.77	40
60	0.58	0.59	0.60	0.60	0.61	0.62	0.62	0.63	0.63	0.64	0.64	0.65	0.65	0.68	0.72	0.75	0.81	60
100	0.59	0.60	0.61	0.61	0.62	0.63	0.63	0.64	0.64	0.65	0.65	0.66	0.66	0.70	0.74	0.77	0.84	100
∞	0.60	0.61	0.62	0.63	0.64	0.65	0.65	0.66	0.67	0.67	0.68	0.68	0.69	0.73	0.77	0.82	1.00	∞

Degrees of freedom for the denominator

$F(0.10)$ Distribution Table

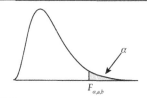

		Degrees of freedom for the numerator																
								(a)										
(b)	1	2	3	4	5	6	7	8	9	10	11	12	13	14	15	16	17	(b)
1	39.86	49.50	53.59	55.83	57.24	58.20	58.91	59.44	59.86	60.19	60.47	60.71	60.90	61.07	61.22	61.35	61.46	1
2	8.53	9.00	9.16	9.24	9.29	9.33	9.35	9.37	9.38	9.39	9.40	9.41	9.41	9.42	9.42	9.43	9.43	2
3	5.54	5.46	5.39	5.34	5.31	5.28	5.27	5.25	5.24	5.23	5.22	5.22	5.21	5.20	5.20	5.20	5.19	3
4	4.54	4.32	4.19	4.11	4.05	4.01	3.98	3.95	3.94	3.92	3.91	3.90	3.89	3.88	3.87	3.86	3.86	4
5	4.06	3.78	3.62	3.52	3.45	3.40	3.37	3.34	3.32	3.30	3.28	3.27	3.26	3.25	3.24	3.23	3.22	5
6	3.78	3.46	3.29	3.18	3.11	3.05	3.01	2.98	2.96	2.94	2.92	2.90	2.89	2.88	2.87	2.86	2.85	6
7	3.59	3.26	3.07	2.96	2.88	2.83	2.78	2.75	2.72	2.70	2.68	2.67	2.65	2.64	2.63	2.62	2.61	7
8	3.46	3.11	2.92	2.81	2.73	2.67	2.62	2.59	2.56	2.54	2.52	2.50	2.49	2.48	2.46	2.45	2.45	8
9	3.36	3.01	2.81	2.69	2.61	2.55	2.51	2.47	2.44	2.42	2.40	2.38	2.36	2.35	2.34	2.33	2.32	9
10	3.29	2.92	2.73	2.61	2.52	2.46	2.41	2.38	2.35	2.32	2.30	2.28	2.27	2.26	2.24	2.23	2.22	10
11	3.23	2.86	2.66	2.54	2.45	2.39	2.34	2.30	2.27	2.25	2.23	2.21	2.19	2.18	2.17	2.16	2.15	11
12	3.18	2.81	2.61	2.48	2.39	2.33	2.28	2.24	2.21	2.19	2.17	2.15	2.13	2.12	2.10	2.09	2.08	12
13	3.14	2.76	2.56	2.43	2.35	2.28	2.23	2.20	2.16	2.14	2.12	2.10	2.08	2.07	2.05	2.04	2.03	13
14	3.10	2.73	2.52	2.39	2.31	2.24	2.19	2.15	2.12	2.10	2.07	2.05	2.04	2.02	2.01	2.00	1.99	14
15	3.07	2.70	2.49	2.36	2.27	2.21	2.16	2.12	2.09	2.06	2.04	2.02	2.00	1.99	1.97	1.96	1.95	15
16	3.05	2.67	2.46	2.33	2.24	2.18	2.13	2.09	2.06	2.03	2.01	1.99	1.97	1.95	1.94	1.93	1.92	16
17	3.03	2.64	2.44	2.31	2.22	2.15	2.10	2.06	2.03	2.00	1.98	1.96	1.94	1.93	1.91	1.90	1.89	17
18	3.01	2.62	2.42	2.29	2.20	2.13	2.08	2.04	2.00	1.98	1.95	1.93	1.92	1.90	1.89	1.87	1.86	18
19	2.99	2.61	2.40	2.27	2.18	2.11	2.06	2.02	1.98	1.96	1.93	1.91	1.89	1.88	1.86	1.85	1.84	19
20	2.97	2.59	2.38	2.25	2.16	2.09	2.04	2.00	1.96	1.94	1.91	1.89	1.87	1.86	1.84	1.83	1.82	20
21	2.96	2.57	2.36	2.23	2.14	2.08	2.02	1.98	1.95	1.92	1.90	1.87	1.86	1.84	1.83	1.81	1.80	21
22	2.95	2.56	2.35	2.22	2.13	2.06	2.01	1.97	1.93	1.90	1.88	1.86	1.84	1.83	1.81	1.80	1.79	22
23	2.94	2.55	2.34	2.21	2.11	2.05	1.99	1.95	1.92	1.89	1.87	1.84	1.83	1.81	1.80	1.78	1.77	23
24	2.93	2.54	2.33	2.19	2.10	2.04	1.98	1.94	1.91	1.88	1.85	1.83	1.81	1.80	1.78	1.77	1.76	24
25	2.92	2.53	2.32	2.18	2.09	2.02	1.97	1.93	1.89	1.87	1.84	1.82	1.80	1.79	1.77	1.76	1.75	25
26	2.91	2.52	2.31	2.17	2.08	2.01	1.96	1.92	1.88	1.86	1.83	1.81	1.79	1.77	1.76	1.75	1.73	26
27	2.90	2.51	2.30	2.17	2.07	2.00	1.95	1.91	1.87	1.85	1.82	1.80	1.78	1.76	1.75	1.74	1.72	27
28	2.89	2.50	2.29	2.16	2.06	2.00	1.94	1.90	1.87	1.84	1.81	1.79	1.77	1.75	1.74	1.73	1.71	28
29	2.89	2.50	2.28	2.15	2.06	1.99	1.93	1.89	1.86	1.83	1.80	1.78	1.76	1.75	1.73	1.72	1.71	29
30	2.88	2.49	2.28	2.14	2.05	1.98	1.93	1.88	1.85	1.82	1.79	1.77	1.75	1.74	1.72	1.71	1.70	30
40	2.84	2.44	2.23	2.09	2.00	1.93	1.87	1.83	1.79	1.76	1.74	1.71	1.70	1.68	1.66	1.65	1.64	40
60	2.79	2.39	2.18	2.04	1.95	1.87	1.82	1.77	1.74	1.71	1.68	1.66	1.64	1.62	1.60	1.59	1.58	60
100	2.76	2.36	2.14	2.00	1.91	1.83	1.78	1.73	1.69	1.66	1.64	1.61	1.59	1.57	1.56	1.54	1.53	100
∞	2.71	2.30	2.08	1.94	1.85	1.77	1.72	1.67	1.63	1.60	1.57	1.55	1.52	1.50	1.49	1.47	1.46	∞

Degrees of freedom for the denominator

F(0.10) Distribution Table

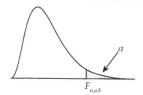

	Degrees of freedom for the numerator																	
	(a)																	
(b)	18	19	20	21	22	23	24	25	26	27	28	29	30	40	60	100	∞	(b)
1	61.57	61.66	61.74	61.81	61.88	61.95	62.00	62.05	62.10	62.15	62.19	62.23	62.26	62.53	62.79	63.01	63.33	1
2	9.44	9.44	9.44	9.44	9.45	9.45	9.45	9.45	9.45	9.45	9.46	9.46	9.46	9.47	9.47	9.48	9.49	2
3	5.19	5.19	5.18	5.18	5.18	5.18	5.18	5.17	5.17	5.17	5.17	5.17	5.17	5.16	5.15	5.14	5.13	3
4	3.85	3.85	3.84	3.84	3.84	3.83	3.83	3.83	3.83	3.82	3.82	3.82	3.82	3.80	3.79	3.78	3.76	4
5	3.22	3.21	3.21	3.20	3.20	3.19	3.19	3.19	3.18	3.18	3.18	3.18	3.17	3.16	3.14	3.13	3.10	5
6	2.85	2.84	2.84	2.83	2.83	2.82	2.82	2.81	2.81	2.81	2.81	2.80	2.80	2.78	2.76	2.75	2.72	6
7	2.61	2.60	2.59	2.59	2.58	2.58	2.58	2.57	2.57	2.56	2.56	2.56	2.56	2.54	2.51	2.50	2.47	7
8	2.44	2.43	2.42	2.42	2.41	2.41	2.40	2.40	2.40	2.39	2.39	2.39	2.38	2.36	2.34	2.32	2.29	8
9	2.31	2.30	2.30	2.29	2.29	2.28	2.28	2.27	2.27	2.26	2.26	2.26	2.25	2.23	2.21	2.19	2.16	9
10	2.22	2.21	2.20	2.19	2.19	2.18	2.18	2.17	2.17	2.17	2.16	2.16	2.16	2.13	2.11	2.09	2.06	10
11	2.14	2.13	2.12	2.12	2.11	2.11	2.10	2.10	2.09	2.09	2.08	2.08	2.08	2.05	2.03	2.01	1.97	11
12	2.08	2.07	2.06	2.05	2.05	2.04	2.04	2.03	2.03	2.02	2.02	2.01	2.01	1.99	1.96	1.94	1.90	12
13	2.02	2.01	2.01	2.00	1.99	1.99	1.98	1.98	1.97	1.97	1.96	1.96	1.96	1.93	1.90	1.88	1.85	13
14	1.98	1.97	1.96	1.96	1.95	1.94	1.94	1.93	1.93	1.92	1.92	1.92	1.91	1.89	1.86	1.83	1.80	14
15	1.94	1.93	1.92	1.92	1.91	1.90	1.90	1.89	1.89	1.88	1.88	1.88	1.87	1.85	1.82	1.79	1.76	15
16	1.91	1.90	1.89	1.88	1.88	1.87	1.87	1.86	1.86	1.85	1.85	1.84	1.84	1.81	1.78	1.76	1.72	16
17	1.88	1.87	1.86	1.86	1.85	1.84	1.84	1.83	1.83	1.82	1.82	1.81	1.81	1.78	1.75	1.73	1.69	17
18	1.85	1.84	1.84	1.83	1.82	1.82	1.81	1.80	1.80	1.80	1.79	1.79	1.78	1.75	1.72	1.70	1.66	18
19	1.83	1.82	1.81	1.81	1.80	1.79	1.79	1.78	1.78	1.77	1.77	1.76	1.76	1.73	1.70	1.67	1.63	19
20	1.81	1.80	1.79	1.79	1.78	1.77	1.77	1.76	1.76	1.75	1.75	1.74	1.74	1.71	1.68	1.65	1.61	20
21	1.79	1.78	1.78	1.77	1.76	1.75	1.75	1.74	1.74	1.73	1.73	1.72	1.72	1.69	1.66	1.63	1.59	21
22	1.78	1.77	1.76	1.75	1.74	1.74	1.73	1.73	1.72	1.72	1.71	1.71	1.70	1.67	1.64	1.61	1.57	22
23	1.76	1.75	1.74	1.74	1.73	1.72	1.72	1.71	1.70	1.70	1.69	1.69	1.69	1.66	1.62	1.59	1.55	23
24	1.75	1.74	1.73	1.72	1.71	1.71	1.70	1.70	1.69	1.69	1.68	1.68	1.67	1.64	1.61	1.58	1.53	24
25	1.74	1.73	1.72	1.71	1.70	1.70	1.69	1.68	1.68	1.67	1.67	1.66	1.66	1.63	1.59	1.56	1.52	25
26	1.72	1.71	1.71	1.70	1.69	1.68	1.68	1.67	1.67	1.66	1.66	1.65	1.65	1.61	1.58	1.55	1.50	26
27	1.71	1.70	1.70	1.69	1.68	1.67	1.67	1.66	1.65	1.65	1.64	1.64	1.64	1.60	1.57	1.54	1.49	27
28	1.70	1.69	1.69	1.68	1.67	1.66	1.66	1.65	1.64	1.64	1.63	1.63	1.63	1.59	1.56	1.53	1.48	28
29	1.69	1.68	1.68	1.67	1.66	1.65	1.65	1.64	1.63	1.63	1.62	1.62	1.62	1.58	1.55	1.52	1.47	29
30	1.69	1.68	1.67	1.66	1.65	1.64	1.64	1.63	1.63	1.62	1.62	1.61	1.61	1.57	1.54	1.51	1.46	30
40	1.62	1.61	1.61	1.60	1.59	1.58	1.57	1.57	1.56	1.56	1.55	1.55	1.54	1.51	1.47	1.43	1.38	40
60	1.56	1.55	1.54	1.53	1.53	1.52	1.51	1.50	1.50	1.49	1.49	1.48	1.48	1.44	1.40	1.36	1.29	60
100	1.52	1.50	1.49	1.48	1.48	1.47	1.46	1.45	1.45	1.44	1.43	1.43	1.42	1.38	1.34	1.29	1.21	100
∞	1.44	1.43	1.42	1.41	1.40	1.39	1.38	1.38	1.37	1.36	1.35	1.35	1.34	1.30	1.24	1.18	1.00	∞

Degrees of freedom for the denominator

F(0.05) Distribution Table

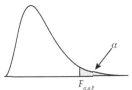

$$F_{\alpha,a,b}$$

(b)					Degrees of freedom for the numerator (a)													(b)
(b)	1	2	3	4	5	6	7	8	9	10	11	12	13	14	15	16	17	(b)
1	161.45	199.50	215.71	224.58	230.16	233.99	236.77	238.88	240.54	241.88	242.98	243.91	244.69	245.36	245.95	246.46	246.92	1
2	18.51	19.00	19.16	19.25	19.30	19.33	19.35	19.37	19.38	19.40	19.40	19.41	19.42	19.42	19.43	19.43	19.44	2
3	10.13	9.55	9.28	9.12	9.01	8.94	8.89	8.85	8.81	8.79	8.76	8.74	8.73	8.71	8.70	8.69	8.68	3
4	7.71	6.94	6.59	6.39	6.26	6.16	6.09	6.04	6.00	5.96	5.94	5.91	5.89	5.87	5.86	5.84	5.83	4
5	6.61	5.79	5.41	5.19	5.05	4.95	4.88	4.82	4.77	4.74	4.70	4.68	4.66	4.64	4.62	4.60	4.59	5
6	5.99	5.14	4.76	4.53	4.39	4.28	4.21	4.15	4.10	4.06	4.03	4.00	3.98	3.96	3.94	3.92	3.91	6
7	5.59	4.74	4.35	4.12	3.97	3.87	3.79	3.73	3.68	3.64	3.60	3.57	3.55	3.53	3.51	3.49	3.48	7
8	5.32	4.46	4.07	3.84	3.69	3.58	3.50	3.44	3.39	3.35	3.31	3.28	3.26	3.24	3.22	3.20	3.19	8
9	5.12	4.26	3.86	3.63	3.48	3.37	3.29	3.23	3.18	3.14	3.10	3.07	3.05	3.03	3.01	2.99	2.97	9
10	4.96	4.10	3.71	3.48	3.33	3.22	3.14	3.07	3.02	2.98	2.94	2.91	2.89	2.86	2.85	2.83	2.81	10
11	4.84	3.98	3.59	3.36	3.20	3.09	3.01	2.95	2.90	2.85	2.82	2.79	2.76	2.74	2.72	2.70	2.69	11
12	4.75	3.89	3.49	3.26	3.11	3.00	2.91	2.85	2.80	2.75	2.72	2.69	2.66	2.64	2.62	2.60	2.58	12
13	4.67	3.81	3.41	3.18	3.03	2.92	2.83	2.77	2.71	2.67	2.63	2.60	2.58	2.55	2.53	2.51	2.50	13
14	4.60	3.74	3.34	3.11	2.96	2.85	2.76	2.70	2.65	2.60	2.57	2.53	2.51	2.48	2.46	2.44	2.43	14
15	4.54	3.68	3.29	3.06	2.90	2.79	2.71	2.64	2.59	2.54	2.51	2.48	2.45	2.42	2.40	2.38	2.37	15
16	4.49	3.63	3.24	3.01	2.85	2.74	2.66	2.59	2.54	2.49	2.46	2.42	2.40	2.37	2.35	2.33	2.32	16
17	4.45	3.59	3.20	2.96	2.81	2.70	2.61	2.55	2.49	2.45	2.41	2.38	2.35	2.33	2.31	2.29	2.27	17
18	4.41	3.55	3.16	2.93	2.77	2.66	2.58	2.51	2.46	2.41	2.37	2.34	2.31	2.29	2.27	2.25	2.23	18
19	4.38	3.52	3.13	2.90	2.74	2.63	2.54	2.48	2.42	2.38	2.34	2.31	2.28	2.26	2.23	2.21	2.20	19
20	4.35	3.49	3.10	2.87	2.71	2.60	2.51	2.45	2.39	2.35	2.31	2.28	2.25	2.22	2.20	2.18	2.17	20
21	4.32	3.47	3.07	2.84	2.68	2.57	2.49	2.42	2.37	2.32	2.28	2.25	2.22	2.20	2.18	2.16	2.14	21
22	4.30	3.44	3.05	2.82	2.66	2.55	2.46	2.40	2.34	2.30	2.26	2.23	2.20	2.17	2.15	2.13	2.11	22
23	4.28	3.42	3.03	2.80	2.64	2.53	2.44	2.37	2.32	2.27	2.24	2.20	2.18	2.15	2.13	2.11	2.09	23
24	4.26	3.40	3.01	2.78	2.62	2.51	2.42	2.36	2.30	2.25	2.22	2.18	2.15	2.13	2.11	2.09	2.07	24
25	4.24	3.39	2.99	2.76	2.60	2.49	2.40	2.34	2.28	2.24	2.20	2.16	2.14	2.11	2.09	2.07	2.05	25
26	4.23	3.37	2.98	2.74	2.59	2.47	2.39	2.32	2.27	2.22	2.18	2.15	2.12	2.09	2.07	2.05	2.03	26
27	4.21	3.35	2.96	2.73	2.57	2.46	2.37	2.31	2.25	2.20	2.17	2.13	2.10	2.08	2.06	2.04	2.02	27
28	4.20	3.34	2.95	2.71	2.56	2.45	2.36	2.29	2.24	2.19	2.15	2.12	2.09	2.06	2.04	2.02	2.00	28
29	4.18	3.33	2.93	2.70	2.55	2.43	2.35	2.28	2.22	2.18	2.14	2.10	2.08	2.05	2.03	2.01	1.99	29
30	4.17	3.32	2.92	2.69	2.53	2.42	2.33	2.27	2.21	2.16	2.13	2.09	2.06	2.04	2.01	1.99	1.98	30
40	4.08	3.23	2.84	2.61	2.45	2.34	2.25	2.18	2.12	2.08	2.04	2.00	1.97	1.95	1.92	1.90	1.89	40
60	4.00	3.15	2.76	2.53	2.37	2.25	2.17	2.10	2.04	1.99	1.95	1.92	1.89	1.86	1.84	1.82	1.80	60
100	3.94	3.09	2.70	2.46	2.31	2.19	2.10	2.03	1.97	1.93	1.89	1.85	1.82	1.79	1.77	1.75	1.73	100
∞	3.84	3.00	2.60	2.37	2.21	2.10	2.01	1.94	1.88	1.83	1.79	1.75	1.72	1.69	1.67	1.64	1.62	∞

Degrees of freedom for the denominator

F(0.05) Distribution Table

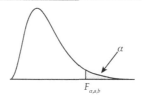

(b)	18	19	20	21	22	23	24	25	26	27	28	29	30	40	60	100	∞	(b)
1	247.32	247.69	248.01	248.31	248.58	248.83	249.05	249.26	249.45	249.63	249.80	249.95	250.10	251.14	252.20	253.04	254.31	1
2	19.44	19.44	19.45	19.45	19.45	19.45	19.45	19.46	19.46	19.46	19.46	19.46	19.46	19.47	19.48	19.49	9.49	2
3	8.67	8.67	8.66	8.65	8.65	8.64	8.64	8.63	8.63	8.63	8.62	8.62	8.62	8.59	8.57	8.55	5.13	3
4	5.82	5.81	5.80	5.79	5.79	5.78	5.77	5.77	5.76	5.76	5.75	5.75	5.75	5.72	5.69	5.66	3.76	4
5	4.58	4.57	4.56	4.55	4.54	4.53	4.53	4.52	4.52	4.51	4.50	4.50	4.50	4.46	4.43	4.41	3.10	5
6	3.90	3.88	3.87	3.86	3.86	3.85	3.84	3.83	3.83	3.82	3.82	3.81	3.81	3.77	3.74	3.71	2.72	6
7	3.47	3.46	3.44	3.43	3.43	3.42	3.41	3.40	3.40	3.39	3.39	3.38	3.38	3.34	3.30	3.27	2.47	7
8	3.17	3.16	3.15	3.14	3.13	3.12	3.12	3.11	3.10	3.10	3.09	3.08	3.08	3.04	3.01	2.97	2.29	8
9	2.96	2.95	2.94	2.93	2.92	2.91	2.90	2.89	2.89	2.88	2.87	2.87	2.86	2.83	2.79	2.76	2.16	9
10	2.80	2.79	2.77	2.76	2.75	2.75	2.74	2.73	2.72	2.72	2.71	2.70	2.70	2.66	2.62	2.59	2.06	10
11	2.67	2.66	2.65	2.64	2.63	2.62	2.61	2.60	2.59	2.59	2.58	2.58	2.57	2.53	2.49	2.46	1.97	11
12	2.57	2.56	2.54	2.53	2.52	2.51	2.51	2.50	2.49	2.48	2.48	2.47	2.47	2.43	2.38	2.35	1.90	12
13	2.48	2.47	2.46	2.45	2.44	2.43	2.42	2.41	2.41	2.40	2.39	2.39	2.38	2.34	2.30	2.26	1.85	13
14	2.41	2.40	2.39	2.38	2.37	2.36	2.35	2.34	2.33	2.33	2.32	2.31	2.31	2.27	2.22	2.19	1.80	14
15	2.35	2.34	2.33	2.32	2.31	2.30	2.29	2.28	2.27	2.27	2.26	2.25	2.25	2.20	2.16	2.12	1.76	15
16	2.30	2.29	2.28	2.26	2.25	2.24	2.24	2.23	2.22	2.21	2.21	2.20	2.19	2.15	2.11	2.07	1.72	16
17	2.26	2.24	2.23	2.22	2.21	2.20	2.19	2.18	2.17	2.17	2.16	2.15	2.15	2.10	2.06	2.02	1.69	17
18	2.22	2.20	2.19	2.18	2.17	2.16	2.15	2.14	2.13	2.13	2.12	2.11	2.11	2.06	2.02	1.98	1.66	18
19	2.18	2.17	2.16	2.14	2.13	2.12	2.11	2.11	2.10	2.09	2.08	2.08	2.07	2.03	1.98	1.94	1.63	19
20	2.15	2.14	2.12	2.11	2.10	2.09	2.08	2.07	2.07	2.06	2.05	2.05	2.04	1.99	1.95	1.91	1.61	20
21	2.12	2.11	2.10	2.08	2.07	2.06	2.05	2.05	2.04	2.03	2.02	2.02	2.01	1.96	1.92	1.88	1.59	21
22	2.10	2.08	2.07	2.06	2.05	2.04	2.03	2.02	2.01	2.00	2.00	1.99	1.98	1.94	1.89	1.85	1.57	22
23	2.08	2.06	2.05	2.04	2.02	2.01	2.01	2.00	1.99	1.98	1.97	1.97	1.96	1.91	1.86	1.82	1.55	23
24	2.05	2.04	2.03	2.01	2.00	1.99	1.98	1.97	1.97	1.96	1.95	1.95	1.94	1.89	1.84	1.80	1.53	24
25	2.04	2.02	2.01	2.00	1.98	1.97	1.96	1.96	1.95	1.94	1.93	1.93	1.92	1.87	1.82	1.78	1.52	25
26	2.02	2.00	1.99	1.98	1.97	1.96	1.95	1.94	1.93	1.92	1.91	1.91	1.90	1.85	1.80	1.76	1.50	26
27	2.00	1.99	1.97	1.96	1.95	1.94	1.93	1.92	1.91	1.90	1.90	1.89	1.88	1.84	1.79	1.74	1.49	27
28	1.99	1.97	1.96	1.95	1.93	1.92	1.91	1.91	1.90	1.89	1.88	1.88	1.87	1.82	1.77	1.73	1.48	28
29	1.97	1.96	1.94	1.93	1.92	1.91	1.90	1.89	1.88	1.88	1.87	1.86	1.85	1.81	1.75	1.71	1.47	29
30	1.96	1.95	1.93	1.92	1.91	1.90	1.89	1.88	1.87	1.86	1.85	1.85	1.84	1.79	1.74	1.70	1.46	30
40	1.87	1.85	1.84	1.83	1.81	1.80	1.79	1.78	1.77	1.77	1.76	1.75	1.74	1.69	1.64	1.59	1.38	40
60	1.78	1.76	1.75	1.73	1.72	1.71	1.70	1.69	1.68	1.67	1.66	1.66	1.65	1.59	1.53	1.48	1.29	60
100	1.71	1.69	1.68	1.66	1.65	1.64	1.63	1.62	1.61	1.60	1.59	1.58	1.57	1.52	1.45	1.39	1.21	100
∞	1.60	1.59	1.57	1.56	1.54	1.53	1.52	1.51	1.50	1.49	1.48	1.47	1.46	1.39	1.32	1.24	1.00	∞

Degrees of freedom for the numerator (a)

Degrees of freedom for the denominator

F(0.025) Distribution Table

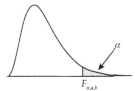

	Degrees of freedom for the numerator																	
	(a)																	
(b)	1	2	3	4	5	6	7	8	9	10	11	12	13	14	15	16	17	(b)
1	647.79	799.50	864.16	899.58	921.85	937.11	948.22	956.66	963.28	968.63	973.03	976.71	979.84	982.53	984.87	986.92	988.73	1
2	38.51	39.00	39.17	39.25	39.30	39.33	39.36	39.37	39.39	39.40	39.41	39.41	39.42	39.43	39.43	39.44	39.44	2
3	17.44	16.04	15.44	15.10	14.88	14.73	14.62	14.54	14.47	14.42	14.37	14.34	14.30	14.28	14.25	14.23	14.21	3
4	12.22	10.65	9.98	9.60	9.36	9.20	9.07	8.98	8.90	8.84	8.79	8.75	8.71	8.68	8.66	8.63	8.61	4
5	10.01	8.43	7.76	7.39	7.15	6.98	6.85	6.76	6.68	6.62	6.57	6.52	6.49	6.46	6.43	6.40	6.38	5
6	8.81	7.26	6.60	6.23	5.99	5.82	5.70	5.60	5.52	5.46	5.41	5.37	5.33	5.30	5.27	5.24	5.22	6
7	8.07	6.54	5.89	5.52	5.29	5.12	4.99	4.90	4.82	4.76	4.71	4.67	4.63	4.60	4.57	4.54	4.52	7
8	7.57	6.06	5.42	5.05	4.82	4.65	4.53	4.43	4.36	4.30	4.24	4.20	4.16	4.13	4.10	4.08	4.05	8
9	7.21	5.71	5.08	4.72	4.48	4.32	4.20	4.10	4.03	3.96	3.91	3.87	3.83	3.80	3.77	3.74	3.72	9
10	6.94	5.46	4.83	4.47	4.24	4.07	3.95	3.85	3.78	3.72	3.66	3.62	3.58	3.55	3.52	3.50	3.47	10
11	6.72	5.26	4.63	4.28	4.04	3.88	3.76	3.66	3.59	3.53	3.47	3.43	3.39	3.36	3.33	3.30	3.28	11
12	6.55	5.10	4.47	4.12	3.89	3.73	3.61	3.51	3.44	3.37	3.32	3.28	3.24	3.21	3.18	3.15	3.13	12
13	6.41	4.97	4.35	4.00	3.77	3.60	3.48	3.39	3.31	3.25	3.20	3.15	3.12	3.08	3.05	3.03	3.00	13
14	6.30	4.86	4.24	3.89	3.66	3.50	3.38	3.29	3.21	3.15	3.09	3.05	3.01	2.98	2.95	2.92	2.90	14
15	6.20	4.77	4.15	3.80	3.58	3.41	3.29	3.20	3.12	3.06	3.01	2.96	2.92	2.89	2.86	2.84	2.81	15
16	6.12	4.69	4.08	3.73	3.50	3.34	3.22	3.12	3.05	2.99	2.93	2.89	2.85	2.82	2.79	2.76	2.74	16
17	6.04	4.62	4.01	3.66	3.44	3.28	3.16	3.06	2.98	2.92	2.87	2.82	2.79	2.75	2.72	2.70	2.67	17
18	5.98	4.56	3.95	3.61	3.38	3.22	3.10	3.01	2.93	2.87	2.81	2.77	2.73	2.70	2.67	2.64	2.62	18
19	5.92	4.51	3.90	3.56	3.33	3.17	3.05	2.96	2.88	2.82	2.76	2.72	2.68	2.65	2.62	2.59	2.57	19
20	5.87	4.46	3.86	3.51	3.29	3.13	3.01	2.91	2.84	2.77	2.72	2.68	2.64	2.60	2.57	2.55	2.52	20
21	5.83	4.42	3.82	3.48	3.25	3.09	2.97	2.87	2.80	2.73	2.68	2.64	2.60	2.56	2.53	2.51	2.48	21
22	5.79	4.38	3.78	3.44	3.22	3.05	2.93	2.84	2.76	2.70	2.65	2.60	2.56	2.53	2.50	2.47	2.45	22
23	5.75	4.35	3.75	3.41	3.18	3.02	2.90	2.81	2.73	2.67	2.62	2.57	2.53	2.50	2.47	2.44	2.42	23
24	5.72	4.32	3.72	3.38	3.15	2.99	2.87	2.78	2.70	2.64	2.59	2.54	2.50	2.47	2.44	2.41	2.39	24
25	5.69	4.29	3.69	3.35	3.13	2.97	2.85	2.75	2.68	2.61	2.56	2.51	2.48	2.44	2.41	2.38	2.36	25
26	5.66	4.27	3.67	3.33	3.10	2.94	2.82	2.73	2.65	2.59	2.54	2.49	2.45	2.42	2.39	2.36	2.34	26
27	5.63	4.24	3.65	3.31	3.08	2.92	2.80	2.71	2.63	2.57	2.51	2.47	2.43	2.39	2.36	2.34	2.31	27
28	5.61	4.22	3.63	3.29	3.06	2.90	2.78	2.69	2.61	2.55	2.49	2.45	2.41	2.37	2.34	2.32	2.29	28
29	5.59	4.20	3.61	3.27	3.04	2.88	2.76	2.67	2.59	2.53	2.48	2.43	2.39	2.36	2.32	2.30	2.27	29
30	5.57	4.18	3.59	3.25	3.03	2.87	2.75	2.65	2.57	2.51	2.46	2.41	2.37	2.34	2.31	2.28	2.26	30
40	5.42	4.05	3.46	3.13	2.90	2.74	2.62	2.53	2.45	2.39	2.33	2.29	2.25	2.21	2.18	2.15	2.13	40
60	5.29	3.93	3.34	3.01	2.79	2.63	2.51	2.41	2.33	2.27	2.22	2.17	2.13	2.09	2.06	2.03	2.01	60
100	5.18	3.83	3.25	2.92	2.70	2.54	2.42	2.32	2.24	2.18	2.12	2.08	2.04	2.00	1.97	1.94	1.91	100
∞	5.02	3.69	3.12	2.79	2.57	2.41	2.29	2.19	2.11	2.05	1.99	1.94	1.90	1.87	1.83	1.80	1.78	∞

Degrees of freedom for the denominator

F(0.025) Distribution Table

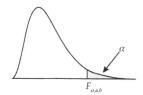

(b)	\multicolumn{17}{c}{Degrees of freedom for the numerator (a)}	(b)
(b)	18	19	20	21	22	23	24	25	26	27	28	29	30	40	60	100	∞	(b)
1	990.35	991.80	993.10	994.29	995.36	996.35	997.25	998.08	998.85	999.56	1000.22	1000.84	1001.41	1005.60	1009.80	1013.17	1018.26	1
2	39.44	39.45	39.45	39.45	39.45	39.45	39.46	39.46	39.46	39.46	39.46	39.46	39.46	39.47	39.48	39.49	39.50	2
3	14.20	14.18	14.17	14.16	14.14	14.13	14.12	14.12	14.11	14.10	14.09	14.09	14.08	14.04	13.99	13.96	13.90	3
4	8.59	8.58	8.56	8.55	8.53	8.52	8.51	8.50	8.49	8.48	8.48	8.47	8.46	8.41	8.36	8.32	8.26	4
5	6.36	6.34	6.33	6.31	6.30	6.29	6.28	6.27	6.26	6.25	6.24	6.23	6.23	6.18	6.12	6.08	6.02	5
6	5.20	5.18	5.17	5.15	5.14	5.13	5.12	5.11	5.10	5.09	5.08	5.07	5.07	5.01	4.96	4.92	4.85	6
7	4.50	4.48	4.47	4.45	4.44	4.43	4.41	4.40	4.39	4.39	4.38	4.37	4.36	4.31	4.25	4.21	4.14	7
8	4.03	4.02	4.00	3.98	3.97	3.96	3.95	3.94	3.93	3.92	3.91	3.90	3.89	3.84	3.78	3.74	3.67	8
9	3.70	3.68	3.67	3.65	3.64	3.63	3.61	3.60	3.59	3.58	3.58	3.57	3.56	3.51	3.45	3.40	3.33	9
10	3.45	3.44	3.42	3.40	3.39	3.38	3.37	3.35	3.34	3.34	3.33	3.32	3.31	3.26	3.20	3.15	3.08	10
11	3.26	3.24	3.23	3.21	3.20	3.18	3.17	3.16	3.15	3.14	3.13	3.13	3.12	3.06	3.00	2.96	2.88	11
12	3.11	3.09	3.07	3.06	3.04	3.03	3.02	3.01	3.00	2.99	2.98	2.97	2.96	2.91	2.85	2.80	2.72	12
13	2.98	2.96	2.95	2.93	2.92	2.91	2.89	2.88	2.87	2.86	2.85	2.85	2.84	2.78	2.72	2.67	2.60	13
14	2.88	2.86	2.84	2.83	2.81	2.80	2.79	2.78	2.77	2.76	2.75	2.74	2.73	2.67	2.61	2.56	2.49	14
15	2.79	2.77	2.76	2.74	2.73	2.71	2.70	2.69	2.68	2.67	2.66	2.65	2.64	2.59	2.52	2.47	2.40	15
16	2.72	2.70	2.68	2.67	2.65	2.64	2.63	2.61	2.60	2.59	2.58	2.58	2.57	2.51	2.45	2.40	2.32	16
17	2.65	2.63	2.62	2.60	2.59	2.57	2.56	2.55	2.54	2.53	2.52	2.51	2.50	2.44	2.38	2.33	2.25	17
18	2.60	2.58	2.56	2.54	2.53	2.52	2.50	2.49	2.48	2.47	2.46	2.45	2.44	2.38	2.32	2.27	2.19	18
19	2.55	2.53	2.51	2.49	2.48	2.46	2.45	2.44	2.43	2.42	2.41	2.40	2.39	2.33	2.27	2.22	2.13	19
20	2.50	2.48	2.46	2.45	2.43	2.42	2.41	2.40	2.39	2.38	2.37	2.36	2.35	2.29	2.22	2.17	2.09	20
21	2.46	2.44	2.42	2.41	2.39	2.38	2.37	2.36	2.34	2.33	2.33	2.32	2.31	2.25	2.18	2.13	2.04	21
22	2.43	2.41	2.39	2.37	2.36	2.34	2.33	2.32	2.31	2.30	2.29	2.28	2.27	2.21	2.14	2.09	2.00	22
23	2.39	2.37	2.36	2.34	2.33	2.31	2.30	2.29	2.28	2.27	2.26	2.25	2.24	2.18	2.11	2.06	1.97	23
24	2.36	2.35	2.33	2.31	2.30	2.28	2.27	2.26	2.25	2.24	2.23	2.22	2.21	2.15	2.08	2.02	1.94	24
25	2.34	2.32	2.30	2.28	2.27	2.26	2.24	2.23	2.22	2.21	2.20	2.19	2.18	2.12	2.05	2.00	1.91	25
26	2.31	2.29	2.28	2.26	2.24	2.23	2.22	2.21	2.19	2.18	2.17	2.17	2.16	2.09	2.03	1.97	1.88	26
27	2.29	2.27	2.25	2.24	2.22	2.21	2.19	2.18	2.17	2.16	2.15	2.14	2.13	2.07	2.00	1.94	1.85	27
28	2.27	2.25	2.23	2.22	2.20	2.19	2.17	2.16	2.15	2.14	2.13	2.12	2.11	2.05	1.98	1.92	1.83	28
29	2.25	2.23	2.21	2.20	2.18	2.17	2.15	2.14	2.13	2.12	2.11	2.10	2.09	2.03	1.96	1.90	1.81	29
30	2.23	2.21	2.20	2.18	2.16	2.15	2.14	2.12	2.11	2.10	2.09	2.08	2.07	2.01	1.94	1.88	1.79	30
40	2.11	2.09	2.07	2.05	2.03	2.02	2.01	1.99	1.98	1.97	1.96	1.95	1.94	1.88	1.80	1.74	1.64	40
60	1.98	1.96	1.94	1.93	1.91	1.90	1.88	1.87	1.86	1.85	1.83	1.82	1.82	1.74	1.67	1.60	1.48	60
100	1.89	1.87	1.85	1.83	1.81	1.80	1.78	1.77	1.76	1.75	1.74	1.72	1.71	1.64	1.56	1.48	1.35	100
∞	1.75	1.73	1.71	1.69	1.67	1.66	1.64	1.63	1.61	1.60	1.59	1.58	1.57	1.48	1.39	1.30	1.00	∞

Degrees of freedom for the denominator

F(0.01) Distribution Table

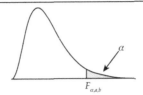

| | Degrees of freedom for the numerator | | | | | | | | | | | | | | | | | |
| | (a) | | | | | | | | | | | | | | | | | |
(b)	1	2	3	4	5	6	7	8	9	10	11	12	13	14	15	16	17	(b)
1	4052.18	4999.50	5403.35	5624.58	5763.65	5858.99	5928.36	5981.07	6022.47	6055.85	6083.32	6106.32	6125.86	6142.67	6157.28	6170.10	6181.43	1
2	98.50	99.00	99.17	99.25	99.30	99.33	99.36	99.37	99.39	99.40	99.41	99.42	99.42	99.43	99.43	99.44	99.44	2
3	34.12	30.82	29.46	28.71	28.24	27.91	27.67	27.49	27.35	27.23	27.13	27.05	26.98	26.92	26.87	26.83	26.79	3
4	21.20	18.00	16.69	15.98	15.52	15.21	14.98	14.80	14.66	14.55	14.45	14.37	14.31	14.25	14.20	14.15	14.11	4
5	16.26	13.27	12.06	11.39	10.97	10.67	10.46	10.29	10.16	10.05	9.96	9.89	9.82	9.77	9.72	9.68	9.64	5
6	13.75	10.92	9.78	9.15	8.75	8.47	8.26	8.10	7.98	7.87	7.79	7.72	7.66	7.60	7.56	7.52	7.48	6
7	12.25	9.55	8.45	7.85	7.46	7.19	6.99	6.84	6.72	6.62	6.54	6.47	6.41	6.36	6.31	6.28	6.24	7
8	11.26	8.65	7.59	7.01	6.63	6.37	6.18	6.03	5.91	5.81	5.73	5.67	5.61	5.56	5.52	5.48	5.44	8
9	10.56	8.02	6.99	6.42	6.06	5.80	5.61	5.47	5.35	5.26	5.18	5.11	5.05	5.01	4.96	4.92	4.89	9
10	10.04	7.56	6.55	5.99	5.64	5.39	5.20	5.06	4.94	4.85	4.77	4.71	4.65	4.60	4.56	4.52	4.49	10
11	9.65	7.21	6.22	5.67	5.32	5.07	4.89	4.74	4.63	4.54	4.46	4.40	4.34	4.29	4.25	4.21	4.18	11
12	9.33	6.93	5.95	5.41	5.06	4.82	4.64	4.50	4.39	4.30	4.22	4.16	4.10	4.05	4.01	3.97	3.94	12
13	9.07	6.70	5.74	5.21	4.86	4.62	4.44	4.30	4.19	4.10	4.02	3.96	3.91	3.86	3.82	3.78	3.75	13
14	8.86	6.51	5.56	5.04	4.69	4.46	4.28	4.14	4.03	3.94	3.86	3.80	3.75	3.70	3.66	3.62	3.59	14
15	8.68	6.36	5.42	4.89	4.56	4.32	4.14	4.00	3.89	3.80	3.73	3.67	3.61	3.56	3.52	3.49	3.45	15
16	8.53	6.23	5.29	4.77	4.44	4.20	4.03	3.89	3.78	3.69	3.62	3.55	3.50	3.45	3.41	3.37	3.34	16
17	8.40	6.11	5.18	4.67	4.34	4.10	3.93	3.79	3.68	3.59	3.52	3.46	3.40	3.35	3.31	3.27	3.24	17
18	8.29	6.01	5.09	4.58	4.25	4.01	3.84	3.71	3.60	3.51	3.43	3.37	3.32	3.27	3.23	3.19	3.16	18
19	8.18	5.93	5.01	4.50	4.17	3.94	3.77	3.63	3.52	3.43	3.36	3.30	3.24	3.19	3.15	3.12	3.08	19
20	8.10	5.85	4.94	4.43	4.10	3.87	3.70	3.56	3.46	3.37	3.29	3.23	3.18	3.13	3.09	3.05	3.02	20
21	8.02	5.78	4.87	4.37	4.04	3.81	3.64	3.51	3.40	3.31	3.24	3.17	3.12	3.07	3.03	2.99	2.96	21
22	7.95	5.72	4.82	4.31	3.99	3.76	3.59	3.45	3.35	3.26	3.18	3.12	3.07	3.02	2.98	2.94	2.91	22
23	7.88	5.66	4.76	4.26	3.94	3.71	3.54	3.41	3.30	3.21	3.14	3.07	3.02	2.97	2.93	2.89	2.86	23
24	7.82	5.61	4.72	4.22	3.90	3.67	3.50	3.36	3.26	3.17	3.09	3.03	2.98	2.93	2.89	2.85	2.82	24
25	7.77	5.57	4.68	4.18	3.85	3.63	3.46	3.32	3.22	3.13	3.06	2.99	2.94	2.89	2.85	2.81	2.78	25
26	7.72	5.53	4.64	4.14	3.82	3.59	3.42	3.29	3.18	3.09	3.02	2.96	2.90	2.86	2.81	2.78	2.75	26
27	7.68	5.49	4.60	4.11	3.78	3.56	3.39	3.26	3.15	3.06	2.99	2.93	2.87	2.82	2.78	2.75	2.71	27
28	7.64	5.45	4.57	4.07	3.75	3.53	3.36	3.23	3.12	3.03	2.96	2.90	2.84	2.79	2.75	2.72	2.68	28
29	7.60	5.42	4.54	4.04	3.73	3.50	3.33	3.20	3.09	3.00	2.93	2.87	2.81	2.77	2.73	2.69	2.66	29
30	7.56	5.39	4.51	4.02	3.70	3.47	3.30	3.17	3.07	2.98	2.91	2.84	2.79	2.74	2.70	2.66	2.63	30
40	7.31	5.18	4.31	3.83	3.51	3.29	3.12	2.99	2.89	2.80	2.73	2.66	2.61	2.56	2.52	2.48	2.45	40
60	7.08	4.98	4.13	3.65	3.34	3.12	2.95	2.82	2.72	2.63	2.56	2.50	2.44	2.39	2.35	2.31	2.28	60
100	6.90	4.82	3.98	3.51	3.21	2.99	2.82	2.69	2.59	2.50	2.43	2.37	2.31	2.27	2.22	2.19	2.15	100
∞	6.63	4.61	3.78	3.32	3.02	2.80	2.64	2.51	2.41	2.32	2.25	2.18	2.13	2.08	2.04	2.00	1.97	∞

Degrees of freedom for the denominator

F(0.01) Distribution Table

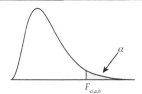

	Degrees of freedom for the numerator																	
	(a)																	
(b)	18	19	20	21	22	23	24	25	26	27	28	29	30	40	60	100	∞	(b)
1	6191.53	6200.58	6208.73	6216.12	6222.84	6228.99	6234.63	6239.83	6244.62	6249.07	6253.20	6257.05	6260.65	6286.78	6313.03	6334.11	6365.86	1
2	99.44	99.45	99.45	99.45	99.45	99.46	99.46	99.46	99.46	99.46	99.46	99.46	99.47	99.47	99.48	99.49	99.50	2
3	26.75	26.72	26.69	26.66	26.64	26.62	26.60	26.58	26.56	26.55	26.53	26.52	26.50	26.41	26.32	26.24	26.13	3
4	14.08	14.05	14.02	13.99	13.97	13.95	13.93	13.91	13.89	13.88	13.86	13.85	13.84	13.75	13.65	13.58	13.46	4
5	9.61	9.58	9.55	9.53	9.51	9.49	9.47	9.45	9.43	9.42	9.40	9.39	9.38	9.29	9.20	9.13	9.02	5
6	7.45	7.42	7.40	7.37	7.35	7.33	7.31	7.30	7.28	7.27	7.25	7.24	7.23	7.14	7.06	6.99	6.88	6
7	6.21	6.18	6.16	6.13	6.11	6.09	6.07	6.06	6.04	6.03	6.02	6.00	5.99	5.91	5.82	5.75	5.65	7
8	5.41	5.38	5.36	5.34	5.32	5.30	5.28	5.26	5.25	5.23	5.22	5.21	5.20	5.12	5.03	4.96	4.86	8
9	4.86	4.83	4.81	4.79	4.77	4.75	4.73	4.71	4.70	4.68	4.67	4.66	4.65	4.57	4.48	4.41	4.31	9
10	4.46	4.43	4.41	4.38	4.36	4.34	4.33	4.31	4.30	4.28	4.27	4.26	4.25	4.17	4.08	4.01	3.91	10
11	4.15	4.12	4.10	4.08	4.06	4.04	4.02	4.01	3.99	3.98	3.96	3.95	3.94	3.86	3.78	3.71	3.60	11
12	3.91	3.88	3.86	3.84	3.82	3.80	3.78	3.76	3.75	3.74	3.72	3.71	3.70	3.62	3.54	3.47	3.36	12
13	3.72	3.69	3.66	3.64	3.62	3.60	3.59	3.57	3.56	3.54	3.53	3.52	3.51	3.43	3.34	3.27	3.17	13
14	3.56	3.53	3.51	3.48	3.46	3.44	3.43	3.41	3.40	3.38	3.37	3.36	3.35	3.27	3.18	3.11	3.00	14
15	3.42	3.40	3.37	3.35	3.33	3.31	3.29	3.28	3.26	3.25	3.24	3.23	3.21	3.13	3.05	2.98	2.87	15
16	3.31	3.28	3.26	3.24	3.22	3.20	3.18	3.16	3.15	3.14	3.12	3.11	3.10	3.02	2.93	2.86	2.75	16
17	3.21	3.19	3.16	3.14	3.12	3.10	3.08	3.07	3.05	3.04	3.03	3.01	3.00	2.92	2.83	2.76	2.65	17
18	3.13	3.10	3.08	3.05	3.03	3.02	3.00	2.98	2.97	2.95	2.94	2.93	2.92	2.84	2.75	2.68	2.57	18
19	3.05	3.03	3.00	2.98	2.96	2.94	2.92	2.91	2.89	2.88	2.87	2.86	2.84	2.76	2.67	2.60	2.49	19
20	2.99	2.96	2.94	2.92	2.90	2.88	2.86	2.84	2.83	2.81	2.80	2.79	2.78	2.69	2.61	2.54	2.42	20
21	2.93	2.90	2.88	2.86	2.84	2.82	2.80	2.79	2.77	2.76	2.74	2.73	2.72	2.64	2.55	2.48	2.36	21
22	2.88	2.85	2.83	2.81	2.78	2.77	2.75	2.73	2.72	2.70	2.69	2.68	2.67	2.58	2.50	2.42	2.31	22
23	2.83	2.80	2.78	2.76	2.74	2.72	2.70	2.69	2.67	2.66	2.64	2.63	2.62	2.54	2.45	2.37	2.26	23
24	2.79	2.76	2.74	2.72	2.70	2.68	2.66	2.64	2.63	2.61	2.60	2.59	2.58	2.49	2.40	2.33	2.21	24
25	2.75	2.72	2.70	2.68	2.66	2.64	2.62	2.60	2.59	2.58	2.56	2.55	2.54	2.45	2.36	2.29	2.17	25
26	2.72	2.69	2.66	2.64	2.62	2.60	2.58	2.57	2.55	2.54	2.53	2.51	2.50	2.42	2.33	2.25	2.13	26
27	2.68	2.66	2.63	2.61	2.59	2.57	2.55	2.54	2.52	2.51	2.49	2.48	2.47	2.38	2.29	2.22	2.10	27
28	2.65	2.63	2.60	2.58	2.56	2.54	2.52	2.51	2.49	2.48	2.46	2.45	2.44	2.35	2.26	2.19	2.06	28
29	2.63	2.60	2.57	2.55	2.53	2.51	2.49	2.48	2.46	2.45	2.44	2.42	2.41	2.33	2.23	2.16	2.03	29
30	2.60	2.57	2.55	2.53	2.51	2.49	2.47	2.45	2.44	2.42	2.41	2.40	2.39	2.30	2.21	2.13	2.01	30
40	2.42	2.39	2.37	2.35	2.33	2.31	2.29	2.27	2.26	2.24	2.23	2.22	2.20	2.11	2.02	1.94	1.80	40
60	2.25	2.22	2.20	2.17	2.15	2.13	2.12	2.10	2.08	2.07	2.05	2.04	2.03	1.94	1.84	1.75	1.60	60
100	2.12	2.09	2.07	2.04	2.02	2.00	1.98	1.97	1.95	1.93	1.92	1.91	1.89	1.80	1.69	1.60	1.43	100
∞	1.93	1.90	1.88	1.85	1.83	1.81	1.79	1.77	1.76	1.74	1.72	1.71	1.70	1.59	1.47	1.36	1.00	∞

Degrees of freedom for the denominator

Bibliography

Abernathy, Robert B. "Dr. E. H. Waloddi Weibull." Last revised July 30, 2003. http://www.barringer1.com/weibull_bio.htm.

Ash, Carol. *The Probability Tutoring Book, an Intuitive Course for Engineers and Scientists (and everyone else!).* New York: IEEE Press, Wiley-Interscience, 1993.

Barro, Josh. "Can You Ever Guarantee a Mega Millions Win?" Forbes.com. March 30, 2012. http://www.forbes.com/sites/joshbarro/2012/03/30/can-you-ever-guarantee-a-mega-millions-win/.

"The Beginnings of Probability." Mathforum.org, Drexel University. Accessed August 19, 2015. http://mathforum.org/isaac/problems/prob1.html.

Champkin, Julian. "Odd Statistical Snippet of the Week: Voltaire and the Statistician Who Won the Lottery and Proved That the Earth Is Not Round." Significance. May 4, 2012. http://www.statslife.org.uk/history-of-stats-science/31-odd-statistical-snippet-of-the-week-voltaire-and-the-statistician-who-won-the-lottery-and-proved-that-the-earth-is-not-round.

Cohen, Micah. "Election Night Replay." FiveThirtyEight (blog). November 8, 2012. http://fivethirtyeight.blogs.nytimes.com/2012/11/08/election-night-replay/.

Crockett, Zachary. "The Time Everyone 'Corrected' the World's Smartest Woman." Priceonomics. February 19, 2015. http://priceonomics.com/the-time-everyone-corrected-the-worlds-smartest/.

Ebeling, Charles E. *An Introduction to Reliability and Maintainability Engineering.* 2nd ed. Long Grove, IL: Waveland Press, 2010.

Encyclopedia Britannica Online. s. v. "Girolamo Cardano." Accessed July 8, 2015. http://www.britannica.com/biography/Girolamo-Cardano.

Encyclopedia of Mathematics. "Negative Binomial Distribution." Last revised May 4, 2012. http://www.encyclopediaofmath.org/index.php?title=Negative_binomial_distribution&oldid=25961.

Gladwell, Malcolm. *Outliers: The Story of Success.* New York: Little, Brown and Company, 2008.

Hogg, Robert V., and Allen T. Craig. *Introduction to Mathematical Statistics.* 4th ed. New York: Macmillan Publishing, 1978.

Hosking, Tony. "An Explanation of Cricket." Last modified December 1, 2009. https://www.cs.purdue.edu/homes/hosking/cricket/explanation.htm.

"Ishtar." IMDb.com. Accessed July 9, 2015. http://www.imdb.com/title/tt0093278/.

Kaye, David H., Valerie P. Hans, B. Michael Dann, Erin J. Farley, and Stephanie Albertson. "Statistics in the Jury Box: How Jurors Respond to Mitochondrial DNA Match Probabilities." Paper 363, Cornell Law Faculty Publications, December 2007. http://scholarship.law.cornell.edu/facpub/363.

Law, Averill M., and W. David Kelton. *Simulation Modeling & Analysis.* 2nd ed. New York: McGraw-Hill, 1991.

Levitt, Steven D., and Stephen J. Dubner. *Freakonomics: A Rogue Economist Explores the Hidden Side of Everything.* New York: William Morrow, 2005.

Lewis, Michael. *Moneyball: The Art of Winning an Unfair Game.* New York: W. W. Norton, 2003.

McDonald, J. H. "Cochran–Mantel–Haenszel Test for Repeated Tests of Independence." In *Handbook of Biological Statistics.* Last revised July 20, 2015. http://www.biostathandbook.com/cmh.html.

Mezrich, Ben. *Bringing Down the House: The Inside Story of Six MIT Students Who Took Vegas for Millions.* New York: Free Press, 2002.

Montgomery, Douglas C. *Introduction to Statistical Quality Control.* 5th ed. New York: John Wiley & Sons, 2005.

Paulos, John Allen. *Innumeracy: Mathematical Illiteracy and Its Consequences.* New York: Hill and Wang, 2001.

Ross, Sheldon M. *Introduction to Probability Models.* 10th ed. New York: Elsevier Academic Press, 2010.

Salsburg, David. *The Lady Tasting Tea: How Statistics Revolutionized Science in the Twentieth Century.* New York: W. H. Freeman and Company, 2001.

Simpson, E. H. "The Interpretation of Interaction in Contingency Tables." *Journal of the Royal Statistical Society Series B* 13 (1951): 238–241.

Stigler, Stephen M. *The History of Statistics: The Measurement of Uncertainty before 1900.* Cambridge, MA: Belknap Press of Harvard University Press, 1986.

The Story of 1. Documentary. Directed by Nick Murphy and narrated by Terry Jones. BBC, 2005.

Student. "The Probable Error of a Mean." Accessed August 4, 2015. http://www.york.ac.uk/depts/maths/histstat/student.pdf.

Sullivan, Michael II. *Statistics: Informed Decisions Using Data.* 3rd ed. Upper Saddle River, NJ: Pearson Prentice Hall, 2010.

Swartz, John. "In Tech Jobs Market, Data Analysis Is Tops." *USA Today*, October 5, 2012. http://www.usatoday.com/story/money/business/2012/10/01/hot-tech-jobs-demand/1593105/.

Triola, Mario F. *Elementary Statistics*. 9th ed. Boston: Pearson Addison Wesley, 2003.

"2015 U.S. News & World Report: ISyE Undergraduate Program Maintains No. 1 Ranking." gatech.edu, September 9, 2014. https://www.isye.gatech.edu/news/2015-us-news-world-report-isye-undergraduate-program-maintains-no-1-ranking.

U.S. News and World Report. "Discrete Mathematics and Combinatorics." Accessed July 20, 2014. http://grad-schools.usnews.rankingsandreviews.com/best-graduate-schools/top-science-schools/discrete-mathematics-rankings.

"Walter A. Shewhart." ASQ.org. Accessed August 21, 2015. http://asq.org/about-asq/who-we-are/bio_shewhart.html.

Weisstein, Eric W. "Witch of Agnesi." MathWorld. Accessed July 21, 2015. http://mathworld.wolfram.com/WitchofAgnesi.html.

Index

Note: Page numbers followed by *f* or *t* refer to figures or tables, respectively.

About the Author

Mary McShane-Vaughn earned her PhD in industrial engineering and MS in statistics from the Georgia Institute of Technology, and a BS in industrial engineering from General Motors Institute (now Kettering University) in Flint, Michigan. She is currently principal at University Training Partners, a company that develops and delivers Lean-Six Sigma and statistical training to hospitals, corporations, and universities, both in-person and online. Previously, Dr. McShane-Vaughn was a tenured faculty member at Southern Polytechnic State University (now Kennesaw State University) in Marietta, Georgia. For eight years she directed and grew the Master of Science in Quality Assurance program and taught Statistics, Statistical Quality Control, Linear Regression, and Design of Experiments in the graduate program.

Before her career in academics, Dr. McShane-Vaughn worked for 15 years as a quality engineer and statistician in the automotive, medical device manufacturing, consumer products testing, and revenue management industries.

Dr. McShane-Vaughn served as the Six Sigma Black Belt exam chair for the American Society for Quality (ASQ) from 2010 to 2012 and was an examiner for the Georgia Oglethorpe Award, Georgia's equivalent of the Malcolm Baldrige National Quality Award. She currently serves on the editorial review board for *Six Sigma Forum*. Dr. McShane-Vaughn is a senior member of ASQ and a member of the American Statistical Association. She holds ASQ certifications as a Six Sigma Black Belt, Quality Engineer, and Reliability Engineer.

The Knowledge Center
www.asq.org/knowledge-center

Learn about quality. Apply it. Share it.

ASQ's online Knowledge Center is the place to:

- Stay on top of the latest in quality with Editor's Picks and Hot Topics.

- Search ASQ's collection of articles, books, tools, training, and more.

- Connect with ASQ staff for personalized help hunting down the knowledge you need, the networking opportunities that will keep your career and organization moving forward, and the publishing opportunities that are the best fit for you.

Use the Knowledge Center Search to quickly sort through hundreds of books, articles, and other software-related publications.

www.asq.org/knowledge-center

Ask a Librarian

Did you know?

- The ASQ Quality Information Center contains a wealth of knowledge and information available to ASQ members and non-members

- A librarian is available to answer research requests using ASQ's ever-expanding library of relevant, credible quality resources, including journals, conference proceedings, case studies and Quality Press publications

- ASQ members receive free internal information searches and reduced rates for article purchases

- You can also contact the Quality Information Center to request permission to reuse or reprint ASQ copyrighted material, including journal articles and book excerpts

- For more information or to submit a question, visit **http://asq.org/knowledge-center/ ask-a-librarian-index**

Visit www.asq.org/qic for more information.

Belong to the Quality Community!

Established in 1946, ASQ is a global community of quality experts in all fields and industries. ASQ is dedicated to the promotion and advancement of quality tools, principles, and practices in the workplace and in the community.

The Society also serves as an advocate for quality. Its members have informed and advised the U.S. Congress, government agencies, state legislatures, and other groups and individuals worldwide on quality-related topics.

Vision

By making quality a global priority, an organizational imperative, and a personal ethic, ASQ becomes the community of choice for everyone who seeks quality technology, concepts, or tools to improve themselves and their world.

ASQ is...

- More than 90,000 individuals and 700 companies in more than 100 countries

- The world's largest organization dedicated to promoting quality

- A community of professionals striving to bring quality to their work and their lives

- The administrator of the Malcolm Baldrige National Quality Award

- A supporter of quality in all sectors including manufacturing, service, healthcare, government, and education

- YOU

Visit www.asq.org for more information.

TRAINING   CERTIFICATION   CONFERENCES   MEMBERSHIP   **PUBLICATIONS**

The Global Voice of Quality®

ASQ Membership

Research shows that people who join associations experience increased job satisfaction, earn more, and are generally happier*. ASQ membership can help you achieve this while providing the tools you need to be successful in your industry and to distinguish yourself from your competition. So why wouldn't you want to be a part of ASQ?

Networking

Have the opportunity to meet, communicate, and collaborate with your peers within the quality community through conferences and local ASQ section meetings, ASQ forums or divisions, ASQ Communities of Quality discussion boards, and more.

Professional Development

Access a wide variety of professional development tools such as books, training, and certifications at a discounted price. Also, ASQ certifications and the ASQ Career Center help enhance your quality knowledge and take your career to the next level.

Solutions

Find answers to all your quality problems, big and small, with ASQ's Knowledge Center, mentoring program, various e-newsletters, *Quality Progress* magazine, and industry-specific products.

Access to Information

Learn classic and current quality principles and theories in ASQ's Quality Information Center (QIC), *ASQ Weekly* e-newsletter, and product offerings.

Advocacy Programs

ASQ helps create a better community, government, and world through initiatives that include social responsibility, Washington advocacy, and Community Good Works.

Visit www.asq.org/membership for more information on ASQ membership.

*2008, The William E. Smith Institute for Association Research

TRAINING   CERTIFICATION   CONFERENCES   **MEMBERSHIP   PUBLICATIONS**